Introductory Ornithology

Introductory

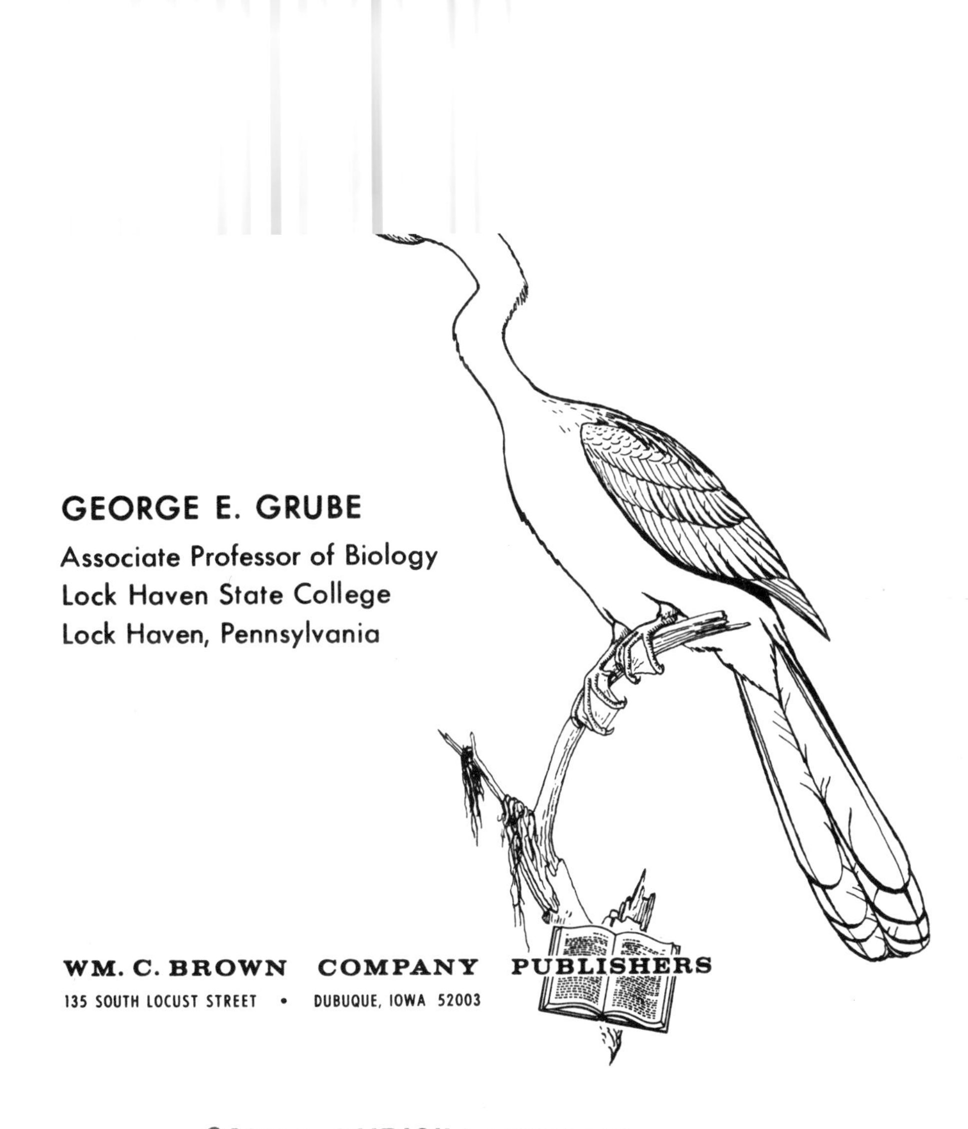

GEORGE E. GRUBE
Associate Professor of Biology
Lock Haven State College
Lock Haven, Pennsylvania

WM. C. BROWN COMPANY PUBLISHERS
135 SOUTH LOCUST STREET • DUBUQUE, IOWA 52003

Library of Congress Catalog Number: 64-66004

Manufactured by WM. C. BROWN CO. INC., Dubuque, Iowa
Printed in U. S. A.

Acknowledgments

Many persons assisted in various ways with the preparation of the work. Dr. William C. Dilger, Laboratory of Ornithology, Cornell University, executed a number of the line drawings. Dr. Ernest P. Edwards, College of the Pacific, Stockton, California, and Dr. Olin Sewall Pettingill, Jr., Laboratory of Ornithology, Cornell University, read early manuscripts and made many helpful suggestions and criticisms. The manuscript was typed by Mrs. John C. W. Riddle. Mrs. Norris Hamner, Mrs. Stanley Karichner, Mrs. Betty Cowfer, and Miss Eleanor Brungard assisted in various ways with secretarial work. Many of some 200 students unknowingly helped in that they showed where elaboration or clarification was needed. My daughter, Louise Grube, assisted in the preparation of two of the illustrations. The help of these and any others who may have escaped my attention is gratefully acknowledged. The author, however, accepts responsibility for the material here presented.

George E. Grube

1964
Lock Haven, Pa.

Preface

Introductory Ornithology is the outgrowth of a small text originally written in 1950. Since then the author has taught ten classes in ornithology. Each has had its impact on the development of the text. The book is meant to be, as the title implies, an introduction to the field. It is not meant as a source book for the graduate or research ornithologist. Yet the text attempts to treat all major phases in the study of birds. Properly managed, it will suffice as an introduction to principles and for indoor laboratory work in a one-semester college course.

Close correlation among the study of principles, laboratory work with structure and identification of orders and families of birds, and field identification of local species is recommended. The text is written with this correlation in mind. The text and suggested exercises should rather thoroughly indoctrinate the student in the principles of ornithology. The keys (Appendix A) should prove adequate for laboratory identification. A field manual, such as Peterson's **A Field Guide to the Birds,** should be used as a source in field identification. A minimal library of the journals and books listed at the end of each chapter should be available to the student.

Preface

Contents

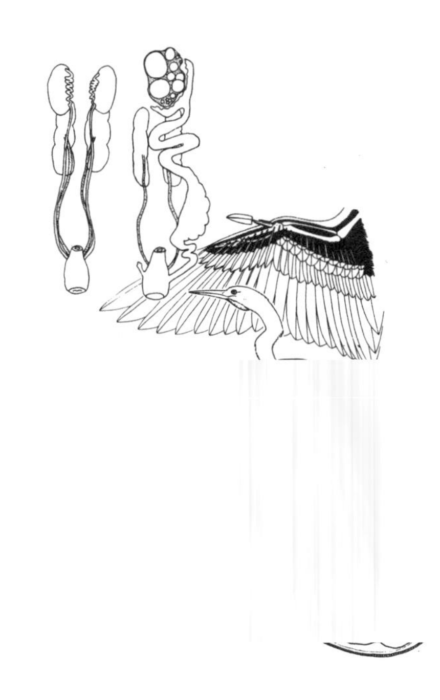

CHAPTER 1

Introduction

Man has displayed an interest in birds for many centuries. Early cave dwellers carved the likenesses of birds on the walls of their caves. Drawings of birds in caves of southern Spain date back to 4,000 – 6,000 B.C. The Mayas of Yucatan made replicas of birds in their early carving. The Bible first records man's use of birds with the sending of the raven, and subsequently the dove, from the ark of Noah.

Birds have been responsible for bringing about some decisions that guided the destiny of man in historic time. Columbus was impelled to change his course, and hence discover the West Indies, when migrating birds were observed overhead. The birds were migrating from the mainland of eastern North America to South America by way of the West Indies. The three tiny Spanish ships followed them and soon reached the Bahamas. Had Columbus persisted on his original course he would have reached Florida, 200 miles farther away, provided his near mutinous crew would have tolerated the additional delay. Quail satisfied the hunger of the Israelites while they were travelling through the wilderness en route from Egypt to the promised land (Exodus 16:13). Thus confidence was again restored in their leader, Moses. The tradition of the Thanksgiving celebration in the United States centers, in large part, on the turkey. These majestic game birds once roamed the forests of much of eastern North America.

The gradual disappearance of some American game and non-game birds resulted in legislation by the colonies, the states, and the federal government to protect this valuable segment of our wildlife heritage. The enactment of the Migratory Bird Treaty Act (by which migratory birds are protected from indiscriminate slaughter) was one of a series of laws to protect birds. The earliest recorded regulation pertaining to birds appears in Deuteronomy 22:6-7, where Moses states, "If a bird's nest chance to be before thee in the way, in any tree or on the ground, with young ones or eggs, and the dam sitting upon the young, or upon the eggs, thou shalt not take the dam with the young: thou shalt in any wise let the dam go, but the young thou mayest take unto thyself; that it may be well with thee, and that thou mayest prolong thy days."

Science is knowledge accumulated and rationally designed to show the mutual relations of observed facts. Knowledge of any particular group of facts and the methodical disposition of these facts constitute a special science. Ornithology (Gr. *ornithos,* of a bird, *logos,* study or discourse) then is the science of birds. Ornithology consists of a rational arrangement of all the facts and theories based on facts to show what is known about birds. The ramifications of the science are many and diverse. They include such contributions to biology as studies in life history, ecology or environmental relationships, food habits, predation, parasitology, epidemiology, distribution, taxonomy, anatomy, coloration and protective coloration, migration, embryology, physiology, behavior, genetics, and population dynamics. Most of these ultimately contribute to the study of evolution and/or conservation. It will be the scope of this work to introduce the reader to many of these fields of bird study.

Birds are vertebrate animals, that is, animals with a backbone, or more precisely a number of bones (the vertebrae) fixed end to end which make the main structural support for the animal. Other vertebrates include such forms as lampreys, sharks and rays or cartilaginous fishes, bony or typical fishes, amphibians, reptiles, and mammals. (See Figure 1.) The presence of feathers on the body surface easily distinguishes the birds from these other vertebrate groups.

Feathers make the bird. No other organism on the earth bears feathers. It is these structures, in large part, that make the bird an extremely interesting animal. Feathers bear color pigments and prismatic surfaces which reflect and refract light and so are responsible for the coloration on most of the bird's body. Feathers enable the bird to fly. Birds are not the only vertebrate animals that fly, and not

Figure 1. Representatives of the classes of vertebrates other than birds. A lamprey (Agnatha or Cyclostomata), a bony fish (Osteichthyes), a shark (Chondrichthyes), a salamander (Amphibia), a tapir (Mammalia), and a lizard (Reptilia).

all birds fly; however, most of them are capable flyers. This fact distinguishes them from all other vertebrates save the bats, whose hairy covering relegates them to the mammals. (See Figure 2.) The power of flight of birds does much to make them more interesting

Figure 2. Bats are the only flying vertebrates other than birds. In prehistoric times (during the Mesozoic Era) a group of reptiles, called Pterosaurs, also were accomplished flyers. Above is *Myotis lucifugus,* a common bat; below is *Pterodactylus,* a Mesozoic flying reptile. Drawings by William C. Dilger.

than other groups of animals. Migration, one of the most distinctive phases of bird life, is a manifestation of flight. Migration itself is a fascinating trait of birds. Much of migration remains a mystery; thus the student of this trait and of birds in general has before him a challenge . . . a challenge to delve into the unknown. Further, migration enables an observer to see many species or kinds of birds

of beak, hence birds do not have fleshy lips. There are no external ear lobes or pinnae. The tail is composed of feathers which are supported internally by a fused series of vertebrae. Internally there are numerous structural modifications. These will be treated in Chapter 3.

It has been indicated that some birds do not fly. The ostriches, natives of Africa, are incapable of flying. They have well developed hind limbs but the forelimbs or wings are reduced and degenerate. Penguins, natives of the Antarctic region, have forelimbs modified for swimming. The rheas of South America, the emus and cassowaries of Australia and Borneo, the kiwis of New Zealand, and other isolated species lack the ability to fly. Many prehistoric birds, known from fossil evidence, were flightless. Some of these will be further discussed in Chapter 4.

Bird study has become a very popular vocation or avocation for thousands of Americans. The rise in ornithology's popularity might be attributed to several factors. First some of the facts about birds were slowly accumulated. With these facts further interest was stimulated and more and more people became bird students. Several early ornithologists banded together and from this nucleus arose a second factor, the formation of organizations such as the American Ornithologists Union (AOU) and Audubon Society (on national, state, and local levels), the Wilson Ornithological Society, the Cooper Ornithological Society, and the several Bird Banding Associations. A third factor lies in the ever-increasing recognition of the fact that our natural resources are gradually dwindling and ornithologists generally are also conservationists. A fourth factor lies in the increasing complexity of our social and economic life. The out-of-doors, with its beauty, fresh air, sunshine, and incidentally nature's own chlorophyll, brings a form of release from care and anxiety.

Bibliography and References

Allen, Elsa Guerdrum, The History of American Ornithology Before Audubon. *Trans. Am. Philosophical Soc.*, Vol. 41, part 3, 1951.

Chapman, Frank M., Birds and Man. *Am. Mus. Natural History Leaflet* No. 115, 1943.

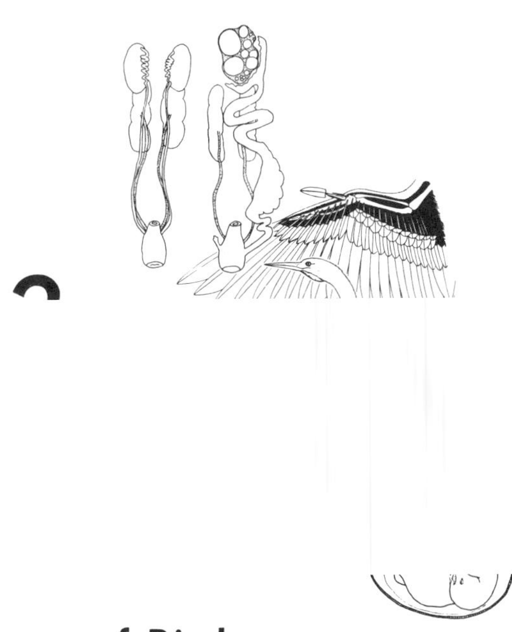

External Features of Birds

A knowledge of the external appearance of birds, both color and form, is essential to the ornithologist. External features provide characteristics for identification in the field or in the hand. Many external characters are used in working out phylogenetic relationships and hence are important in bird taxonomy. Topographic features and the terminology pertaining to topography should be learned early by the student so that the descriptions of species, by field trip leader or in field manual, will be thoroughly understood. Figures 3 and 4 show topography of birds. It will be advantageous to study these illustrations carefully, for the terms will be used frequently in the field.

The body of any bird can be divided into four parts — the head, the neck, the trunk, and the tail. The comparative size of any of these parts often deviates considerably from the normal. For example, the head of a kingfisher is comparatively large. The neck of an Anhinga is comparatively long. The trunk or body of the game birds is comparatively large and the tail of a cuckoo is comparatively long. (See Figure 5.) It may be somewhat difficult to differentiate accurately among some of these parts externally. The neck may be so folded or covered with feathers that the head appears to be attached directly to the trunk. These parts must necessarily be defined by recourse to internal anatomy. The **head** is that part of the bird which is supported

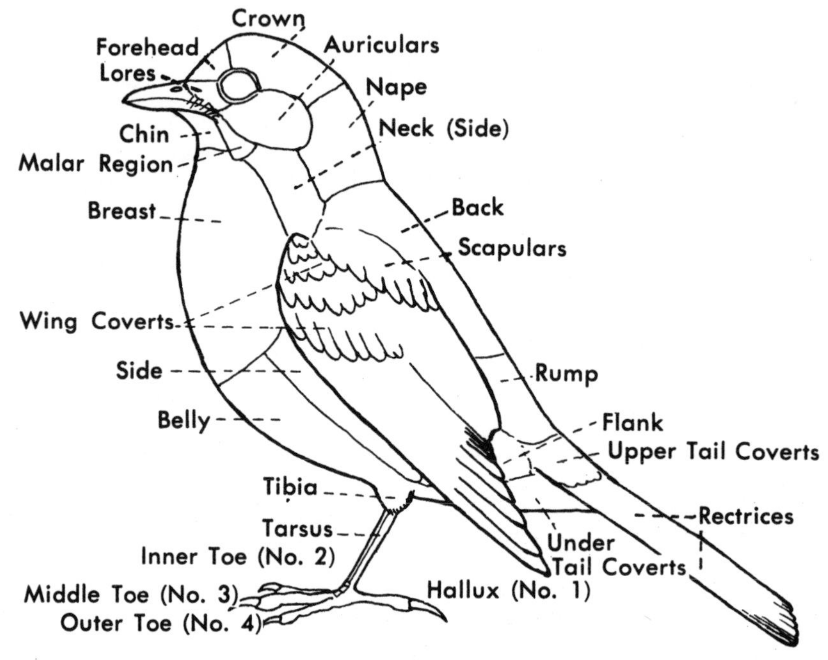

Figure 3. Topography of a song bird.

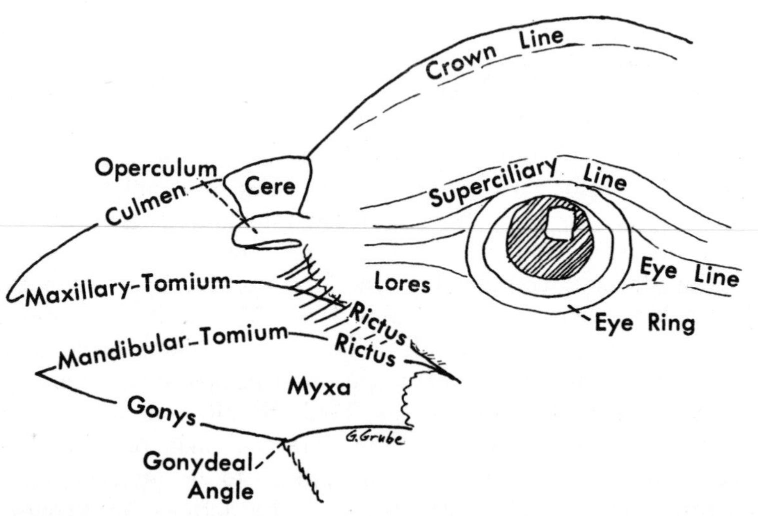

Figure 4. Topography of the head and external features of the head and bill of a bird.

Figure 5. Relative size of head, neck, trunk, and tail of some birds. The body of the Bobwhite, the head of the Belted Kingfisher, the tail of the Yellow-billed Cuckoo, and the neck of the Anhinga are comparatively large. Drawings by William C. Dilger.

internally by the skull. The **neck** is that portion supported by the **cervical vertebrae** or by that part of the segmented backbone between the vertebrae which bear ribs at the posterior end of the neck and the skull at the anterior end. The remainder of the skeletally supported body is the **trunk.** The **tail** is composed only of feathers, known as the **rectrices.** These are attached to the flesh which is supported by the underlying fused tail vertebrae called the **pygostyle.**

The **bill** is a highly specialized structure, supported internally by the **premaxillary bone** in the **upper mandible** and by the **dentary bone** (principally) in the lower mandible. (See Figure 4.) Externally these bones are covered by a horny sheath, the **ramphotheca.** The ramphotheca is a modification of the integument or skin which covers the rest of the body. The dorsal angle of the upper mandible is known as the **culmen** which, in some birds, leads into the **cere** proximally (as in birds of prey and parrots and their allies). The cere is a dense membranous structure of uncertain function. In pigeons, doves, and their kin (the Order Columbiformes) a large membranous **operculum** occupies the same position and partially overlies the **nostrils.** The nostrils open into the upper respiratory channels through the ramphotheca of the upper mandible. The operculum partially closes over the nostrils of many species but only in the birds of the Order Columbiformes is it swollen and membranous. The hard cutting edge of the upper mandible is called the **maxillary tomium.** On the lower mandible the cutting edge is known as the **mandibular tomium.** The **rictus** is the soft edge which continues proximally with both the maxillary and mandibular tomia. The ventral edge of the lower mandible is the **gonys.** (See Figure 4.) The lower mandible is Y-shaped with the **rami** (singular-**ramus**) extending laterally and proximally. The angle formed by the rami is known as the **gonydeal angle.** The line on which the upper and lower mandibles meet is known as the **commissure** or **gape.** The **commissural point** is the proximal terminus of the commissure. The term **gape** may refer also to the extent to which the bill may be opened. (This can further be related to the distance between commissural points as demonstrated by the goatsuckers of the Order Caprimulgiformes and the swifts of the Order Apodiformes.) On the upper mandible of some birds a small depression, the **nasal fossa,** leads into the nostrils. The term **myxa** is frequently applied to the sides of the lower mandible and extends from the tip to the proximal ends of the rami. Most of the foregoing structures are illustrated in Figure 4.

The bill has changed considerably since the time of the earliest known bird, *Archeopteryx,* which lived in Jurassic times, some 150 million years ago. *Archeopteryx* had teeth imbedded in the bones of its jaws as do most of the reptiles. The shape of the bill varies greatly in birds of the present time. It may be long, short, tapering to a point, compressed (flattened from the sides), depressed (flattened dorsoventrally), arched, vaulted, bent, decurved (curved downward), recurved (curved upward), straight, spatulate, lamellate, sulcate, dentate, serrate, denticulate, carunculate, punctate, hypogna-

shape of bill which accidentally evolved in each species. Most species have food habits which can be explained by the adaptation of the bill. It would appear, then, that as new environments appeared on the earth mutant bill forms which were capable of utilizing the foods provided by that new environment were able to survive, while others less well adapted had to find more suitable environment or become extinct. The subject of adaptation to environment is treated in Chapter 7.

The bills of birds may display both convergent and divergent evolution. **Convergent evolution** can be defined as the phenomenon in which distantly related species resemble each other or are similarly adapted in one or more respects. The bill of the Green Heron (Order Ciconiiformes) is similar to that of the Belted Kingfisher (Order Coraciiformes) and they have somewhat similar feeding habits. The bills of these two unrelated species are illustrated in Figure 7. **Divergent evolution** involves the situation in which closely related species have considerably different structures or bear diverse adaptations. The bills of the Evening Grosbeak, the Seaside Sparrow, and the White-winged Crossbill (see Figure 8), all of which are in the Order Passeriformes and the Family Fringillidae, demonstrate divergence in closely related species.

Except for the bill and the feet, the body of the bird is covered with **feathers,** which are among the most distinctive anatomical features of all birds. The earliest evidence of feathers appeared in the Jurassic fossil bird, *Archeopteryx*. These distinctive integumentary structures are specially adapted for birds' habits and sustenance. Feathers have numerous functions. They protect the bird from mechanical injury by absorbing shock – a virtue of their pliable character – and

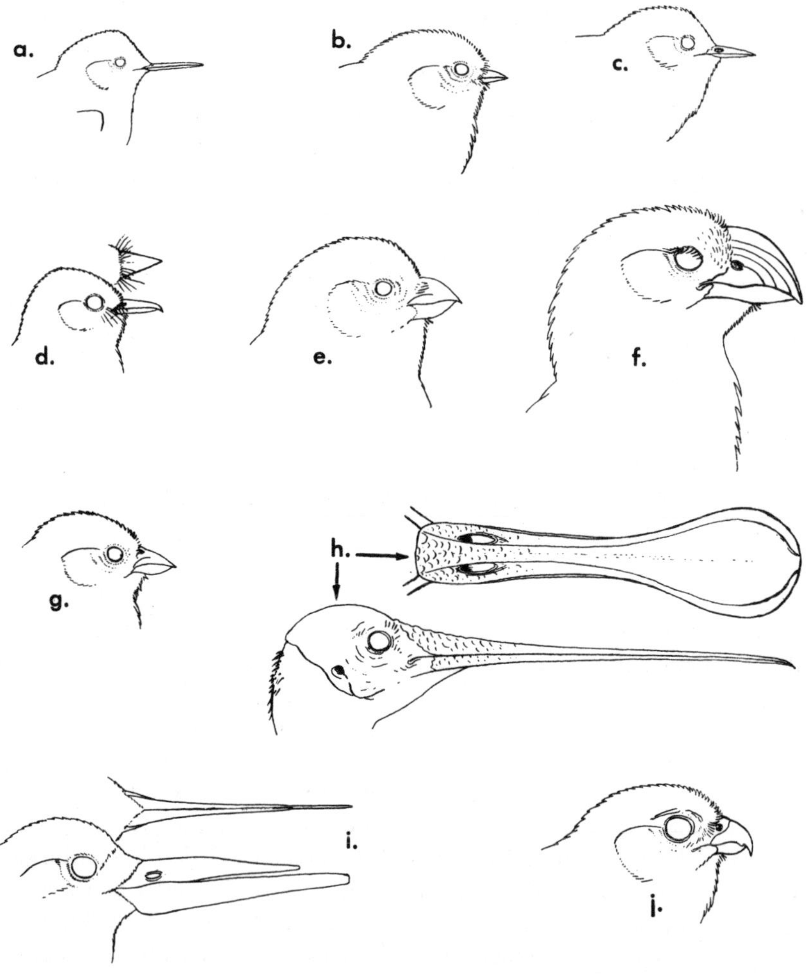

Figure 6. Some representative types of bills of birds. (*a*) Long (Ruby-throated Hummingbird); (*b*) short (Black-capped Chickadee); (*c*) pointed (Winter Wren); (*d*) depressed (Alder Flycatcher); (*e*) vaulted (Pine Grosbeak); (*f*) sulcate (Groove-billed Ani); (*g*) arched (Vesper Sparrow); (*h*) spatulate and depressed Roseate Spoonbill); (*i*) compressed and hypognathous (Black Skimmer); (*j*) toothed (Pigeon Hawk); (*k*) bent (American Flamingo); (*l*) straight (Robin); (*m*) hooked (Sharp-shinned Hawk); (*n*) decurved (Hudsonian Curlew); (*o*) recurved (Avocet); (*p*) dentate (Motmot); (*q*) crossed (Red Crossbill); (*r*) notched and straight (Wood Thrush); (*s*) carunculate (King Vulture); (*t*) soft and punctate (Common Snipe); (*u*) lamellate (Blue Goose); (*v*) serrate (Hooded Merganser.) Drawings by William C. Dilger.

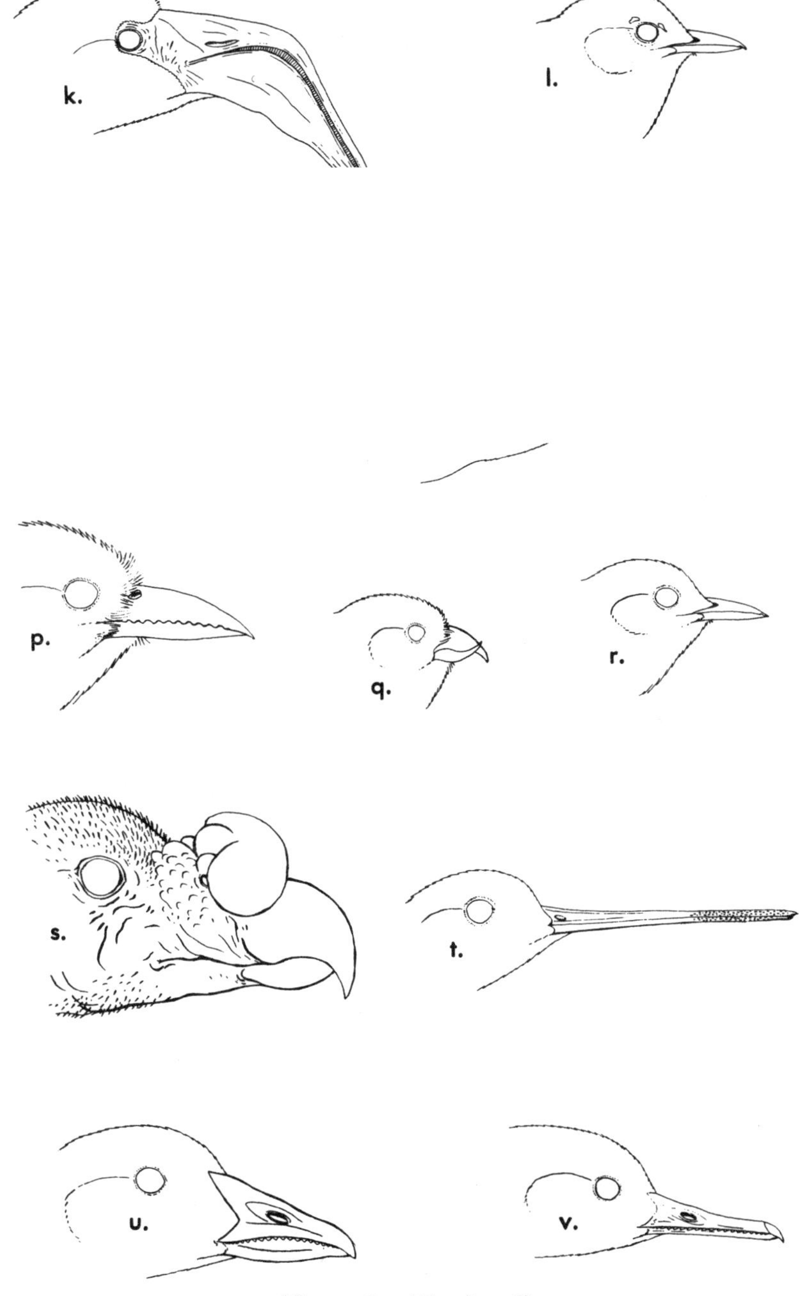

Figure 6. (Continued)

Figure 7. Convergent evolution is demonstrated by the bills of a Belted Kingfisher (above) and a Green Heron (below). Drawings by William C. Dilger.

Figure 8. Divergent evolution is demonstrated by the bills of an (*a*) Evening Grosbeak, a (*b*) Seaside Sparrow, and a (*c*) White-winged Crossbill. Drawings by William C. Dilger.

by preventing cuts and scratches – a virtue of their toughness. They protect from exposure to low temperatures, for they serve as insulators which can be easily adjusted by subcutaneous muscles to regulate heat loss. Birds are **warm-blooded** or **homothermous,** that is, they have a constant body temperature (within a few degrees) which is, to some extent, controlled by the feathers. When cold, the bird's subcutaneous muscles contract and pull the feathers out and away from the body in such a way that small air pockets provide "dead air" insulation. When the bird is hot the feathers are held close to the body so that heat can be lost by direct conduction. There are no sweat glands in the bird's

blood supply is cut off, and the feather exists as a "dead" structure until it is lost with the next molt or through some accident. **Molting** or **ecdysis** is the regular periodic shedding of the feathers. This frequently provides for seasonal changes in the plumage so that birds may appear quite different in the fall than in the spring. The feathers are found only on certain rather well defined areas of the skin. These areas are called **feather tracts** or **pterylae.** Those areas of the skin where no feathers are found are called **apteria.** Figure 9 shows pterylosis, the arrangement of feather tracts on the bird's body.

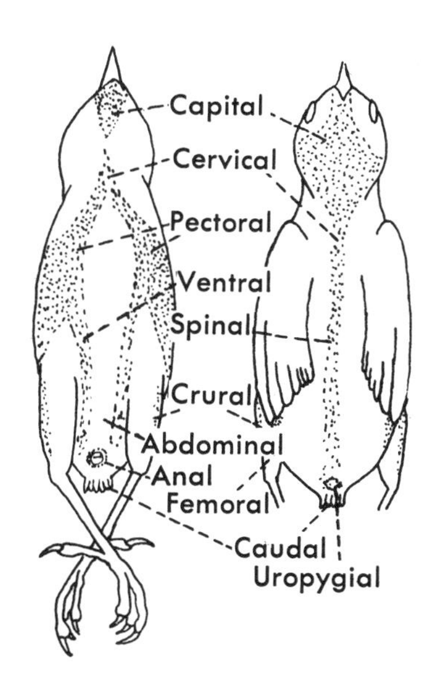

Figure 9. Pterylosis of a nestling Red-winged Blackbird.

The typical feather consists of an axial support called the **shaft** and the flattened surfaces called the **vanes.** (See Figure 10.) The shaft is divided into the **calamus,** the proximal part below the vanes, and the **rachis** which bears the lateral vanes or webs. The vane is composed of many **barbs** which arise from the rachis and in turn bear the branching **barbules** which interlock with the barbules of the neighboring barbs. **Barbicels,** small hook-like structures, are attached to the barbules and serve to hold the vane intact. These small hooks clasp over the barbules and bind them together thus forming a tight network, the vane. If the barbs become unbound, the bird is likely to preen. When a bird

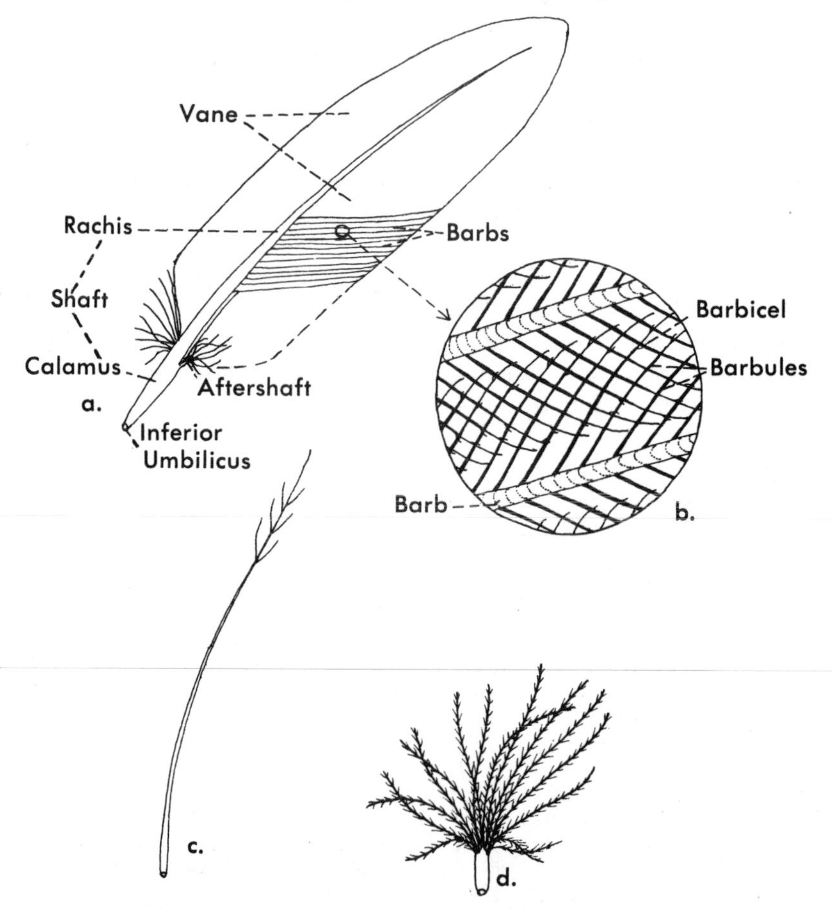

Figure 10. Structure and types of feathers. (*a*) teleoptile; (*b*) an enlargement of the vane of a teleoptile; (*c*) filoplume; (*d*) down feather.

preens, or pulls a part of the vane through its bill, the barbicels snap into position over a barbule and the damaged feather is restored to its original condition. Proximally the typical feather frequently bears no barbicels so that that portion of the vane is downy, a condition which provides further insulation against heat loss. Figure 10 shows the structure of a typical feather.

[illegible]

down feathers. These are replaced shortly by the teleoptiles which push the neossoptiles out, for the latter are attached to the tips of the developing teleoptiles. After a varying period of time the neossoptiles wear off, never to appear again on the growing bird. Teleoptiles are of five types. First are the **contour feathers,** which include the wing primaries, secondaries, tertials, coverts, the tail feathers or rectrices, and all other features that are exposed on the body. Second are the **down feathers** which lie beneath the contour feathers and vary greatly in their occurrence in different species of birds. They often lack the rachis and always lack the barbicels. Third are the **semiplumes,** which are intermediate between the preceding two types, for they have the rachis and vanes but lack the barbicels. Fourth are the **filoplumes,** which are sparsely distributed hair-like feathers with only a few barbs, and fifth, the **powder down feathers** which occur in only a few groups of birds, for example the herons and bitterns. The powder down feathers are similar to the down feathers but the barbs continually break off at the tips and produce a powdery substance which frequently can change the color of a bird. This is demonstrated by the Swallow-tailed Kite in which the back often appears gray instead of black. The feather types are illustrated in Figure 10.

The flight or wing feathers are given names according to their points of insertion. All the long flight feathers are called **remiges.** The remiges that are attached to the digits and manus are called **primaries,** those attached to the ulna (larger of the bones of the forearm) are the secondaries, and those attached to the humerus (proximal bone of the arm) are the **tertials.** Three rows of **wing coverts** generally cover the bases of the row of feathers posterior to them. The **major coverts** cover the primaries, secondaries, and tertials; the **middle coverts** cover the major coverts, and the **lesser coverts** cover the bases of the middle coverts. At the distal end of the row of lesser coverts and attached to the first digit (actually this is the second digit, the first having been lost through the evolution of birds) is the **alula** or bastard wing. This is composed of a group of feathers which apparently function as flaps which brake flight when the bird alights. The **marginals** are the coverts which cover the leading edge of the wing and extend around to the ventral side. Most of the ventral side bears no feathers. Figure 11 illustrates the feather arrangement of the wing of a bird.

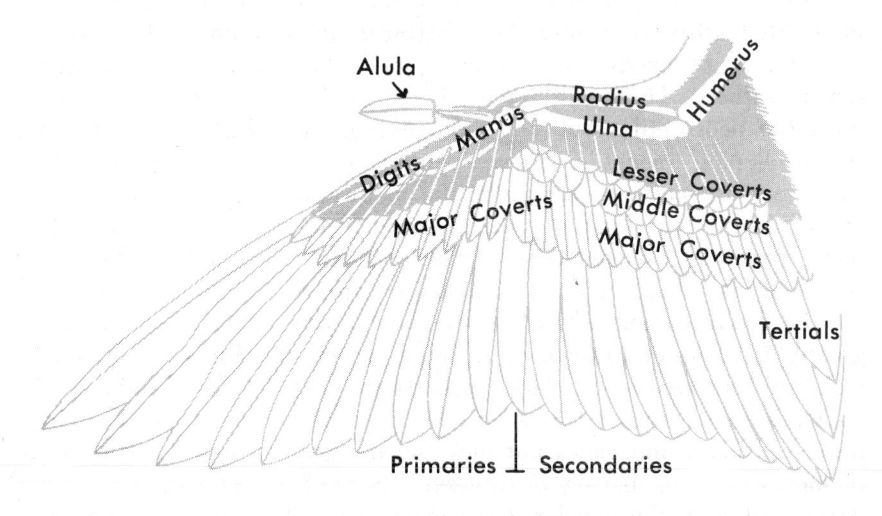

Figure 11. The wing of a song bird, showing the arrangement of the feathers. Feathers cut away over the wing bones reveal the attachment of the remiges. Drawing by William C. Dilger.

The coloration of feathers is due to two factors. **Pigments** are deposited in the feather at the time of its formation. Three principal pigments are present. They are red (zoonerythrin), yellow (zooxanthin), and brown or brown-black (melanin). A few less important pigments are found in some birds. The second factor involves both pigments and feather structure. Blue, green, and iridescent colors are brought about by the presence of microscopic thin plates called lamellae, which lie over the pigmented parts and serve to refract light rays. A mature feather changes color only by wear, fading, or staining. The plumage of a bird may change from light to dark when the white tips of the feathers wear off as illustrated in Figure 12.

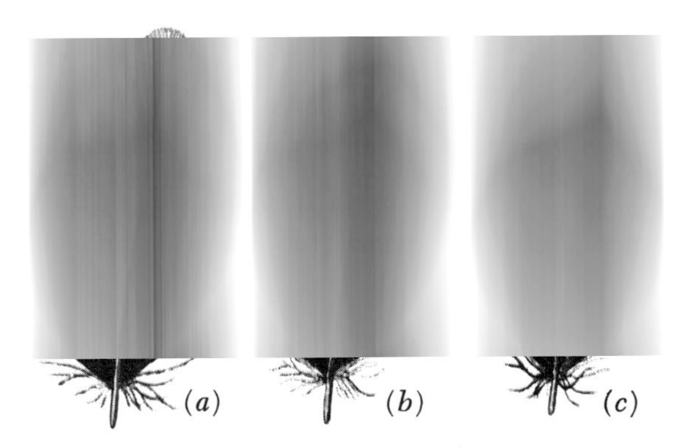

Figure 12. Wearing of the feathers may cause a marked change in the appearance of the bird. These are feathers from the back of a Snow Bunting. (*a*) fall; (*b*) winter; (*c*) late spring.

A complete lack of pigments results in **albinism.** Albinism may be either partial or complete. Partial albinism is usually symmetrical and the eye color is usually normal. Complete or pure albinos usually lack pigment in the irises of the eyes so that they appear pink, because the capillary blood shows through. Other abnormal colorations in plumage are melanism (caused by excessive brown pigment), xanthochroism (excessive yellow), and erythrism (excessive red). Sometimes abnormal coloration has interesting correlations with geographic distribution. The Screech Owl (*Otus asio*) in the eastern United States is often erythristic while in the western United States it is always normal gray.

The actual mode of replacement of feathers was only recently described for all molts (Watson, 1963). The newly emerging replacement feather grows a sheath which is continuous with the calamus of the old feather. The new feather develops within the sheath. As it pushes outward, it pushes the old feather out of the follicle until finally the old feather breaks off with part of the tip of the new sheath attached. Previously it was thought that the loss of the old feather at ecdysis stimulated the growth of the new one, except in natal down replacement. This idea developed from the fact that artificially and untimely plucking of a feather usually results in its replacement within a short period of time.

The sequence of plumages is quite variable in different species of birds and sometimes varies within species depending upon geographical distribution. The photoperiod appears to affect plumage sequences through its influence on hormonal cycles. Thus equatorial birds tend to have no regular annual or perennial plumage sequences, whereas periodic plumage sequences become rather firmly fixed in near polar populations. Numerous examples of intergradations can be cited.

A thorough review of plumage sequences appears in a paper by P. S. Humphrey and K. C. Parkes (1959) in which they propose a new terminology. An eloquent rebuttal appears in Erwin Stresemann's (1963) paper in which he argues for a retention of the terminology of Dwight (1900) and subsequent modifications. The reader is referred to these papers.

Meanwhile the new terminology has already been accepted in the most recent analysis of North American birds (Palmer, Ralph S., 1962). Thus it appears that we are due to find both terminologies in the literature for the next decade or more. The fundamental difference between the two systems lies in the Dwight system's stressing the biological cycles of plumage and the Humphrey-Parkes system's emphasizing the incoming plumage.

The following table compares the terminology employed in the two systems of nomenclature of plumage sequences in birds:

Dwight System	Time	Humphrey-Parkes System
Juvenal Plumage	fledgling	Juvenal Plumage
Postjuvenal Molt		Prebasic I Molt
First Nonnuptial Plumage	1st winter	Basic I Plumage
First Prenuptial Molt		Prealternate I Molt
First Nuptial Plumage	1st breeding	Alternate I Plumage
First Postnuptial Molt		Prebasic II Molt
Second Nonnuptial Plumage	2nd winter	Basic II Plumage
Etc.	Etc.	Etc.

It must be emphasized that many birds do not molt completely. Some birds change appearance by contour feather wear rather than by plumage change at the onset of the breeding season. Others shed wing and tail feathers in one season, body contour feathers in another. Thus it is apparent that there are many modifications of the plumage sequences.

colies, natives of Africa, all four toes are directed forward (pamprodactyl). Many of our native American species (woodpeckers, trogons, and cuckoos) have two toes directed forward and two directed to the rear. Owls are able to hold the outer toe either forward or back. Those birds with three toes forward and one behind are said to be **anisodactyl.** In these birds the first toe is the rear one, the second is in the inner forward position, the third in the middle front, and the fourth in the outer front. They are given numbers in that order, number one being to the rear and so on to number four which is the outer forward toe. By adding one to the toe number one can usually arrive at the number of bones in each toe. This number provides the digital formula which typically is 2– 3 – 4 – 5.

Those birds which have two toes directed to the rear may have either numbers 1 and 2 back or numbers 1 and 4 back. Trogons have toes 1 and 2 directed to the rear and are said to be **heterodactyl.** Woodpeckers and cuckoos are **zygodactyl,** that is, they have toes 1 and 4 in the rear position. Some birds, such as the owls, have toe number 1 permanently fixed to the rear but can turn the fourth toe either forward or to the rear at will. This condition is described as "outer toe reversible" or **semi-zygodactyl.** The kingfisher and some other birds have two or more toes fused at their bases, a condition known as **syndactylism.**

Loons, ducks, geese, swans, gulls, terns, and some other birds have toe numbers 2, 3, and 4 connected by a web and are **natatorial.** (See Figure 13.) Natatorial feet are well adapted for swimming and diving. In the birds of the Order Pelecaniformes all four toes are joined in a web and are said to be **totipalmate.** Grebes, rails, gallinules, coots, etc., have laterally **lobed** toes. Lobed toes are well adapted for swimming or

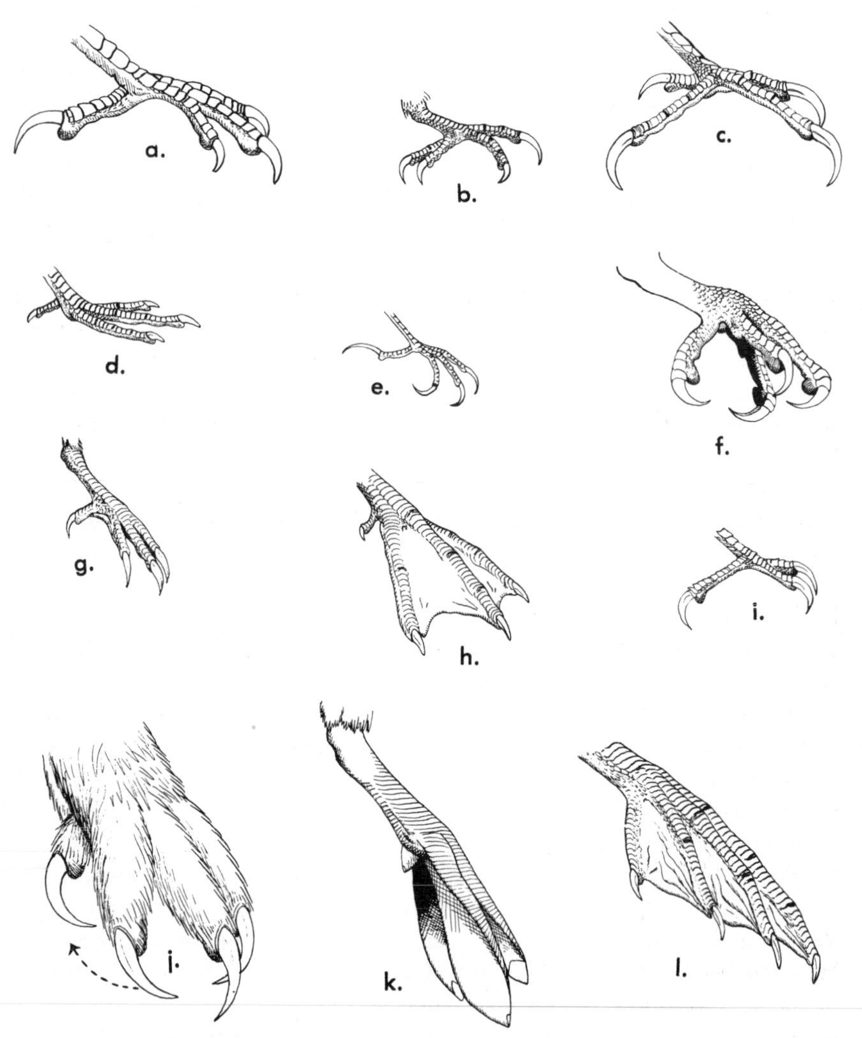

Figure 13. Some representative types of feet of birds. (*a*) anisodactyl (Common Crow); (*b*) heterodactyl (Coppery-tailed Trogon); (*c*) zygodactyl (Pileated Woodpecker); (*d*) rasorial or scratching (Bobwhite); (*e*) scansorial (Brown Creeper); (*f*) raptorial (Duck Hawk); (*g*) syndactyl (Belted Kingfisher); (*h*) natatorial or webbed (Ring-billed Gull); (*i*) three-toed (Arctic Three-toed Woodpecker); (*j*) semi-zygodactyl and raptorial (Great Horned Owl); (*k*) lobed (Horned Grebe); (*l*) totipalmate (Double-crested Cormorant). Drawings by William C. Dilger.

paddling in water or for walking on mucky land. In most birds the toes are free. The hind toe or **hallux** may be elevated (raised) or incumbent (inserted on the same level as the other toes). At their tips the toes are equipped with **nails** or **claws.** These too are variable. In the grebes they are flattened, and in barn owls, herons, and goatsuckers the third toe bears a **pectinate nail** or one with a comb-like ridge along the side.

tarsus. The tarsus may be feathered, as on the grouse, or bare as on most birds. A bare tarsus is actually covered by scales. This scale covering varies greatly in the different families of birds and thus frequently serves as a taxonomic character. A number of terms are employed to describe the tarsus. Some of these are **holothecal,** having the tarsal covering in one continuous piece wrapped around the tarsus like a scroll; **scutellate,** bearing rather large and distinctive scales on the tarsus, usually only on the foretarsus; **reticulate** or **granular,** having a tarsal covering that bears a network of small or fine scales which are bordered by furrows thus giving the feet a granular appearance; **cancellate,** having short but wide scales that extend across the foretarsus and frequently across the top of lobed toes as in the grebes; **cylindrical,** having the tarsus circular in cross section; **compressed,** having the tarsus somewhat flattened from the sides; **ridged,** having the tarsus cylindrical or compressed but bearing a rather sharp ridge which extends from top to bottom on the rear surface of the tarsus.

The external appearance of birds is due largely to the color and arrangement of the feathers. The great variety of bill types and variations of the feet also contribute much to the external appearance. A thorough working knowledge of the material presented in this chapter is essential for every phase of study in ornithology. The taxonomist will pursue this subject farther. The geneticist will study inherited variations. The bird-watcher whose principal interest is "bird listing" will be able to tell decoys from the real thing.

Bibliography and References

Allen, Arthur A., The Book of Bird Life. Princeton, N. J.: D. Van Nostrand Co., pp. 198-239, 1961.

Allen, Glover Morrill, Birds and Their Attributes. Boston: Marshall Jones Co., pp. 35-105, 1925. (Also reprint: 1962, Dover Publications, New York.)

Chapman, Frank M., Handbook of Birds of Eastern North America, 2nd ed. New York: D. Appleton-Century Co., pp. 91-104, 1940.

Dwight, J., Jr., The Sequence of Plumages and Molts of the Passerine Birds of New York. *Ann. N. Y. Acad. Sci.,* 13:76-360, 1900.

Humphrey, P. S. and K. C. Parkes, An Approach to the Study of Molts and Plumages. *Auk,* 76:1-31, 1959.

Palmer, Ralph S. (Editor), Handbook of North American Birds. Vol. 1. New Haven: Yale Univ. Press, pp. 1-19, 1962.

Stresemann, Erwin, The Nomenclature of Plumages and Molts. *Auk,* 20:1-8, 1963.

Watson, George E., Feather Replacement in Birds. *Science,* 139 (3549): 50-51, 1963.

EXERCISE ON EXTERNAL FEATURES

The use of study skins of birds for examination of external structure is a standard procedure. Study skins are produced by skinning the entire bird except feet and bill. The skin is then filled with soft cotton and wood or wire support. The bill is generally oriented directly forward, the feet crossed and extended posteriorly, and the wings tied against the back of the body. In this position, the skin is allowed to dry. The dried skin is somewhat fragile and should be handled carefully. Following are some suggestions on the care of museum-type study skins of birds.

1. Pick up the study skin by firmly grasping the bird by both sides of the body, gently pinching the skin between thumb and forefingers. Very small birds can be handled by gently but firmly pinching a few of the breast feathers and holding between thumb and index finger. Very large birds must be handled by using both hands.

2. Lay the study skin in its proper position. Most birds are dried in a position with the dorsal side down. Look for the flat side of the skin and keep that side down when not handling the bird.

3. Never force the wings. The correct method for examining the wing feathers, particularly the primaries, is to firmly place thumb and forefinger over the base of both wings. The flexible feathers can then be bent as needed to count or examine them. Never bend feathers beyond the flexing point so that they break.

4. Tail feathers should be held firmly by pinching the base of the feathers when counting or otherwise examining rectrices.

5. Feet sometimes present a problem. They cannot be moved at all. Never hold the specimen by the feet. Never hold the specimen by the label that may be tied to the feet. Examine feet only by holding study skin and maneuvering the entire bird. Forcing a toe or

A. Examine the listed species of birds and complete the table as indicated:

Species (General)	Species Examined	Type of Feet	Type of Bill
Loon			
Grebe			
Petrel			
Pelican			
Heron			
Mallard			
Hawk			
Grouse			
Rail			
Skimmer			
Gull			
Auk			
Jacana			
Woodcock			
Killdeer			

Species (General)	Species Examined	Type of Feet	Type of Bill
Stilt			
Barn Owl			
Night Hawk			
Hummingbird			
Kingfisher			
Woodpecker			
Lark			
Brown Creeper			
Starling			
Grosbeak			

B. Examine a prepared microscope slide of the feather. Prepare a drawing of your observations or briefly describe the specimen observed.

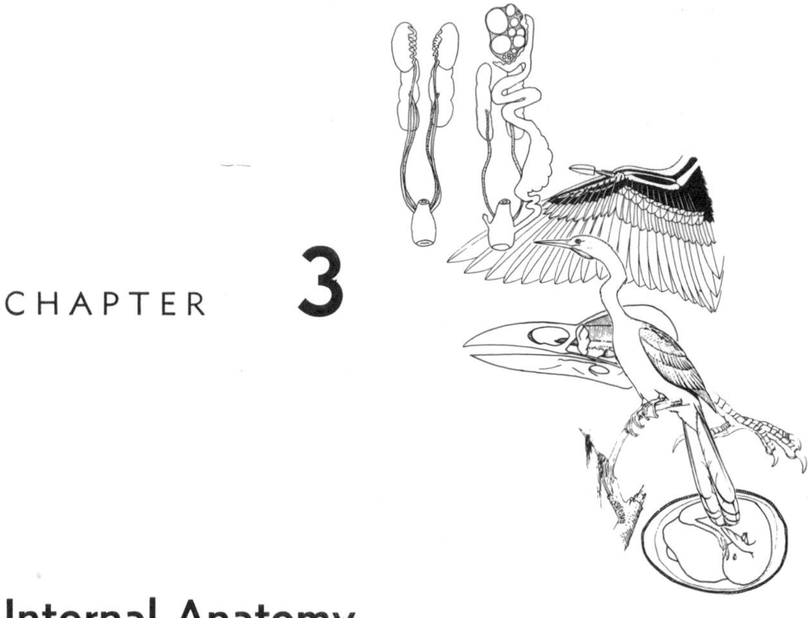

CHAPTER 3

Internal Anatomy

The bird is a vertebrate and the structures of other vertebrates are, for the most part, similar to those of the bird or vice versa. This chapter therefore will not delve into a detailed anatomical description of a bird but instead will endeavor to point out the major modifications of the avian anatomy compared to that of a mammal in particular.

Most of the anatomical differences between mammals and birds can be traced directly to the flying habit of birds. There is a general tendency for organs, which in mammals are situated toward the extremities, to be shifted toward the center in birds. For example, the large oral cavity, which in mammals bears the teeth, is replaced by a comparatively small oral cavity without teeth. The mastication of food is accomplished by a large muscular gizzard (ventriculus) or muscular stomach. The breast muscles which perform the strong down-stroke of flight are highly developed in birds that fly.

The skeleton bears many modifications. (See Figures 14-15.) Most of them serve to provide a more rigid support or a greater surface for the attachment of muscles. The **skull** is composed of numerous bones which are rigidly fused. It serves to house the brain and supports the bill, eyes, and ears. The backbone or **vertebral column** is essentially like that of mammals. In all but a few mammals there are seven **cervical** or **neck vertebrae,** while in the birds they number twelve to twenty-

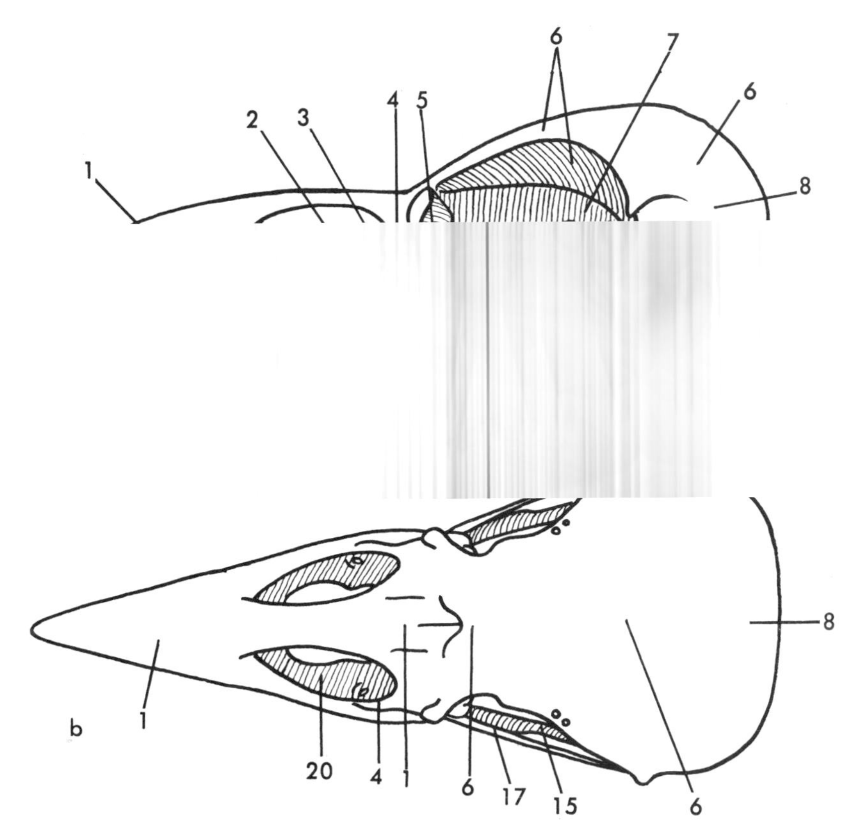

Figure 14. Skull of the Raven (*Corvus corax*); a. lateral view, b. dorsal view. 1. Premaxillary; 2. Vomer; 3. Maxillary; 4. Nasal; 5. Ethmoid; 6. Frontal; 7. Mesethmoid; 8. Parietal; 9. Squamosal; 10. Occipital; 11. Otic; 12. Quadrate; 13. Quadratojugal; 14. Angulare; 15. Pterygoid; 16. Surangulare; 17. Jugal; 18. Basisphenoid; 19. Splenial; 20. Palatine; 21. Dentary. Drawing by William C. Dilger.

five. The first cervical vertebra, that one next to the skull, has but one articulating surface with the skull. The process on the skull which moves on the atlas or first vertebra is known as the **occipital condyle.** Mammals have two occipital condyles. Here birds show relationship with the reptiles, which also have a single condyle articulating with the atlas. The cervical vertebrae are followed by the **thoracic** or **dorsal vertebrae.** These bear lateral projections, the **ribs,** which bend sharply ventrally and forward. The ribs bear special projections, the **uncinate processes,** which serve to form a more rigid support for the trunk. The uncinate processes project, one from each rib except the last, posterodorsally from one rib to the next. The lumbar, sacral, and urosacral vertebrae are usually fused into a single bone, together with the pelvic girdle. This fused structure is known as the **synsacrum.** Following the urosacral vertebrae are the **caudal vertebrae,** which articulate freely except for the last (usually) six, which are fused to form the **pygostyle.** The pygostyle supports the feathers of the tail. It articulates rather freely with the last of the free caudal vertebrae. (See Figure 15.)

The pelvic girdle, which was mentioned in the foregoing paragraph, supports the hind limbs. The "upper leg" or **femur** is similar to that of mammals and articulates with the synsacrum at the **acetabulum.** The acetabulum is a somewhat spherical cavity situated at the meeting point of the **ilium, ischium,** and **pubis** (the bones of the pelvic girdle which are fused with the synsacrum). The "drumstick" or **tibiofibula** is a combination of several bones, the tibia, the fibula, and some of tarsals, all of which are fused. The **tarsometatarsus** has been mentioned in the previous chapter in connection with the external features of the feet. It is composed of some of the tarsals and all of the metatarsals, which again are fused into a single bone which supports the **digits** or bones of the toes. The bird walks only on its toes and not on the whole foot as do many of the mammals, including man.

The ribs are composed of two parts. The **vertebral ribs** extend ventrally and connect with the **sternal ribs,** which extend anteriorly to connect with the breastbone or **sternum.** This is a rather large bone compared to its homolog in mammals. On the mid-ventral surface of the sternum of most birds is a large plate-like process, the **keel** or **carina.** The carina extends ventrally and serves to increase the surface for the attachment of the pectoral or flight muscles. The sternum supports the two **coracoid** bones, which, together with the **scapulae** and the fused **clavicles** or wishbone, support the forelimbs or wings. The bones of the wings are more similar to those of the forelimbs of mammals than are the hind limbs to their homologs. Proximally the **humerus** articulates with the **glenoid fossa,** which is a depression in the ends of the coracoid and the scapula. The **radius** (smaller bone of the forearm) and the **ulna** articulate with the distal end of the humerus. The radius and ulna are not fused and can move freely, thus allowing the wing a partial rotary motion. Three carpal and metacarpal bones, variously fused, form the **carpometacarpus,** which supports the three digits. The second, third, and fourth digits remain in the wing of birds. (See Figure 15.)

The **palate,** or bony portion of the roof of the mouth, varies considerably in different orders of birds. The five major types of palates

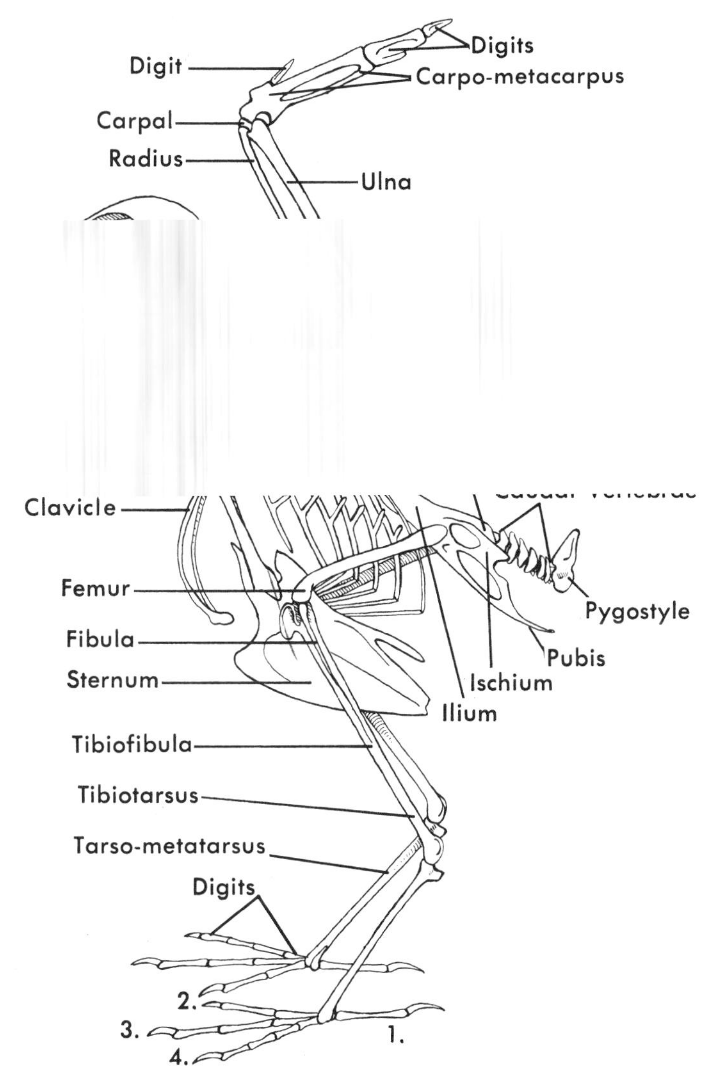

Figure 15. Skeleton of a Robin (*Turdus migratorius*). Drawing by William C. Dilger.

are exemplified by emus (dromaeognathous), geese (desmognathous), gulls (schizognathous), woodpeckers (saurognathous), and song birds (aegithognathous). The significance of the bony palate is principally taxonomic and is presented here only briefly to introduce the student to terminology which may be important later.

Many fusions are apparent in the skeleton of birds. These fusions form a more rigid skeletal structure which provides better support for the body under the stress of flight. Further, the larger bones bear large cavities so that, while large, they are light in weight. These cavities house air sacs which are diverticula of the lungs.

The digestive system bears several important modifications. The bill has been dealt with previously. It forms the roof, floor, and sides of the **oral cavity.** The tongue is housed in this cavity where it is superficially attached to the floor. The tongue has, however, additional bony or cartilaginous support in the **hyoid** apparatus which anchors in the tissues at the posterior part of the skull. There are no teeth. Teeth are last known in *Ichthyornis* and *Hesperornis,* both of which lived in western North America in the Cretaceous period (some 100 million years ago).

Posteriorly the oral cavity opens into the pharynx, where the air channel (which leads air to and from the lungs and the nostrils) and the food channel cross. (See Figure 16.) A relatively long esophagus leads from the pharynx and extends through the neck and through the thoracic region of the trunk. In its posterior portion the **esophagus** is generally quite elastic and capable of storing much food. This distensible portion is called the **crop.** Its major function is food storage; however in pigeons and doves it is glandular and secretes a milky fluid (pigeon milk) which is regurgitated into the mouths of their young. The esophagus empties into the glandular stomach or **proventriculus** which is followed immediately by the muscular stomach or **gizzard.** The proventriculus has glandular walls which secrete some digestive enzymes. The gizzard serves as a substitute for teeth in masticating food. Pebbles or grit that are ingested by the bird assist the muscles in grinding the food. These remain in the gizzard, where their action is similar to that of millstones in grinding the food.

The **small intestine** leads from the gizzard and proximally the **duodenum** loops around and more or less encases the **pancreas.** The bile duct from the liver and the pancreatic ducts empty into the duodenum. The liver and the pancreas have among their functions the secreting of digestive enzymes. The remainder of the small intestine is long and coiled. Posteriorly it opens into the short **large intestine** or **rectum.** At the point of union of the small and large intestines, two large **ceaca** diverge. The large intestine empties into the **cloaca,** a structure common to the urogenital systems and the digestive system. The cloaca is a short and enlarged portion of the tract which serves as a storage organ for

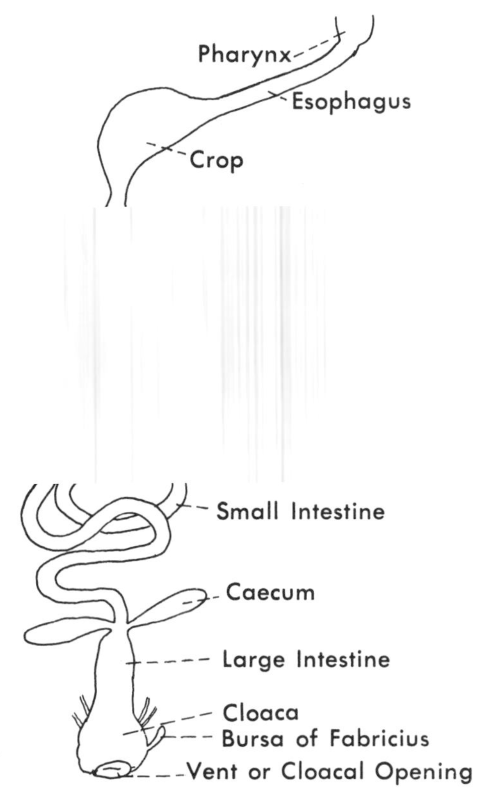

Figure 16. The digestive system of a bird.

digestive wastes and the wastes of the excretory system. These wastes escape to the outside through the anus or **vent.** The digestive system is illustrated in Figure 16.

The excretory system of birds differs in several respects from that of mammals. There is no urinary bladder. Excreta is not a watery fluid as is the case with mammals but rather it is a white paste which requires less space for storage until it is eliminated. The **kidneys** function more efficiently in reabsorbing aqueous materials. This efficiency in water reabsorption enables birds to consume comparatively less water. The cloaca functions in storing the excreta until it is passed out of the body through the vent along with the wastes of the digestive system. Figure 17 illustrates the excretory system.

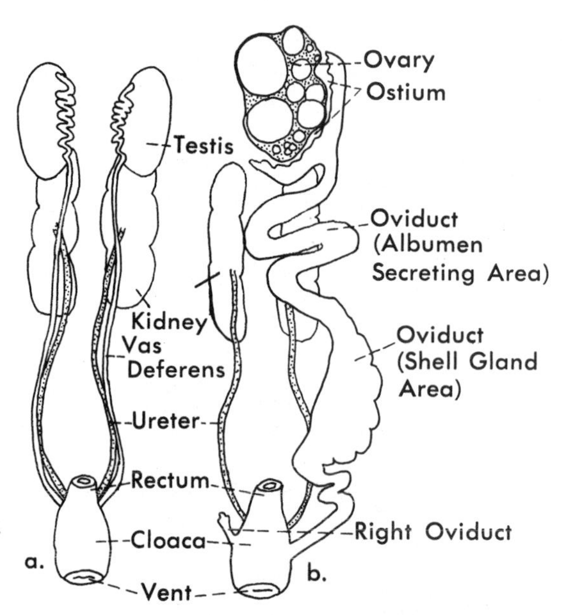

Figure 17. The urogenital system of a bird. (*a*) male; (*b*) female.

The male reproductive system (see Fig. 17) is somewhat similar to that of mammals. In most birds, however, there is no copulatory organ. The testes are permanently located dorsal to the coelom or body cavity and anterior to the kidneys. The testes become enlarged and are functional only during the breeding season.

The female reproductive system (see Fig. 17) differs substantially from that of mammals, for it is adapted for **oviparous** reproduction (egg laying). All the mammals except the platypus and the spiny anteaters are viviparous, that is, they bear living young which during development have a placental attachment to the mother. The female bird has lost the right half of the system. Traces of the right portion may be found, but unless the left portion is injured or destroyed the right half is abortive and nonfunctional. The left **ovary** is small and apparently degenerate throughout the winter months, but with the approach of spring and the mating season the ovary becomes very large. This increase in size is due largely to the growth of the eggs which are produced therein. When the egg is properly matured (ripe) in the ovary it ruptures from its parent tissues and enters the oviduct via the **ostium** (the opening of the inner end of the oviduct). The oviduct, too, is small during most of the year but becomes enlarged during the breeding and nesting seasons. The upper portion of the oviduct bears glands which secrete the albumen (the **albumen secreting area**), while the lower region bears the **shell glands.** Fertilization necessarily occurs in the upper reproductive system before the egg passes through the shell gland area.

female for some time. An entire clutch of eggs thus may be fertilized by sperm deposited in the cloaca of the female a day or more before the first egg was laid.

The activities of the ovary in birds are truly amazing. Most people are more or less familiar with the domestic hen, which may lay around 200 to 275 eggs per annum. This has been accomplished by selection of breeding stock, supplementary light, and improved foods. Wild birds normally lay a more or less definite number of eggs per set or **clutch,** the number varying with each species. Experiments have shown that if one egg is removed and a "nest egg" or two is left behind, the bird may continue to lay one egg daily (more or less) for some time before its egg-laying capacity is reached or before it quits the nest in question and builds a new one elsewhere. The classical case of the flicker that is said to have laid approximately seventy eggs in this manner is perhaps the record. Normally, however, when the clutch is complete the female stops laying eggs and begins incubating them. The physiological control of such a phenomenon is truly a mysterious one, especially when one considers that it normally takes the egg from 3 to 12 hours to pass from the ovary to the cloaca in the domestic hen and as much as 18 hours in some wild birds.

The shell glands, especially those near the cloaca, secret the pigment which gives the egg its color. Color in birds' eggs portrays something of the evolution of the species concerned. In general, those birds that nest in cavities or the like lay white eggs whereas those that lay their eggs in open nests produce pigmented ones. The thrush family presents an interesting case. Most of the thrushes, such as the Robin and Wood Thrush, lay more or less uniformly blue eggs. These thrushes nest in open nests so the eggs can be seen from above when not covered by the adult in incubation. The Bluebird, on the other hand, nests in cavities in posts, or trees, or in bird houses provided by man. This species lays eggs which vary from bluish-white to white. Apparently the cavity-nesting habit of the Bluebird is not very ancient, for the egg color has not been lost entirely. Two hypotheses attempt to explain this phenomenon.

Modern ideas of the mechanics of evolution would present the case this way: At one point in the phylogeny of the Bluebird a gene, or a combination of several genes, was affected in some manner so that the eggs lost their blue coloration. **Genes** are structures situated in the chromosomes of cells. They are responsible for passing on characters from one generation to the next. This gene would have had to affect the previously normal functioning of the shell gland or more particularly that part of the shell gland which has to do with the secreting of pigments. Then the Bluebird was faced with the problem of adjusting itself to this change in its inheritance and it changed its nesting habits so that now it nests in cavities. A change in egg color is actually inherited. In a sense, inheritance might be called internal environment. In this sense the change of the color of the Bluebird's eggs might be considered a change in its environment. If the species could not survive by laying white eggs in an exposed nest, then the Bluebird was faced with two alternatives. It could adapt itself to this change or it could fail to adapt itself and become extinct. Similar situations faced many organisms throughout geologic time and many failed to make the necessary adjustments. If this was the case those Bluebirds that did not make the change were exterminated and only a select portion of the former population remained to carry on the species.

On the other hand, for some unknown reason, the Bluebird may have changed its habits from open nesting to cavity nesting. This may have occurred simultaneously with the origin of the Bluebird as a new species. The change of color of the eggs may have been a part of the evolutionary change involved with the origin of the new species. Or the genes involved with pigment production may have been altered as a result of the change in environment when the change in nesting habits occurred. The altered genes failed to allow the continuation of the production of blue pigments.

The respiratory system, illustrated in Figure 18, bears a few specialized structures that are worthy of mention here. The larynx is present as in the mammals, but some of its functions are performed by a unique structure, the **syrinx.** The syrinx is usually located at the bifurcation of the trachea or windpipe. The larynx is in the same position

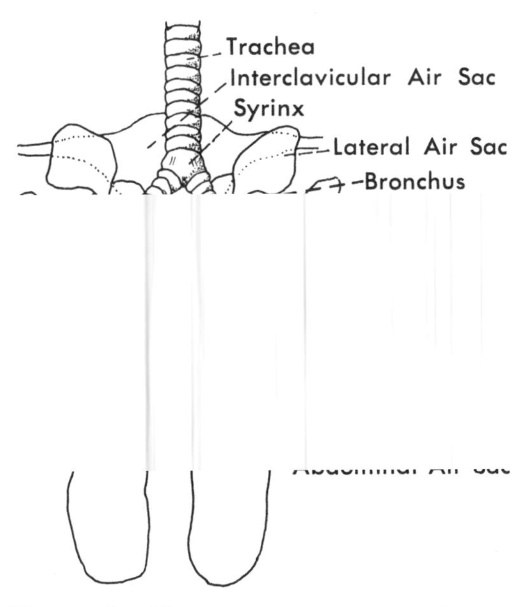

Figure 18. The respiratory system of a pigeon showing the arrangement of the air sacs.

as in mammals, just behind the pharynx. In mammals the larynx houses the sound-producing organs, whereas in birds this is the function of the syrinx. There are several **tympanic membranes**, which lie along the inner surface of the trachea and the bronchi at the syrinx. These membranes are the sound-producing structures. Each of the membranes can be adjusted by a set of special muscles to produce various tones. Another structure, the **semilunar membrane,** projects like a flap from the internal point of jointure of the two bronchi. This also produces vibrations. These structures and their muscles are variously modified in various bird groups and are best developed in the passerine or song birds.

The lungs are equipped for maximum efficiency by the addition of nine or ten major **air sacs** which extend from the lungs. In mammals only about two-thirds of the lung capacity can be utilized. One-third of the capacity holds residual air which serves to prevent the lungs from collapsing. In birds this residual air is forced into the air sacs with each breath. The respiratory system thus has increased efficiency, enabling the cells to receive a sufficient oxygen supply during the exertion of flight. The air sacs extend from the lungs into the hollow bones and into other free spaces in the body cavity. They do not occupy any additional space nor tend to increase the size of the bird as compared to a mammal. The air sacs include one interclavicular or two cervicals, two laterals, two anterior thoracics, and two abdominals (see Figure 18).

The sense of sight is very keen in birds. Essentially, the avian eye is similar to the eye of mammals but there are two major differences. The comparison of the structures can be studied from Figure 19. The

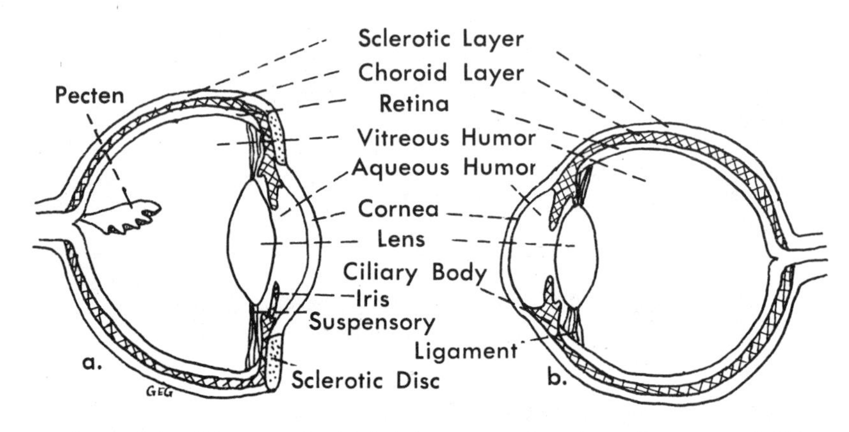

Figure 19. The eye of a bird (*a*) compared to that of a mammal (*b*).

forward or lateral side of the bird's eye is flattened somewhat. This modification is caused by an underlying bony ring, the **sclerotic disc.** The sclerotic disc is composed of a circular series of small bony plates. It provides added support to the eye for an animal that places this organ under unusual stresses in flight at rather high speeds. The sclerotic disc is not peculiar to birds, for it is present in some of the fishes and many of the reptiles.

The second modification of the avian eye is the **pecten,** a highly vascular structure which is attached near the point at which the optic nerve leaves the eye. The pecten's size can be changed at will by the bird. It can be moved about somewhat, in the region occupied by the fluid vitreous humor. The function of the pecten is unknown. Because of its vascular structure it has been suggested that it serves as an agent in nourishing the vitreous humor. Others believe it functions in accommodation, that is, adjusting the lens so that objects can be kept in focus as the bird flies or dives through the air. A more likely function, perhaps merely auxiliary, is that its rod-shaped mass projects through the vitreous humor, thus casting a shadow on the retina. This shadow would automatically move with the movement of light rays coming from any moving object within range. Thus the bird would be provided with a keen power for seeing moving objects, while those that are stationary

[illegible]

the movement of the soil as the worm moves under the surface. The range of hearing in most species is probably far less than that of humans. Man can hear frequencies ranging from about 20 cycles per second to 16,000 cycles per second. The Starling showed a hearing range of 700 c.p.s. to 15,000 c.p.s. in experiments (Brand and Kellogg, 1939). Furthermore, it showed a decided loss of sensitivity below 1000 c.p.s. and above 14,000 c.p.s., so that the Starling hears best between 1000 and 14,000 cycles per second. The following table shows the hearing ranges of the indicated species:

Species	Low (c.p.s.)	High (c.p.s.)	Authority
Great Horned Owl	60	7,000	Edwards, 1943
Canvasback	190	5,200	"
Domestic Pigeon	200	7,500	Brand & Kellogg, 1939
Horned Lark	350	7,600	Edwards, 1943
Snow Bunting	400	7,200	"
House Sparrow	675	11,500	Brand & Kellogg, 1939
Starling	700	15,000	"

Birds and mammals are homothermous animals. The temperature of most birds is in the vicinity of 110° F. to 115° F. and on the average is considerably higher than the body temperature of mammals. Body temperature is more or less directly proportional to metabolic rate. Birds require more food to produce more energy and they expend their energy more rapidly. In general, the numerous structural and physiological modifications of birds can be linked to flight. Structures that show relation to the flying habit are present in the skeleton, the digestive system, the excretory system, the reproductive systems, the respiratory system, the circulatory system, the musculature, the integument, and the sense organs.

Bibliography and References

ALLEN, GLOVER MORRILL, Birds and Their Attributes. Boston: Marshall-Jones Co., pp. 78-197, 1925. (Reprinted: 1962, Dover Publications, New York.)

BERGER, ANDREW J., Bird Study. New York: John Wiley & Sons, pp. 279-307, 1961.

BRAND, ALBERT R., and P. PAUL KELLOGG, Auditory Responses of Starlings, English Sparrows, and Domestic Pigeons. *Wilson Bull.*, 51:38-41, 1939.

EDWARDS, ERNEST P., Hearing Ranges of Four Species of Birds. *Auk*, 60:239-241, 1943.

HYMAN, LIBBIE HENRIETTA, Comparative Vertebrate Anatomy, 2nd Ed. Chicago: University Chicago Press, pp. 121-122, 279-286, 351-359, 410-411, 1942.

MARSHALL, A. J. (Editor), Biology and Comparative Physiology of Birds, Volumes I and II. New York: Academic Press, 1960, 1961.

WELTY, JOEL CARL, The Life of Birds. Philadelphia: W. B. Saunders Co., pp. 55-155, 1962.

EXERCISE ON INTERNAL FEATURES

The author has long felt that a valuable biological resource is being completely wasted. This resource is the millions of day-old cockerels of light breeds of domestic chickens. Light breeds (Leghorns) are maintained commercially primarily for egg production, and since the males produce no eggs they are destroyed immediately after being separated from the females. These day-old cockerels may be used satisfactorily to illustrate, through dissection, the major internal anatomical features of birds.

Day-old cockerels (Leghorn varieties) can be obtained, generally without charge, from almost all hatcheries. They can be killed by gassing and should then quickly be preserved by injecting 15 percent to 20 percent formalin solution into the body cavity at two or three points. They can then be stored in 5 percent formalin solution in a tight container. They are sufficiently hardened for ease in dissecting after three days.

With sharp dissecting scissors, make an incision in the ventral abdominal wall about five millimeters to the left (bird's left) of the midline. Note that the body wall is quite thin in this region. Do not cut too deeply. Continue the incision anteriorly into the thoracic region. [illegible] from making the incisions.

Under the abdominal wall a large pale yellow **yolk sac** will be found. It is connected to the **abdominal peritoneum** at the navel and to the **intestines.** Carefully sever its connection to the peritoneum. Now the two flaps of body wall can be forced open to reveal the visceral organs. It is helpful to cut the small intestine anterior to the yolk sac and fold the posterior portion of the alimentary tract back to allow for easier inspection of the anterior structures.

Using the discussion of these structures in the text, examine and identify the organs of the digestive system, the respiratory system, the urogenital system, and the heart.

Prepare a series of drawings to record your observations of the internal anatomy of the baby chick.

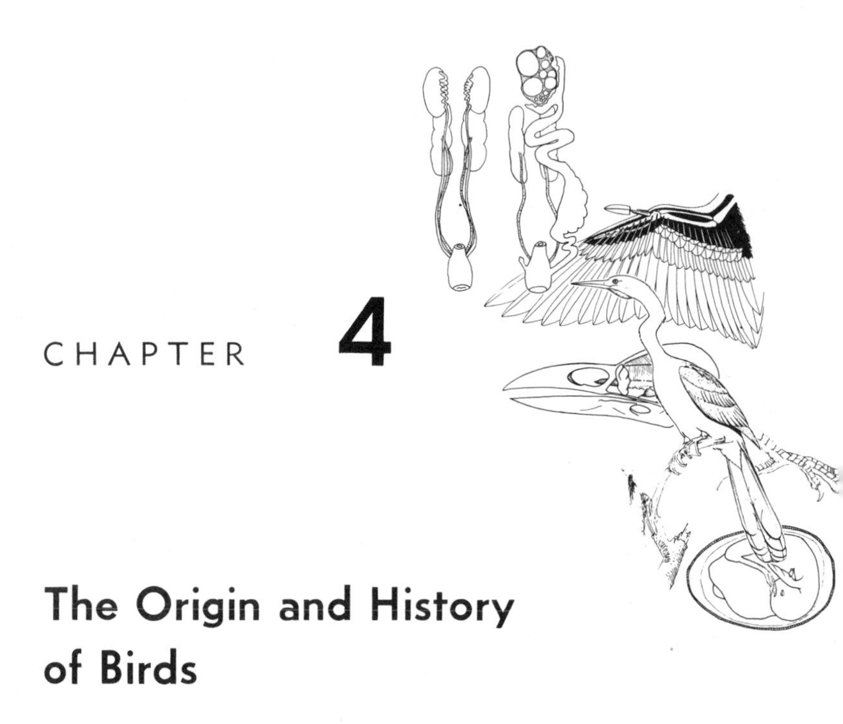

CHAPTER 4

The Origin and History of Birds

The story of the origin and early evolution of birds must necessarily be incomplete. Such facts as can be gleaned from the few fossil remains of early avian forms and other animal and plant remains or traces in the rocks are the only valid source materials. By using the present as a key to the past, these materials can be interpreted. A complete story is impossible, for the evidence is only fragmentary. Considering the requisites for fossilization, however, we are extremely fortunate to have what little evidence has been found. A brief investigation into the history of the earth will give us a better understanding of the origin of birds.

The earth's history has been divided into five eras. (See the geologic time table on page No. 45.) These were separated by great and rather widespread revolutions in the earth's crust. In areas where the rock deposits of two successive eras meet, there is a great difference between the two. Revolutions themselves were slow and may have covered a million or more years. They may have involved a raising or a submergence of the earth's crust, or both raising and submergence may have occurred simultaneously in adjacent areas. The latter is more likely. Mountains are constantly moving about. They are not the dead masses they appear to be. They are dynamic. An area which was an extensive swamp for thousands or perhaps millions of years may have become a young mountain. An ancient mountain may have gradually submerged and left in its place a lake or swamp. Climatic changes accompanied these topographic changes. In comparatively recent geologic time, glaciers covered the northern portion of the United States and Canada. Agents such as glaciers, while caused by cold climate and high precipitation, brought about topographic changes. Most of the lakes in the [illegible]

Essentially this is how evolution works. Changes in environment apparently are frequently responsible for changes in genetic constitution. This is an involved process and through it new species are often derived.

A glance at the geologic time table on page 45 will provide the reader with an idea of the large picture and further will show how small a part has been occupied by the birds and mammals. It may be highly desirable to memorize the table.

The great dinosaurs, as well as the less well known smaller dinosaurs, made their appearance in the early portion of the Mesozoic era. This **era** of geologic time has been divided into three **periods:** the most ancient Triassic, the middle Jurassic, and the most recent Cretaceous. It was in the Jurassic that the dinosaurs, which were rather highly evolved reptiles, first appeared. These dinosaurs are generally believed to have a common ancestor with the birds in the primitive thecodonts. Thecodonts first appeared in the Triassic. This same group may have given rise to the pterosaurs, or flying reptiles, which appeared about the same time as the first known bird.

Paleontological records of the birds are not very satisfactory. In order that a form could become fossilized it had to possess hard parts such as teeth, scales, shells, and bones, for they decay slowly. Furthermore, the organism must have been buried rapidly, so that predators and scavengers would not have eaten it. The burial must have been deep or in some medium which preserved the material. Fossilization required extremely slow decay processes.

Fossils can be of several types, classed according to the method by which they were preserved. Some bones, mollusk shells, teeth, etc., may have been preserved as **original material.** These fossils generally are from comparatively recent times. In many older burials there has been a slow **replacement** of the original organic molecules by molecules of some mineral. As the original ones slowly decayed, mineral molecules replaced them. Such fossils are a rock model of the original and they are very durable. Other **traces** remain as **tracks** or **prints.** A bird may have left his footprints on soft mud. The mud then dried and hardened. A flood over the area may have left a layer of mud on top of the original layer. This subsequently dried and hardened, and the process was frequently repeated. As more and more layers were added the mud, under pressure, became rock. When quarried, the rock tends to break at the planes where mud layers joined. Thus, with the breaking of the rock at the point at which the bird's footprint was marked in the mud, two fossils may be found. The original footprint, a depression, is a **mold**, and the superimposed mud which filled in this depression is a **cast.** Feathers flattened out on mud surfaces left **prints** similarly. The original feathers had completely decomposed and no replacement had occurred.

At Rancho la Brea in Los Angeles, California, there are pits or wells of sticky asphalt. Water collects on their surfaces and many animals are lured there for a drink. Many become mired in the underlying pitch and sink down in this natural preservative. Ninety species of birds, of which 73 are modern forms, have been recorded as fossils from the Pleistocene of Rancho la Brea. Quicksands provide other means for rapid burial, and alkaline lakes or ponds may provide preservation to a degree sufficient to permit slow burial. All told, however, fossilization of an organism obviously involves a great deal of chance. The chances are probably less than one in a million, especially in birds, which can fly, and get out of possible situations where death and rapid burial could occur. The hollow bones of birds lend themselves poorly to preservation.

In the Jurassic period, nearly 200 million years ago, a vast tropical sea with coral islands occupied what is now Central Europe. Silt deposits were laid down and an ancient bird met its demise on the silt. As the years passed, layer after layer of the fine silt covered this bird until the deposit became hundreds of feet thick and, under the great pressure, changed to stone. The stone was of a very fine texture which has come to be known as lithographic limestone, for it has been quarried for use in the reproduction of color pictures. The ancient bird was first known from a single feather print. In 1861, a nearly complete specimen was found in the lithographic limestone quarries at Solenhofen, Bavaria. This specimen, discovered by Andreas Wagner, was named *Archeopteryx*. It is now in the British Museum. In 1877 a third speci-

TABLE 1. GEOLOGIC TIME TABLE

Era and duration	Period	Epochs	Important events in animal evolution
million years)	Quaternary Triassic	Recent	first dinosaurs
Paleozoic (300 million years)	Permian Pennsylvanian Mississippian Devonian Silurian Ordovician Cambrian		spread of amphibs and reptiles first reptiles rise of amphibians first amphibs, age of fish first air breathing fish first primitive vertebrates dominance of invertebrates
Proterozoic		(600 million years)	origin of invertebrates
Archeozoic		(900 million years)	viruses, bacteria, primitive algae.
Azoic (? years)			no life

The list of important events in animal evolution is necessarily incomplete, for the invertebrates played a great role in the picture, especially through the Paleozoic. The diagram below shows the relative duration of the eras.

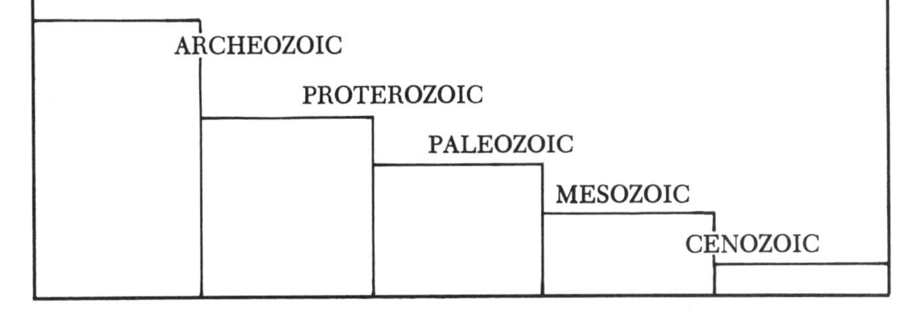

men was found in the same deposits. It was named *Archeornis,* the same name given to the specimen of the single feather. The fossil was housed in the Berlin Museum, which is now in the Russian-occupied zone. The specimen of *Archeopteryx* lacked the head, while the second specimen of *Archeornis* was more nearly complete.

Archeopteryx and *Archeornis* were long considered to be closely related. Recent studies show a more distant relationship, and now the two are in separate families. These birds show many reptilian characters. The remains are so similar to some of the smaller bipedal dinosaurs that they probably would not have been recognized as birds were

Figure 20. The Jurassic reptile-bird, *Archeornis.* A scratchboard reproduction of the fossil specimen.

it not for the prints of feathers associated with the outlines of bones. They differ from modern birds in several outstanding details. The bills bore well-developed teeth, which were implanted in sockets in the maxillary and premaxillary bones of the upper mandible and in the dentary bone of the lower mandible. All of the vetebrae were free. The caudal vertebrae extended well out beyond the trunk. Feathers lined

northern South America, are able to climb about with the aid of two clawed digits on each wing. The Hoactzin is a gallinaceous bird. Both *Archeornis* and *Archeopteryx* were about the size of a crow.

More than 35 million years elapsed before any further known records of bird life were preserved. According to Wetmore (1940), fifteen species, in seven genera, five families, and three orders, have been described from the Upper Cretaceous of the United States and Canada. Some of these are described from very small bone fragments. The two most important genera are *Hesperornis* (three species) and *Ichthyornis* (seven species). *Hesperornis* was somewhat similar to a modern loon in habits. It had powerful hind limbs which spread out laterally at the ankles. These suggest swimming and diving ability. *Hesperornis* was already a degenerate form, for its wings had almost completely disappeared. The sternum was not carinate. *Ichthyornis* was a tern-like bird with highly developed wings and with a carinate sternum. Both *Ichthyornis* and *Hesperornis* had fused caudal vertebrae; both had the lumbar, sacral, and urosacral vertebrae fused with the pelvic girdle to form the synsacrum; both had teeth. *Ichthyornis* had its teeth inserted in separate sockets (like *Archeornis*), while *Hesperornis* had teeth inserted in a groove. Both lacked teeth on the premaxillary bones. They probably had horny beaks. In many respects these two birds were intermediate between *Archeopteryx* or *Archeornis* and modern birds. (See Figure 21.)

Upper Cretaceous beds in Alberta, Canada, yielded a fossil believed to be of a bird similar to the ostrich. This fossil, named *Caenagnathus*, is believed to be avian; however, there is some doubt as to its status. *Caenagnathus* is known from a nearly complete mandible.

Figure 21. *Ichthyornis* (on rock) and *Hesperornis* (swimming) in a Cretaceous scene. Drawing by William C. Dilger.

Early Cenozoic deposits reveal little that cannot be learned from modern living forms. About half of the modern orders of birds are known from Eocene representatives. Eocene deposits in Wyoming provide a highly evolved form, *Diatryma,* which has been placed taxonomically above the cranes and rails of the present. *Diatryma* was a large ground bird, about seven feet in height, somewhat like the South American cariamas. The wings were reduced, the skull large. The legs were heavy and apparently powerful. Like present flightless birds, *Diatryma* lived in an area where there were no carnivorous mammals. It is possible that the rise of carnivorous mammals led to its extinction. (See Figure 22.)

The late Pleistocene and Recent epochs have witnessed the extermination of many forms. The Dodo, a relative of the pigeons, from Madagascar; the Great Auk, from the North Atlantic; and the Carolina Parakeet, the Passenger Pigeon, and the Heath Hen from eastern United States have recently been eliminated from our fauna for all time. The

Figure 22. *Diatryma,* an Eocene land bird of North America. Drawing by William C. Dilger.

Elephant Birds, *Aepyornis,* former natives of Madagascar, were flightless species which became extinct during historic time. *Aepyornis* was the largest bird known. The largest species was about ten feet tall and produced eggs which measured more than a foot in length and had a capacity of over two gallons. The moas, *Dinornis,* of New Zealand were also large, flightless, ostrich-like birds. *Aepyornis, Dinornis,* and the other birds listed were exterminated by man or through the influence of man. When man invades a new land he changes the environment and frequently introduces predators, and many native species are unable to adjust to the change. (See Figure 23.)

The Ivory-billed Woodpecker (*Campephilus principalis*), now nearly extinct, demonstrates how man indirectly affects a species. The Ivory-bill has very specialized feeding habits. It feeds on insect larvae which invade the dead tissues of large trees such as are found in virgin for-

Figure 23. *Aepyornis* (left), the Elephant Bird of Madagascar, and *Dinornis* (right), a Moa of New Zealand. Both lived in recent times. Drawings by William C. Dilger.

ests. Many square miles of virgin forest are needed to provide the necessary food for a single nesting pair of these birds. Man has slowly but surely removed these forests from North America so that now only a few suitable habitats remain. The Ivory-billed Woodpecker is doomed to extinction as soon as the swampland forests of Florida and Louisiana are cut.

The Carolina Parakeet (*Conuropsis carolinensis*) was a fruit eater of the southeastern United States. When man set out orchards he provided an abundant food supply, and at first the species thrived. The paroquet had no fear of guns, and the fruit growers shot them to protect their crops. Other factors contributed to the extermination of this once abundant member of the parrot family. Professional bird trappers took many for the pet markets. Many others were shot for the colorful feathers, and worse, many were killed for the sake of killing. Man is one of few predators that kill without apparent reason. (See Figure 24.)

Figure 24. The Carolina Parakeet, *Conuropsis carolinensis*, a former resident of Eastern United States. The last observation reported was in February 1920. Drawing by William C. Dilger.

At the present time other species are in extreme danger of extermination. The National Audubon Society, the ornithological societies, conservation groups, other private groups, and government agencies of the United States and Canada are trying to preserve rare and vanishing birds for posterity.

The present United States population of Trumpeter Swans (*Olor buccinator*) is found mainly in a 60 mile radius encompassing parts of southwestern Montana, eastern Idaho, and northwestern Wyoming. This area contains Yellowstone National Park and Red Rock Lakes Migratory Waterfowl Refuge. The latter contains an area of some 40,682 acres set aside largely to protect breeding and wintering areas of the Trumpeter Swan. The refuge is managed by the Bureau of Sport Fisheries and Wildlife, Fish and Wildlife Service, of the United States Department of the Interior.

The Trumpeter Swan has responded to protection and care as shown by the following table (modified from Banko, 1960):

TABLE 2. TRUMPETER SWAN CENSUS DATA –1931 TO 1957

Year	Red Rock Lakes Refuge	Yellowstone National Park	Other	Total
1931	*	30	5	35
1932	26	31	12	69
1933	24	35	7	66
1934	42	33	22	97
1935	46	27	*	73
1936	57	51	9	117
1937	85	64	9	158
1938	70	44	34	148
1939	109	64	26	199
1940	106	53 #	32	191
1941	96	59	57	212
1942	88	*	63	151
1943	113	*	58	171
1944	164	49	66	279
1945	163	*	72	235
1946	170	51	140	361
1947	180	53	119	352
1948	194	62	162	418
1949	193	75	183	451
1950	146	73	157	376
1951	246	74	215	535
1952	239	68	264	571
1953	249	61	267	577
1954	380	87	175	642
1955	283	68	239	590
1956	332	57	199	588
1957	204	60	224	488

* No census. # Incomplete census.

The steady increase in population of Trumpeter Swans can be attributed to several factors. First, the habits of the bird lend themselves well to generally established waterfowl management practices. The birds do not migrate over wide areas, hence it has been comparatively easy for one agency and one group of individuals to manage them. Second, they have been afforded complete protection by federal and state laws. Third, the establishing of the large Red Rock Lakes Refuge has made possible management and protection on a continuing basis.

Thus, while far from having attained a completely satisfactory situation with respect to the Trumpeter Swan population, it is apparent that good management practices can restore a species which is nearly extinct.

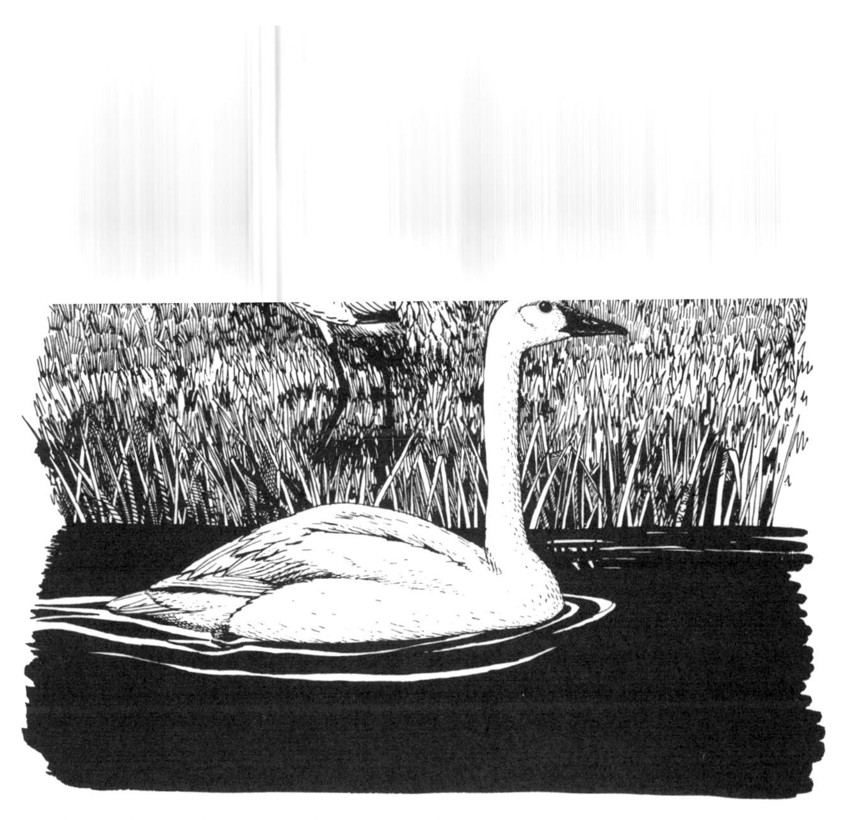

Figure 25. Whooping Crane (standing) and Trumpeter Swan (swimming). These two species may be among the extinct North American bird species in a few decades. Drawing by William C. Dilger.

The case of the Whooping Crane (*Grus americana*) presents an entirely different picture. The whooper nests in a vast muskeg region in the Northwest Territory of Canada. The present world population of some 30 individuals (32 in 1962-1963) winters on the Aransas National Wildlife Refuge and adjacent areas in coastal Texas. This dangerously small population of our largest wading bird thus travels about 3,000 miles in the round trip involved in spring and fall migrations. The breeding ground is in a very remote area and is considered to be relatively safe from the inroads of man. The small wintering area also seems to be quite effective in preserving the birds. However, the combination of low fertility, poor hatching, and the hazards encountered during migration have held the population down to 25 to 38 individuals for several decades. Plans are now formulating which are aimed at rearing Whooping Cranes in captivity so that they can be released to augment the wild population.

Many other birds face extinction. Man's activities are generally responsible for these losses. Hunting pressures, oil and other pollutants, and drainage of wetlands have seriously reduced the populations of most species of ducks, geese, and swans. A growing national concern for our water resources may, if pressed soon enough and hard enough, relieve the pressures on waterfowl populations. It has been a paradox in governmental administration that it has supported an ever-increasing surplus of grains, while at the same time subsidizing the drainage of marshlands which serve only to increase the surpluses. Marshlands typically are areas in which the ground water or water table comes above the soil surface. Drainage means a lowering of the water table not only over the area of the wetland but over wide areas surrounding the immediate area. A valuable water reservoir thus is lost. Wetland drainage eliminates the home of many birds in addition to the waterfowl.

It has been suggested that insecticide spraying has been a major contributing factor to serious decimation of the Bald Eagle (*Haliaeetus leucocephalus*) population in its Florida breeding range. In this case the sprayed insects and some of the spray itself fall into water bodies. Here aquatic organisms absorb some of the spray material (halogenated hydrocarbons or organic phosphates) directly or by eating dead or dying insects. These in turn are consumed by fish. Fish comprise the principal part of the diet of eagles. There is no evidence that adult eagles are seriously harmed by accumulation of insecticides in their tissues; however there is considerable evidence to indicate that these insecticides affect fertility of the eggs adversely. New generations therefore are not produced and the population rapidly declines.

All species seem doomed to extinction sooner or later. Man seems simply to be hastening the process. The big difference between natural and man-provoked exterminations is time. Natural extinction of a species generally can be measured in terms of tens of thousands or even millions of years. Man has exterminated whole species in a few centuries.

With the constant development of bigger and better forces for destruction (such as detergents, halogenated hydrocarbons in ever increasing array, and ditchers and bulldozers to speed drainage operations) it seems likely that the number of threatened species will increase sharply . . . unless there is an awareness of the problems along with vigilance and perseverance in remedying detrimental practices. Natural processes

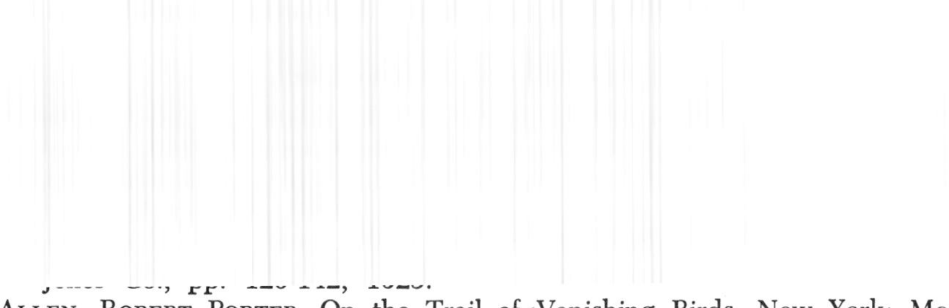

ALLEN, ROBERT PORTER, On the Trail of Vanishing Birds. New York: McGraw-Hill, 1957.

A. O. U. Committee on Bird Protection, Report of the Committee on Bird Protection, 1962. *Auk*, 80:352-364, 1963. (See also reports by this committee which appear in each volume of *The Auk*.)

BANKO, WINSTON E., The Trumpeter Swan, Its History, Habits and Population in the United States. *USFWS N. Am. Fauna*, No. 63, 1960.

BRODKORB, PIERCE, A Giant Flightless Bird from the Pleistocene of Florida. *Auk*, 80:111-115, 1963.

CARSON, RACHEL, Silent Spring. Boston: Houghton Mifflin Co., 1962.

MCCOY, JOHN J., The Fossil Avifauna of Itchtucknee River, Florida. *Auk*, 80:335-351, 1963.

SCHORGER, A. W., An Ancestral Pueblo Turkey. *Auk*, 78:138-144. 1961.

WETMORE, ALEXANDER, How Old Are Our Birds? *Bird Lore*, 38:321-326, 1936.

WETMORE, ALEXANDER, A Checklist of the Fossil Birds of North America. *Smithsonian Inst. Misc. Coll.*, Vol. 99, No. 4, Publication 3587, 1940.

EXERCISE ON EXTINCT AND VANISHING BIRDS

1. From the literature, prepare a list of birds which have become extinct during the past five or six centuries.

2. Prepare a similar list of species which are presently threatened with extinction.

In addition to the section on "Bibliography and References," the following references are suggested as sources from which much of your list may be compiled. These in turn may lead you to other references and these to still more. It should be noted that literature searches are often carried out in this manner.

Biological Abstracts contain brief abstracts of many papers in the whole area of biologv. *The Aves* Section will direct your attention to the recent literature on all aspects of avian biology.

Ornithological Journals – *The Auk, The Condor,* and *The Wilson Bulletin* are the major American ones – are indexed at the end of each volume. In addition these journals may contain occasional or regular reports by appropriate committees (such as the report of the Committee on Bird Protection of the American Ornithologists Union cited) on the status of threatened species.

STREET, PHILIP, Vanishing Animals, Preserving Nature's Rarities. London: Faber and Faber, Ltd., 1961. A popular account of threatened and recently extinct species. One chapter is devoted to birds.

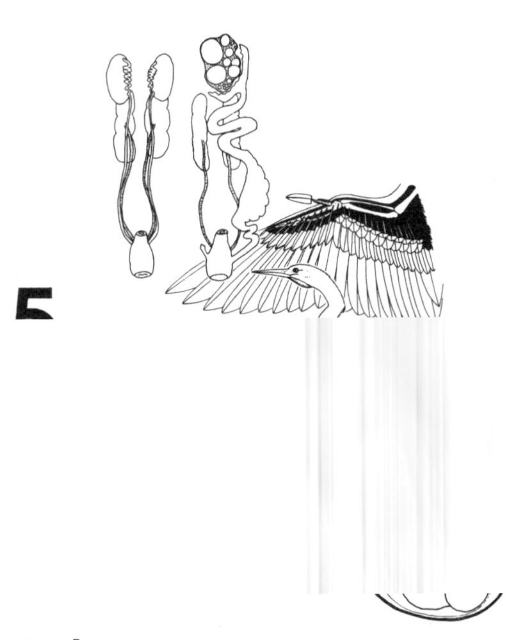

Taxonomy of Birds

Every group of workers which labors with a large number of animate or inanimate objects uses some system to make order out of what otherwise would be chaos. The librarian, if he knows the author, or the title, or the subject of any work, can put his hand on that piece of literature in a few minutes. This is possible because he has classified his books, pamphlets, and periodicals in such a way that he and his helpers can find them by following a few simple rules. The rules become somewhat more complex as the number of volumes in the library is increased. Similarly, biologists have a system for arranging the plants and animals of the world. The term **taxonomy** is employed to designate the study and practice of this system. Other terms such as **systematics, classification,** and to a certain degree **nomenclature,** are synonyms. Nomenclature more specifically refers to the naming of organisms, but they are named, in part at least, according to their relationship to other forms. Hence, nomenclature is a part of taxonomy. It is a common error to confuse taxonomy with identification.

The present system of nomenclature had its origin with the tenth edition of Carl von Linné's (Linnaeus) *Systema Naturae* which appeared in 1758. Linné introduced a workable system for classifying and naming animals. His tenth edition was the first to use a binary nomenclature consistently. The names are of two parts, first the generic name and second the specific or trivial name. When combined, the two comprise the species name. The advantages of this system are many. W. L. McAtee recently published a booklet in which he listed the local common names of game birds. He listed 106 common names for the Ruddy Duck (*Oxyura jamaicensis*). Obviously the one species or scientifc name, if used by everyone, will enable all to communicate freely about this species, while in 106 names there would be the confusion of Babel. Furthermore, the species name is used by biologists throughout the whole world. The terms employed are Latin or Latinized. Latin was, and still is to some extent, the language of scholars of the world. It is a "dead" language or one in which the rate of evolution has decreased substantially. Modern languages are constantly changing and hence would not be suitable for a more permanent system of classification.

The general scheme of the system employed at present in the classification of animals is shown following. The arrangement is from the largest group through the subgroups to the individuals which comprise a race or subspecies. The Eastern Robin is presented as an example.

Regnum – the animal kingdom and the plant kingdom.
Phylum – Chordata, animals with a hollow, dorsal nerve cord and a notochord as the main skeletal support at some time in their life history.
Subphylum – Vertebrata, chordates with a backbone.
Class – Aves, animals with feathers; birds.
Subclass – Neornithes, modern or toothless birds.
Superorder – Neognathae, birds with a more highly developed palate, typical birds.
Order – Passeriformes, perching birds.
Suborder – Passeres, song birds.
Family – Turdidae, thrushes.
Genus – *Turdus*, typical thrushes. (The generic name.)
Species – *migratorius*, migrating thrush or Robin. (The **trivial** name.)
Subspecies or **race** – *migratorius*, Eastern Robin.

The **species name** or scientific name of an organism is composed of all terms applied to the generic name and the categories which fall under it. In the foregoing example the scientific name of the Eastern Robin is *Turdus migratorius migratorius*. In every case there are at least two parts to the species name, thus it is a **binomial nomenclature.** Since the work of Linné, however, most of the readily available species have been named and taxonomists are now frequently concerned with comparative studies of the morphology and life history of a group of similar organisms. Often through such research it becomes apparent that some of the individuals of a species are separable from others, especially when from a different geographical area, so they are designated by subspecific names. Much of the present work on nomenclature might therefore be called **trinomial.** This is largely true of the vertebrates in which most of the original naming of species has been done. The [illegible]

How does this work in actual practice? Let us suppose that you have found a new form of bird which you believe has never been described. When you collected this specimen, you carefully noted the exact location and something of the conditions of its habitat. You recorded the exact date. The specimen was prepared in the form of a study skin in the generally accepted method. Then you carefully studied the literature for a description of the species. Let us say that the bird was collected from a nest in central Pennsylvania. Thus the bird was definitely a breeding resident of that area. If the bird has been described, it will be listed in the American Ornithologists' Union's *Check-list of North American Birds,* Fifth Edition, its supplements, or in the literature (which might be any scientific work, periodical or book) since 1957, the date of publication of the latest A. O. U. Check-list. The search through the literature, let us suppose, revealed nothing. Having thus established the fact that your specimen has not been described, you describe the species.

If the alleged new species does not fit into any of the existing orders, you may originate a new order, family, genus, and species. Generally, however, it will be possible to place the new form in an already described genus so that only a specific or trivial description will be necessary. The original description must be **published** in some form, in this case probably in one of the American ornithological journals. This new name then stands as the species name for the new form for all time. As the original describer of the form, you will be honored by having your family name affixed to the species name after the trivial name. Thus the Robin is *Turdus migratorious* Linné.

In writing the description you must have followed certain rules. The locality from which the specimen was taken, the date of collecting, colors, measurements, diagnostic features, etc., must be mentioned. The actual word used by you as a trivial name must be unused in other species names in the same genus. If a new genus was described, then the word must be unused as a generic name for any living or fossil animal. The specimen must be properly labeled and should be housed in a permanent collection. It may be kept in a private collection provided it is available for the inspection of others. Actually, nothing in the rules prevents one from keeping his specimens out of the sight of others but such practice is definitely frowned upon. The catalog number of the collector and, if possible, of the museum or other collection agency should be published with the description. This will enable future workers to locate the specimen.

This specimen of yours now becomes a very important object and is called a **type specimen.** If you had collected several individuals of this new form, then the type, or the particular specimen on which your description was based, may be called the **holotype.** The other specimens which you collected at the same time and place, if used to supplement the description, may be designated **paratypes.** If you based your description on all or several of the specimens instead of only a single one, they may all be called **syntypes,** provided they are of equal value. If someone later selects one of the syntypes to serve as a holotype it becomes known as a **lectotype.** The foregoing are primary types since all involve specimens available to the original author of the species.

Secondary types include the following:

topotype — a specimen collected from the same locality as the original primary type. A specimen from the **type locality.**

hypotype — a figured, listed, or described specimen not a primary type. Important when the primary type material is lost or destroyed.

homoeotype — a specimen compared by a competent observer with a primary type and found to be precisely like it.

plastotype — a cast of a type. Important especially in paleontology.

Primary and secondary type materials are used in comparison and enable zoologists to formulate a concept of the species, to identify the species, and to draw conclusions as to the relationship of the species to others in the genus. The value of the additional categories, other than the holotype, lies in the fact that they need not be housed in the same place; thus there will be more ready access to important specimens.

Let us suppose, further, that you were wrong in concluding that your supposed new species had not been described previously, but the previous description went unnoticed by zoologists and your description was widely accepted. Later some student, working with the group in which the new species was placed, found the earlier description and established that your description was superfluous. In the meantime,

students. The trivial name which you applied will persist and your surname will be placed in parenthesis after the new species or scientific name. Again your generic name will be retained as a synonym. This is accomplished by authority of the **rules of preoccupation**, for no two species may have the same name, nor may two genera in different families have the same name. Homonyms are not permitted, although they do sometimes occur for some time before they are discovered. This is understandable in view of the fact that there are more than a million species of plants and animals known and described in the world.

The genus is generally considered the most important category, and upon it the relationships are based. The family is named by using the root or stem of the generic name of the **type genus** and adding the ending -idae; the subfamily name consists of the stem plus the ending -inae. Thus the type genus of the family Turdidae is *Turdus*.

The distinction among generic, species or specific, and trivial names was made by Linné. The combination of generic and trivial name constitutes the species or specific name. In *Turdus migratorius, Turdus* is the generic name, *migratorius* is the trivial name, and *Turdus migratorius* is the species name. The trivial name should never stand alone unless the name is being discussed as a name or word and not as an organism. The generic name may stand alone when the group of species which compose the genus is under discussion. The generic name may be abbreviated to the initial letter when a genus is being reviewed or its species are being compared. In all instances both generic and trivial components of the species name should be italicized.

Trivial names as well as generic names can be grouped into five general classes; descriptive, geographic, geologic, patronymic, and miscellaneous. *Turdus migratorius* illustrates the descriptive name. *Turdus* is a Latin word meaning thrush, and *migratorius* refers to the migratory habit of the bird. The species name of the Canada Goose, *Branta canadensis,* is descriptive in its generic component and geographic in its trivial component. *Colymbus oligoceanus,* an Oligocene grebe, illustrates a geologic name. Patronymic names are designed to honor any person the describer wishes to honor. The warbler genus *Wilsonia* honors Alexander Wilson, early American ornithologist. Miscellaneous names include meaningless terms or names formed by arbitrary arrangement of letters. An entomologist recently described a new genus of insects which he called *Zyzzyx* simply to insure that it would be the last entry in any alphabetical listing.

American ornithologists, especially amateurs, show a strong tendency to favor common names rather than scientific or species names. Common names are more or less accepted by the Committee on Classification and Nomenclature, which prepares and publishes the American Ornithologists' Union's Check-list, when new names are entered on the list. This is a rather unfortunate trend, for the generic names show relationships with which it is well to be familiar.

The keys to the orders and families of birds of North America, Appendix A, will further consider the taxonomy of birds. It must be remembered, however, that keys are largely artificial and serve primarily in identification and not in classification.

Bibliography and References

Allen, Arthur A., The Book of Bird Life, 2nd Ed. Princeton, N. J.: D. Van Nostrand, pp. 9-59, 1961.

Allen J. A., The Influence of Physical Condition on the Genesis of Species. *Radical Review,* 1:108-140 (Reprinted 1905, *Smithsonian Report,* pp. 375-402.) 1877.

A.O.U., Check-list of North American Birds. Am. Ornithologists' Union. 691 pp., 1957.

Chapman, Frank M., Handbook of Birds of Eastern North America, 2nd Ed. New York: D. Appleton-Century, pp. 96-99, 1940.

Lack, David, Darwin's Finches. London: Cambridge Univ. Press, 1947.

McAtee, W. L., Local Names of Migratory Game Birds. *U.S.D.A. Misc. Circular* No. 13, 1937.

Mayr, Ernst, Systematics and the Origin of Species. New York: Columbia Univ. Press, 1942.

Mayr, Ernst, E. Gorton Linsley, and Robert L. Usinger, Methods and Principles of Systematic Zoology. New York: McGraw-Hill Book Co., 1953.

MILLER, ALDEN H., Concepts and Problems of Avian Systematics in Relation to Evolutionary Processes. (In: Recent Studies in Avian Biology, Albert Wolfson, Editor.) Urbana: Univ. Illinois Press, pp. 1-22, 1955.
SCHENK, EDWART T., and JOHN H. MCMASTERS, Procedure in Taxonomy. 2nd Ed. Stanford, Calif.: Stanford Univ. Press, 1956.
SIMPSON, GEORGE GAYLORD, Principles of Animal Taxonomy. New York: Columbia Univ. Press, pp. 147-186, 1961.

2. Examine the description and naming of new species listed in the references at the end of Chapter 4.

3. Appended at the end of this work are outline forms for listing characteristics of each North American family of birds and for outlining the distribution of each family. Using the key to the orders and families (Appendix A), identify the families from specimens provided. Then properly fill in the appropriate form for each family.

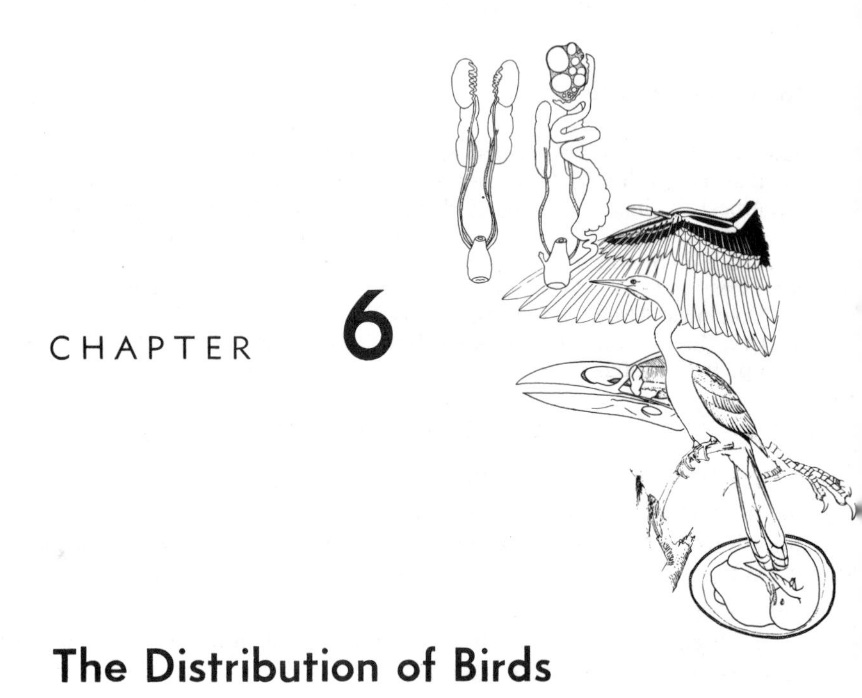

CHAPTER 6

The Distribution of Birds

Every species of plant or animal occurs within only a certain more or less well defined area. That area may be world-wide or cosmopolitan for some species and very small or local for others. Whatever the size, the area is known as the **range** of the species. The factors which limit the range are the concern of the ecologist. The factors which pertain to the range in its entirety are the concern of the zoogeographer and phytogeographer. The study of the development of present ranges is complicated and involves ecology, geology, paleontology, meteorology, geography, and taxonomy. With regard to birds, orders tend to be cosmopolitan in distribution, families tend to be limited to continents or zoogeographic regions (see following), and genera and species more commonly are restricted to smaller areas.

The study of animal distribution is termed **zoogeography** and of plants **phytogeography.** This distribution is four dimensional, that is, it involves time as well as space, and there is a close correlation between them. Throughout the past one and one-half billion years or more, plants and animals have been dispersing over the surface of the earth, on land, in sea, in air.

Evolutionists generally agree that life had its origin in one particular spot on the earth's surface and that that memorable event occurred only one time. From this primordial protoplasm plants and animals arose. Each species arose similarly at one time and in only one place. The area in which a species had its origin was undoubtedly very small. It is called the **center of origin.** The center of origin must necessarily have been a part of the early range of the species, and if the species has persisted it may be within the present range; however, species may become extinct at their center of origin and persist in outlying areas. For instance, a [illegible]

In a sense, plants are far more dependent than animals on their environment. To a degree, their capacity for locomotion makes animals independent of their environment. They are at least able to move toward food or water and need not die because these requirements are lacking in the immediate vicinity. Plants are relatively passive in their distribution, whereas animals are frequently active in extending their ranges. The ability of animals to move from place to place is not limitless. Terrestrial animals cannot cross oceans. Aquatic animals cannot cross land masses. Fresh-water fishes cannot survive in the saline marine waters. With their ability to fly, birds can sometimes cross areas which are impassable to other animals. Thus, in some respects, birds are not ideal subjects for the study of general principles of distribution.

The most interesting examples of distribution are those animals which have a **discontinuous distribution.** The tapirs (Figure 26) are now confined to the wet tropical forests of the Amazon basin in South America and the tropical forests of Malaysia. The camel family (Camelidae) is represented by three species at the present time. Their distribution is such that there are two species, both *Camelus,* in Eurasia and northern Africa and one species, *Lama,* in South America. The true alligators are found in the southeastern United States and the middle and upper reaches of the Yangtze River in China. How did such discontinuous distribution come to be?

There are several factors to consider. These forms, like all others, had a center of origin. After origin the ranges spread out radially or lineally or both. The gradual increase in the population of each species after origin, and the consequent competition for food and living room,

Figure 26. Malayan Tapir (left) and the South American Tapir (right) are outstanding examples of discontinuous distribution. Drawing by William C. Dilger.

necessitated an increase in the range. The enlargement of the range continued until ecological barriers prevented further increase. In the case of the tapirs and camelids, it was necessary that they walk across either the Atlantic Ocean or the Pacific Ocean. Obviously, this was not possible, but it is possible that at some time in the history of the earth there was a land connection between the eastern and western hemispheres. The land connection may have been a continuous **land bridge** or a chain of islands which slowly raised from and descended into the sea. Such a chain of islands now exists in the Aleutians. A similar chain loosely connects Australia with the Asiatic mainland. (See map in Figure 27.) Land bridges occur now between North and South America at the Isthmus of Panama and farther to the northwest at the Isthmus of Tehuantepec. Marine deposits at the mountain tops of the Isthmus of Tehuantepec prove that the area was submerged throughout most of the Tertiary Period. It emerged in the Pliocene and has remained since. In all probability the Bering Strait was a land bridge; it is generally accepted as the link between the eastern and the western hemispheres. Many other land bridges have been proposed but with little

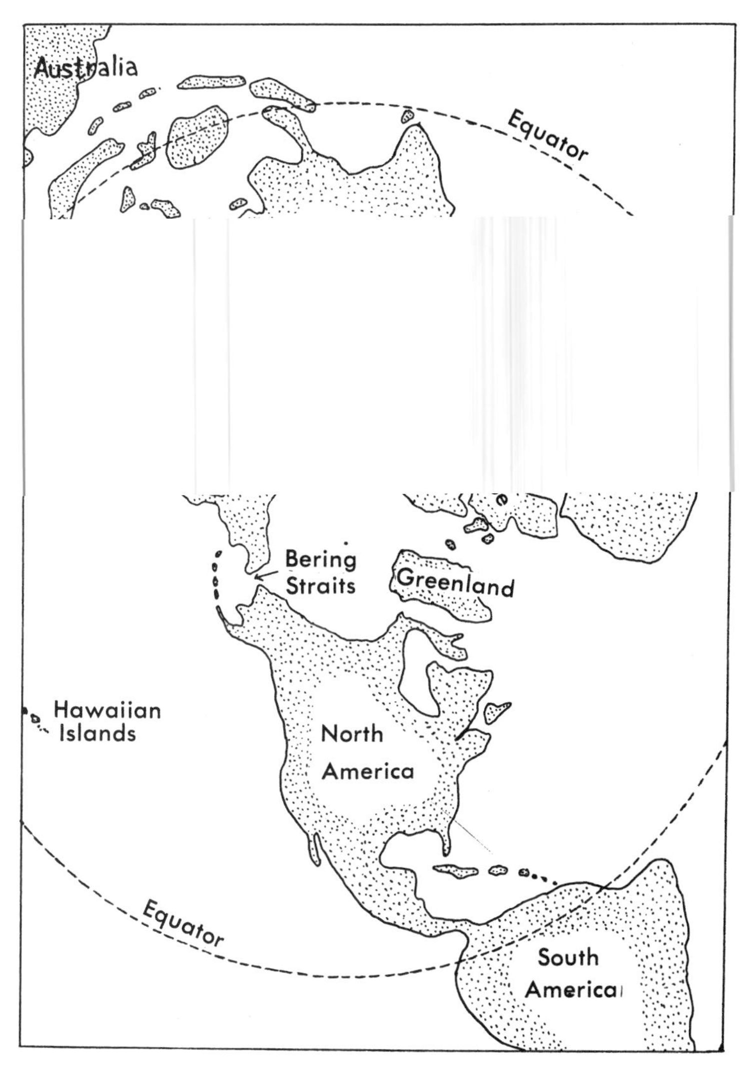

Figure 27. North polar projection map of the world. The northern regions of the Earth probably provided several routes for dispersal of animals in the geologic past.

substantiating evidence. At the height of the Pleistocene glaciers, it has been estimated that some 500 feet of the waters of all oceans were locked in ice above the land masses. While this conceivably could have allowed land bridges to occur in the North Atlantic and in the North

Pacific, those areas probably were too cold to permit much life to exist there at that time. It is necessary to keep in mind that the earth's crust is constantly changing; undoubtedly many possible routes for dispersal existed at one time or another and have disappeared, leaving no traces.

Geologists have been known to propose theories pertaining to supposed former land structures on the basis of present distribution of animals. Certain similarities in the fauna of eastern South America and western Africa have been used as arguments to support the Continental Drift hypothesis. According to this hypothesis, the western continents (North and South America) were separated from the continents of Europe and Africa by some gigantic geologic force. The likelihood of such a drifting of the continents seems very remote, for there is little similarity in geologic formations built up on the two hemispheres. The idea has been substantiated by the similarity of the eastern coastline of North and South America and the western coastline of Europe and Africa.

It is necessary to consider the restricting influences on distribution. Many obstacles or **barriers** prevent movement of a species from its center of origin or any part of its established range. These can be considered under three general categories: physical or topographic, climatic, and biological.

Physical barriers include mountains, high plateaus, oceans, seas, rivers (for terrestrial animals), and land masses (for marine and freshwater inhabitants). Mountains may affect distribution in two distinct and opposite ways. Those mountain ranges which run more or less north and south serve as ideal paths for dispersal for arctic or high latitude species. This phenomenon is a climatic barrier, or lack of it, rather than a physical one. Animals that normally are restricted to colder northern climates find similar conditions in higher altitudes farther to the south. Mountains which extend east and west, on the other hand, present a definite obstacle to the north-south dispersal of these animals. Animals attempting to move against a mountain are confronted by the physical barriers of steep slopes and the lowered atmospheric pressure as well as the climatic factor of sharp decline in temperature and often greater precipitation. Oceans form formidable barriers for terrestrial animals. The fauna of many islands is extremely interesting and it is always a difficult problem to try to trace the origin of island inhabitants. Natural rafts of vegetation have been suggested as the means by which land animals were transported to many islands. Birds, especially the more capable flyers, have little problem here; however, many of the smaller land birds are not physiologically equipped to fly over hundreds of miles of open water. Island faunas will be discussed in greater detail later.

Climatic barriers are numerous and complicated. They include such factors as relative humidity, temperature, and quantity and distribution of precipitation. These are directly related to such phenomena as deserts, floods, glaciers, and freezing or torrid temperatures, all of which exert

parasitism, disease, and general adaptability to the environment. Animals are dependent upon plants for replacing the oxygen to the atmosphere, and all animals are either directly or indirectly dependent upon plants for their food. Plants depend upon animals for the carbon dioxide from which, together with water, they synthesize their food. Further, many plants depend upon animals to distribute the seeds or fruits, thus not restricting but actually extending their ranges.

The world has been divided into biotic areas called **regions** by zoogeographers and phytogeographers. These regions bear certain groups of animal life which are peculiar to them. The regions have been further divided into subregions and provinces but they will not be dealt with in detail here. A brief outline of the regions and some of their characteristics are given. These areas are demonstrated on the map, Figure 28.

The **Australian Region.** The most primitive of the regions includes the continent of Australia, New Zealand, the South Pacific Islands and east to Hawaii, New Guinea, and the East Indies as far north and west as **Wallace's Line**. Wallace's Line extends between the islands of Bali (just east of Java) and Lombok, north through the Straits of Makassar (between Borneo and Celebes Islands), and northeast through the Celebes Sea, south of Mindanao (in the Philippine Islands) into the Pacific. The Australian Region is the exclusive host to twelve families of birds. Two of these are restricted to the New Zealand subregion, one to New Caledonia, and one to the Hawaiian Islands. Every part of the Australian Region is an island, so that all birds which are found there faced oceanic barriers.

New Zealand bears no native land mammals; consequently, no mammalian predators could molest birds, and the "selective action" in avian evolution was minimized there. The islands have many species of flightless birds (the moas, kiwis, a rail, a goose, a hawk, etc.) The absence of mammals indicates that New Zealand was definitely separated from Australia or any other body of land before mammals could invade it.

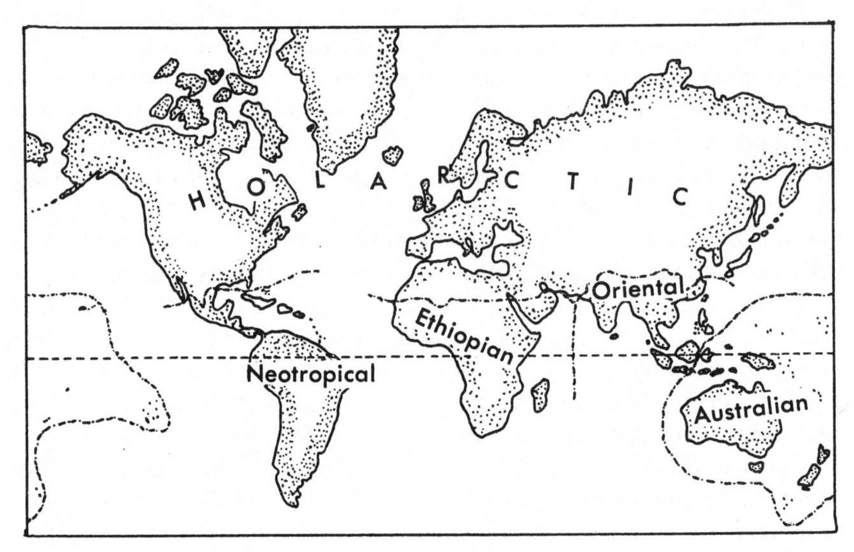

Figure 28. Outline map showing the Zoogeographic regions of the world. Mercator projection.

An excellent discussion on the origin, evolution, and distribution of some of these islandic birds appears in Rollin H. Baker's (1951) *The Avifauna of Micronesia, Its Origin, Evolution and Distribution.* Micronesia includes the Palau Islands, the Marianas, the Carolines, the Marshalls, the Radak Chain, the Ralik Chain, and Wake Island. These islands apparently were formed independently of any present day continental land mass. Any land animals which inhabit them therefore had to penetrate the oceanic barrier. Baker reports the origins of the birds of these islands to be Polynesia, Melanesia, the Moluccas, Celebes, Philippines, and the Asiastic mainland. Oceanic or pelagic birds apparently arrived first. (These left phosphate deposits, derived from the decomposition of guano, on some of the elevated islands.) The land birds and freshwater birds, of which there are 104 native residents, have become so differentiated that 93.5 percent of them can be taxonomically separated from the ancestral stock from which they originated. Most of the species were derived from Melanesia, which lies to the south, and from the Moluccas, Celebes, and Philippines, which lie to the west and southwest. The direction and intensity of the winds, the small size and isola- [illegible]

Hawaii bears a distinctive family, the Drepanididae, which contains some twenty species. The bills of these birds vary from finch-like, short and stout, to long and slender and conspicuously curved. The various species feed on the nectar of flowers, beetle grubs taken from the bark and twigs of trees, and seeds. It is believed that their ancestors lived in South America.

Wallace's Line is extremely interesting because it presents a surprisingly clear-cut line across which many groups of animals have never passed. The finch family (Fringillidae), for instance, is distributed throughout the remainder of the world and is found in Java and Borneo, but none are found to the southeast in the Australian Region. Only six species of the cosmopolitan woodpecker family (Picidae) have successfully trespassed into the land down under.

The **Oriental Region.** The Oriental or Indian Region includes the area which is bounded by Wallace's Line on the Southeast, the Indian Ocean on the south and west, the Indus River on the northeast, the Himalaya Mountains on the north, and from there roughly along the 30th degree of latitude east to the East China Sea. On the family level the avifauna of this region is not particularly distinctive. Only one family (Paradoxornithidae, the parrot-bills and sutheras) is restricted to it, and this is a group of somewhat doubtful relationship. On the generic level, however, there are many distinctive forms. Twenty-one genera of birds are native or **endemic** to Malaysia. Seven genera are endemic in the Philippines. The Oriental Region is essentially tropical and is similar in some ways to tropical areas of Africa, and to a lesser extent South and Central America.

The **Ethiopian Region**. Africa, Arabia (south of the Tropic of Cancer), and Madagascar comprise the Ethiopian Region. With the exception of Madagascar, the region is not separated by sea. There are fifteen endemic bird families. Of these, five are found only in the Madagascar Subregion. This large island bears 129 endemic species of birds. Like New Zealand and the Pacific islands, it demonstrates the effects of geographic isolation on the evolution of animals. Some of the characteristic groups of birds of the Ethiopian Region are ostriches, shoebills, hammerheads, secretary birds, Guinea fowl, trumpeters, colies, hoopoes, wood shrikes, and vanga shrikes.

The Holarctic Region. The northern hemisphere, roughly north of the Tropic of Cancer and including most of Mexico, the United States, Canada, Alaska, Greenland, the northern part of Africa, and Eurasia excepting that part in the Oriental Region and the "foot" of the boot-shaped Arabian Peninsula, makes up the largest of the zoogeographic regions of the world. The Holarctic is a sort of melting pot for the distribution of animals, for it is the center which connects with all the others. The avifauna is abundant but not particularly distinctive. There are five endemic families and two more which only slightly trespass into other regions. One family, the Prunellidae (commonly called hedge sparrows and accentors) is restricted to the Palearctic Subregion (the Holarctic of the Old World) and another, Chamaeidae (the wren-tit), is restricted to the Nearctic (the Holarctic of the New World). The family Chamaeidae consists of but one species, whose range is restricted principally to the coast and valleys of California and Oregon. It is of doubtful taxonomic status. The auks and their allies, the grouse, and the loons are the other Holarctic families. The waxwings and the kinglets are nearly restricted to the Holarctic.

The **Neotropical Region.** South and Central America and the West Indies comprise the richest region in the world. The avifauna consists of 31 endemic families, plus several more which it shares with the southern edges of the Nearctic. The West Indies, like other islands, have many endemic forms. Two families, the palm chats (Dulidae) and the todies (Todidae) (See Figure 29.), are restricted to these islands and approximately 140 species are found only there. Three species, a rail, a wren, and a finch, are found only in the Zapata Swamp of Cuba. The tody family illustrates well the reason for so many endemic species in groups of islands. Todies are related to the kingfishers, which are cosmopolitan in their distribution, and the motmots, which are neotropical. There are five species, all in the genus *Todus*. The five species are so distributed throughout the West Indies that only one island, Hispaniola, bears two

Figure 29. The Cuban Tody, *Todus multicolor,* one of the five species of *Todus* endemic in the West Indies. Drawing by William C. Dilger.

of the species. They are obviously very closely related, and yet with geographical isolation specific differences have developed.

Of the 165 families of birds of the world, 31 are found only in the Neotropical, one is found only in the Nearctic, and eleven more are found only in both. If the rate of differentiation of species into separable genera and of genera into separable families were constant, then one would be led to conclude that birds must have lived in the Neotropical Region longer than elsewhere. On the other hand, if one looks at the distribution of the most primitive families, he finds a noticeable discontinuity. The penguins (Spheniscidae) are Antarctic; the ostriches (Struthionidae) are found in Africa; the rheas (Rheidae) in South America; the Cassowaries (Casuariidae) and Emus (Dromiceidae) in the Australian Region; the elephant birds (now extinct and in family Aepyornithidae) in Madagascar; the moas (now extinct and in family Dinornithidae) in New Zealand; the kiwis (Apterygidae) in New Zealand, and the tinamous (Tinamidae) in South and Central America. Note that these forms are widely separated and without exception are found south of the Holarctic. Yet another factor to consider is the fact that our known Mesozoic fossil birds all occurred in the Holarctic, and the earliest of these (*Archeopteryx* and *Archeornis*) were uncovered in Europe.

The trogons (Trogonidae) (Figure 30) have an interesting distribution. The family is composed of 34 species in eight genera. They are

Figure 30. A trogon, *Priotelus temnurus*, a member of a family which is discontinuously distributed in tropical America, Africa, and tropical Asia. Drawing by William C. Dilger.

distributed as follows: twenty species in five genera in the Neotropical Region, three species in two genera in the Ethiopian Region, and eleven species in one genus in the Oriental Region. This would tend to show that the group had its origin in South America, for there the most differentiation has occurred and such differentiation requires much time. It is quite possible, on the other hand, that trogons may be on their

sharp line at the 100th meridian, which falls in North Dakota, South Dakota, Nebraska, and Texas. East of this line is a humid area, and to the west it is comparatively arid.

A more recent, and in many respects more satisfactory, classification of North America lies in the **Biotic Community** concept (as presented by Frank A. Pitelka, *American Midland Naturalist,* vol. 25, 1941). Under this system the continent has been separated into eight major biotic communities: the tundra, coniferous forest, deciduous forest, grassland, sagebrush, southwestern woodland, southwestern chaparral, and the creosote bush desert. This system will be discussed in the next chapter. A map showing the biotic communities or biomes appears on page 160 in Pettingill (1956).

Man has been an important factor in animal distribution in recent times. Domestic and game animals have frequently been introduced to great advantage, but the introduction of many forms has been most ungratifying. Some of the introductions of **exotic** (not native) animals have been accidental (as the Japanese beetle), and others have been purposely imposed upon native faunas. When such introductions are successful (many are unsuccessful) and the species becomes naturalized it is frequently regretted later. Many of our undesirable animals in America are not native; witness the House Sparrow (*Passer domesticus*), the Starling (*Sturnus vulgaris*), the Norway rat, the house mouse, the Japanese beetle, and the German roach. The Colorado potato beetle was originally a native of the sage plains of the West. It moved eastward as soon as it developed a taste for potato leaves. That happened when man introduced potatoes in an area that was adapted for sagebrush.

The study of distribution of animals is a fascinating one. In toto, it is the cumulation of the work of many persons, each generally contributing but a small part. For ornithologists, local or regional lists of breeding birds have been very important. Continued studies of this type reveal the dynamics of distribution – for distribution is a continually changing phenomenon.

Bibliography and References

Baker, Rollin H., The Avifauna of Micronesia, Its Origin, Evolution, and Distribution. *Univ. Kansas Publications*, Vol. 3, No. 1., 1951.

Chapman, Frank M., Handbook of Birds of Eastern North America. New York: D. Appleton-Century Co. Inside cover papers and pp. 30-34, 1940.

Griscom, Ludlow, Modern Bird Study. Cambridge: Harvard Univ. Press, pp. 112-163, 1947.

Grube, George E., Observations on Gnatcatcher Range Extension. *Auk*, 74:494-496, 1957.

Peters, James Lee, Check-list of Birds of the World. Vols. I-VI Harvard Univ. Press, Vol. VII Museum of Comparative Zoology, Cambridge, 1931-1951.

Pettingill, Olin Sewall, Jr., A Laboratory and Field Manual of Ornithology, 3rd Ed. Minneapolis: Burgess Pub. Co., pp. 152-176, 1956. (See p. 160 for reproduction of Pitelka's map showing biotic communities.)

Pitelka, F. A., Distribution of Birds in Relation to Major Biotic Communities. *Am. Midland Nat.*, 25:113-137, 1941.

VanTyne, Josselyn and Andrew J. Berger, Fundamentals of Ornithology. New York: John Wiley & Sons, pp. 155-181, 385-552, 1959.

EXERCISE ON DISTRIBUTION

Using the literature cited and the keys provided in Appendix A (page 178) of this book: (1) identify to Order and Family, (2) list family characteristics, and (3) plot the distribution of each family identified. Record these data on the pages provided in Appendix A (beginning on page 201).

VanTyne, Josselyn and Andrew J. Berger, Fundamentals of Ornithology. New York: John Wiley & Sons, pp. 385-552, 1959.

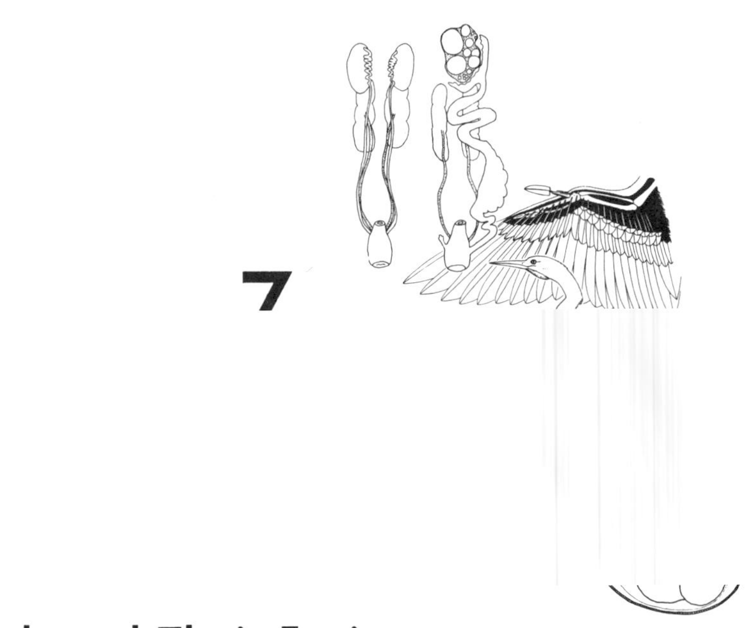

7

Birds and Their Environment

In Chapter 6 numerous references were made to the ecological factors which aid or limit the dispersal of birds. These factors not only pertain to dispersal but are associated with the very survival of all species. **Ecology** includes the study of the relationship between the organism and its whole environment. Environment must necessarily include everything animate and inanimate. A bird reacts as it does to its environment not only because of the other individuals of the same species, but also because of the other species of plants and animals, because of the temperature, the humidity, the type of soil, the density of sunlight, the magnetic forces of the earth, the tides, and/or any other phenomena which occur either naturally or unnaturally.

Ecological factors can be classified into three groups: climatic, edaphic, and biotic. Climatic factors include temperature, light, atmospheric humidity, precipitation, wind, and chemical components of the air (oxygen, carbon dioxide, etc.). Edaphic factors generally affect birds indirectly through their effect on vegetation. They include those things which act on an individual from the earth, such as water in the soil, temperature of the soil, quantity and nature of soluble chemicals of the soil, gravitational pull of the earth, the magnetic field of the world, and the coriolis effect due to the rotation of the earth. Biotic factors include such things as population pressure, food, and all other plants and animals. These may affect the individual in various ways. Predators, parasites, disease-causing organisms and the like generally act adversely. A parasite on one species may actually be beneficial to a nonparasitized competing species. Cattle and quail might be considered noncompetitive. Yet grazing by cattle may destroy the ground cover needed by quail for nesting sites and protection from predators. In cutting down America's forests man destroyed the habitat for many species of birds and other animals but at the same time created a new habitat for different species. Seed-eating birds are affected by plant-eating insects, and seed-eating birds might limit the plants made available to insects and thus affect the food supply of insect-eating birds. Such examples could become more and more complicated.

Like all other organisms, birds are adapted to live in habitat types in which they can thrive. Each species has its particular requirements. It would be as unnatural for a House Sparrow (*Passer domesticus*) to build a nest in a cattail swamp as for a Black Tern (*Chlidonias niger*) to nest in a gutter on a house. Each species nests in a more or less specialized type of environment; each has its **ecological habitat.** With some species this ecological habitat is extremely well defined, whereas with others it is rather broad and does not lend itself well to definition.

Three general groups of habitats or environments have been suggested: land, water, and the intermediate shore. In these habitats birds spend at least a part of their lives, and one can expect to find them here if the time is right. The three general types can be broken into many subgroups. Certain land birds, for example, might be found only in the forest. Furthermore, some are found only in deciduous woods, and there some are restricted to the forest floor; others generally occupy the brush or lower branches, and still others are found only in the treetops. Other land birds occupy coniferous forests or open fields. Many are classed in the intermediate group called **forest edge** birds. An example of a highly specialized habitat is that of Kirtland's Warbler (*Dendroica kirtlandii*). This interesting species breeds only in an area of about 60 miles by 100 miles in central Michigan. In that small breeding range the Kirtland's Warbler nests only in jack pine forests where the trees are between five and fifteen feet tall. Here it nests on the ground.

An outline classification of the major natural ecological groups follows.

- Land Environments
  - Tundra
  - Evergreen or Coniferous Forest
    - Forest floor
  - Desert Shrubland
    - Sagebrush
    - Creosote bush
    - Chaparral
- Water Environments
  - Marine or Salt Water
    - Open seas
    - Salt water marshes
    - Seacoasts or shores
  - Fresh water
    - Open lakes
    - Streams and rivers
    - Marshes
      - Cattail marsh
      - Sedge marsh
    - Swamps

The **tundra** is characterized by low, sometimes scanty, vegetation. It is bounded on the north by the polar ice caps and on the south by "tree line." Low temperature and little sunlight do not permit lush plant growth. The soil is frozen throughout much of the year, and even in summer it thaws only to a few inches or a few feet. Caribou and Willow Ptarmigan are typical inhabitants of the tundra. The Willow Ptarmigan (*Lagopus lagopus*) is a permanent resident. Many other birds, such as Golden Plover (*Pluvialis dominica*), Stilt Sandpiper (*Micropalama himantopus*), Hudsonian Curlew (*Numenius phaeopus*), and Hoary Redpoll (*Acanthias hornemanni*) breed on the tundra. Tundra plants

Figure 31. Alpine Tundra. Tree line occurs at around 12,500 feet above sea level in the Rocky Mountains of Colorado. Above tree line is the tundra.

include lichens, grasses, sedges, *Sphagnum* or peat moss (in bogs), heaths, and shrubby willows and birches.

The tundra is often divided into two broad types: 1. the **arctic tundra** or **muskeg** tundra (largely described in the foregoing) and 2. the **alpine tundra.** The latter is characteristic of high mountain areas, including a few peaks in the Appalachian chain in the east as well as the more abundant peaks of the Rocky Mountains of the west. The four races of the Water Pipit (*Anthus spinoletta*) are tundra-nesting species. Three of these are found as breeding residents in alpine tundra areas in North America. *Anthus spinoletta alticola* is exclusively an alpine tundra subspecies that nests on mountain tops from Utah and Colorado to Northern Arizona and North-central New Mexico.

The **coniferous forest** region bears principally tall, slender evergreen trees such as white spruce, balsam fir, jack pine, and tamarack. Much of the coniferous forest has been cut, and frequently deciduous aspens, poplars, and birches temporarily replaced the conifers. The coniferous region covers most of Canada south of the tundra, and extends south into the United States in regions of high altitude in the Appalachian and Rocky Mountains. The moose is a typical coniferous forest inhabitant. Breeding birds of this habitat include Bohemian Waxwing (*Bombycilla garrula*), Northern Shrike (*Lanius excubitor*), Tennessee Warbler (*Vermivora peregrina*), Bay-breasted Warbler (*Dendroica castanea*), Blackpoll Warbler (*Dendrioca striata*), Connecticut Warbler (*Oporornis agilis*), Pine Grosbeak (*Pinicola enucleator*), Common Redpoll (*Acanthias flammea*), White-winged Crossbill (*Loxia leucoptera*), and

Figure 32. Coniferous forest. Photograph courtesy of the South Dakota Department of Game, Fish and Parks.

Tree Sparrow (*Spizella arborea*). The Northern Shrike occurs principally in brush-bordered swamps and bogs in the coniferous forests. Kirtland's Warbler (*Dendroica kirtlandii*) breeds only in second growth jack pine forests or jack pine plantings in central Michigan. The pines apparently must be between five and fifteen feet tall. This species appears to have depended upon forest fires to maintain its ecological requirements.

The **hardwood** or **deciduous forest** habitat covers most of the eastern United States in the humid zone roughly east of the 95th meridian. This area receives a comparatively heavy and well distributed rainfall. Most of the land area has lost its original character in favor of agriculture. Maples, chestnut, hickories, oaks, and southern pines are the dominant plant forms. The Virginia deer is a fairly typical deciduous forest inhabitant. Breeding birds include Turkey (*Meleagris gallopavo*), Red-bellied Woodpecker (*Centurus carolinus*), Tufted Titmouse (*Parus bicolor*), Brown Thrasher (*Toxostoma rufum*), Wood Thrush (*Hylocichla mustelina*), Worm-eating Warbler (*Helmitheros vermivorus*), Hooded Warbler (*Wilsonia citrina*), and Scarlet Tanager (*Piranga olivacea*). The Hooded Warbler is a bird of the underbrush, while the Scarlet Tanager is generally restricted to the higher branches of tall trees. The Brown Thrasher is usually a brush edge resident. The Ovenbird (*Seiurus aurocapillus*) is a bird of forest floors which are relatively free of underbrush.

The **grasslands** lie between the eastern deciduous forests and the Rocky Mountains from Alberta, Canada, to Texas. Grasses and low herbaceous plants formerly formed the dominant flora. The nature of the climate is such that trees were not adapted for survival. Rainfall is generally less (20 inches to 30 inches per annum) and it is irregular in its distribution throughout the year. Many of the grassland plants have large root systems which enable them to survive droughts. Settlement of the area has largely destroyed the original characteristics, and grains are now extensively farmed. Before settlement this was the grazing land of millions of herbivorous mammals such as bison, antelopes, jack rabbits, prairie dogs, and pocket gophers. Characteristic breeding birds of the prairies include Prairie Chicken (*Tympanuchus cupido*), Scissor-tailed Flycatcher (*Muscivora forficata*), Sprague's Pipit (*Anthus spragueii*), Lark Bunting (*Calamospiza melanocorys*), McCown's Longspur (*Rhynchophanes mccownii*), and Chestnut-collared Longspur (*Calcarius ornatus*).

The **desert shrublands** cover much of the Far West and Southwest. This area can be divided into three more or less distinct habitats. The

Figure 33. A deciduous forest. Photograph courtesy of the Commonwealth of Pennsylvania, Department of Forests and Waters.

northern desert or sagebrush desert extends from southeastern Washington to southern Utah. Sagebrush, black sage, white sage, shadscale, and some grasses form the principal flora. The southern desert or creosote bush desert includes the area from southern Nevada south into northern Mexico. Characteristic plants of the creosote bush desert are creosote

Figure 34. The short grasslands of the Great Plains of west-central United States.

bush, bur sage, mesquite, giant cactus, yucca, Joshua tree, and palo verde. The third desert region is less desert-like and includes southern California and much of Lower California. Chaparral, sagebrush, and plains grasses are the predominant plants. The animals are not as clearly restricted to these three divisions. Large mammals are not characteristic and are generally scarce; rodents and other small mammals are more common. Lizards and snakes attain their greatest diversification and prominence in these regions. Desert breeding birds include Harris's Hawk (*Parabuteo unicinctus*), Scaled Quail (*Callipepla squamata*), Gambel's Quail (*Lophortyx gambeli*), Sage Hen (*Centrocercus urophasianus*), Roadrunner (*Geococcyx californianus*), Gila Woodpecker (*Centurus uropygialis*), Cactus Wren (*Heleodytes brunneicapillus*), Curve-billed Thrasher (*Toxostoma curvirostre*), Lucy's Warbler (*Vermivora luciae*), and Desert Sparrow (*Amphispiza bilineata*).

The tundra, coniferous forest, deciduous forest, grasslands, sagebrush, creosote bush, and chaparral habitats are the principal biomes generally recognized by modern ecologists. A **biome** is a major category in the ecological classification of plant and animal communities. It is related to temperature, humidity, and precipitation. A **community** can

Figure 35. The desert shrublands, Arizona.

be defined as a group of interdependent organisms living together in an area. The area of transition between two types of communities is called an **ecotone.** These categories are more or less based on the climax vegetation. The term **climax** applies to that community in which the composition of the flora has attained comparative stability. The climax vegetation is the end product of a **sere** or series of communities that follow one another from barren ground or lake to the comparatively stable vegetation.

For example, the glaciers of the Pleistocene completely destroyed most of the vegetation of the northern part of the North American continent. In a certain area the glaciers may have gouged out a deep depression. Later, when the last of the glaciers retreated, the depression became a lake. Lakes are temporary phenomena from the geologist's point of view. As soon as they are formed they begin to be filled, by the forces of erosion and gravity, with soil from surrounding land. The young and deep lake is generally relatively poorly stocked with plants and animals. An old lake, filled with sediments so that it is shallow, supports comparatively more life. The sediments continue to pour in and the lake becomes a marsh or a swamp or a bog. (A marsh can be defined as an area in which water covers the soil, and herbaceous plants, such as cattails and sedges, abound. A swamp is similar but bears woody plants or trees, while a bog supports *Sphagnum* mosses). Aquatic plants which extend above the surface replace subsurface plants. The area may continue to build up through numerous stages, such as cattails, sedges, willows, and poplars, until the climax deciduous or coniferous forest or a grassland community replaces the previous vegetation stages. The succession of plants constitutes a **sere.**

At any point in the succession, fire, change of climate, change of topography, or other phenomena may retard or hasten the succession. Fire may cause it to return to an earlier stage. A change of climate may alter the course of the succession and lead to a different climax. A change in topography would hasten the process of an emergence of a marsh or swamp.

Each of the stages of a sere bears characteristic plants and animals. The open deep lake may support diving ducks such as Canvasback (*Aythya valisneria*), and Greater Scaup (*Aythya marila*). The older shallow lakes support underwater vegetation on which dabbling ducks,

Figure 36. A marsh.

Figure 37. A swamp.

such as Mallard (*Anas platyrhynchos*) and Black Duck (*Anas rubripes*), feed. The deeper cattail marsh supports breeding birds such as Common Gallinule (*Gallinula chloropus*) and Long-billed Marsh Wren (*Telmatodytes palustris*). The Short-billed Marsh Wren (*Cistothorus platensis*) and Yellow Rail (*Coturnicops noveboracensis*) breed in sedge or grass marshes.

Many other aquatic habitats can be recognized. Belted Kingfishers (*Megaceryle alcyon*) and Dippers or Water Ouzels (*Cinclus mexicanus*) are commonly found along streams. The Common Tern nests on sandy shores of lakes. Many shore birds (Order Charadriiformes) are fairly well restricted to shores of either fresh or marine water bodies. Brackish or salt swamps and marshes have distinctive faunas. The Eastern Willet (*Catoptrophorus semipalmatus semipalmatus*), Clapper Rail (*Rallus longirostris*), and Seaside Sparrow (*Ammospiza maritima*) are restricted to marine marshes during the breeding season. Pelagic species, or birds of the open seas, include Shearwaters (*Puffinus*), Fulmar (*Fulmarus glacialis*), the several genera of Petrels (*Oceanordroma, Hydrobates, Oceanites, Pelagodroma*), Albatrosses (*Diomedea*).

It must be remembered that most species of birds migrate to and from their breeding grounds. Avian ecology is concerned primarily with the breeding grounds. In migration many species can be observed in atypical habitats. There are many species whose ranges overlap into neighboring habitats or which are well adapted for survival in several habitat types. Many species have changed their habitat requirements or preferences since man disturbed the normal environment. For example, the Red-winged Blackbird (*Agelaius phoeniceus*) was primarily a bird of cattail marshes, but as man drained many vast marshes the Red-wing moved into grain or grass fields and pastures. The food habits of this bird are such that the transition was easy; if this were not the case, the Red-wing might be a comparatively rare species now.

The effects of man on the environment of birds in the Americas cannot be overestimated. Consider the habits of the Chimney Swift (*Chaetura pelagica*) which now numbers countless thousands of individuals.

Figure 38. A Nighthawk on its nest. Here is an example of adaptation to change in environment. The nest is situated on a flat gravelled roof.

This species earlier depended on hollowed dead trees for nesting sites. Now it nests in chimneys. The Common Nighthawk (*Chordeiles minor*) now rests on the graveled flat roofs of large buildings in our cities. Before the arrival of man and his cities this bird nested principally on the graveled flat tops of overhanging cliffs or rock outcrops. In the rural areas these sites still serve the Nighthawk. The many common species

a hold on its new home, but after about 20 years the House Sparrow was firmly established to the point that it has been one of our most serious pests. With the decline of the horse and the rise of the automobile, the population has diminished somewhat!

Consider also the effects of man as a factor in the environment of such forms as the Passenger Pigeon (*Ectopistes migratorius*), which was extremely abundant in migration in eastern North America. Alexander Wilson, early American ornithologist, wrote about a flock he observed at Frankfort, Kentucky, which he estimated at 2,230,272,000 individuals early in the nineteenth century. They nested in gigantic rookeries. A "moderate" sized one was described as "perhaps eight miles long," and the largest known was 28 miles long and averaged three to four miles wide. By the end of the nineteenth century the passenger pigeon was virtually exterminated. Man's guns and nets and the appetite of city dwellers were entirely responsible for the mass slaughter of this species. The last known specimen died in the Cincinnati Zoo, September 1, 1914.

The influence of environment in natural selection is related to nearly all aspects treated in this book. Both external and internal structural features result from gene changes. In cases where gene changes provided structural modifications related to habit, such modifications may make for better or poorer adaptation for survival. More poorly adapted forms die out. Better adapted forms are better prepared for survival. In some instances changes in habit must have accompanied or followed structural changes. Thus the Jacana (*Jacana spinosa*) became well adapted for feeding on the surface of lily pads and other aquatic vegetation on tropical and subtropical ponds and rivers. Its toes are long and equipped with long slender nails which provide a broad area for walking over surface vegetation.

Taxonomy, distribution, and history of development of species have obvious ecological relationships. The influence of environment on the life history of any species is obvious. Migration and behavior (song, territory establishment, courtships, etc.) are ecologically related. Many aspects of behavior are poorly understood and comprise an area in which there is ever increasing research. Of more immediate and practical importance is the study of ecological relationships partaining to population dynamics — another rapidly developing and important area of ecology.

Bibliography and References

Allee, W. C., Alfred E. Emerson, Orlando Park, Thomas Park, and Karl P. Schmidt, Principles of Animal Ecology. Philadelphia: W. B. Saunders Co., 837 pp., 1949

Allen, Glover Morrill, Birds and Their Attributes. Boston: Marshall Jones Co., pp. 150-171, 1925. (Reprinted 1962, Dover Publications, New York.)

Farner, Donald S., Birdbranding in the Study of Population Dynamics. In: Albert Wolfson, editor. Recent Studies in Avian Biology. Urbana: Univ. Illinois Press, pp. 397-449, 1955.

Gibb, John A., Bird Populations. In: A. J. Marshall, editor. Biology and Comparative Physiology of Birds. New York: Academic Press, pp. 413-440, 1961.

Herman, Carlton M., Diseases of Birds. In: Albert Wolfson, editor, Recent Studies in Avian Biology. Urbana: Univ. of Illinois Press, pp. 450-468, 1955.

Hinde, R. A., Behavior. In: A. J. Marshall, editor. Biology and Comparative Physiology of Birds. New York: Academic Press, pp. 373-412, 1961.

Kendeigh, S. C., et al., Nature Sanctuaries in the United States and Canada. *The Living Wilderness,* Vol. 15, No. 35, 1950.

Pettingill, Olin Sewall, Jr., A Laboratory and Field Manual of Ornithology, 3rd Ed. Minneapolis: Burgess Pub. Co., pp. 227-239, 1956.

Welty, Joel Carl, The Life of Birds. Philadelphia: W. B. Saunders Co., pp. 368-393, 1962.

EXERCISE ON AVIAN ECOLOGY

The literature on ecology of birds is very extensive. Practically every published report has some bearing on ecology. Frank M. Chapman's (1940) *Handbook of Birds of Eastern North America,* for example, lists the nesting habitat for each species. Other handbooks and identification manuals often provide similar general ecological information.

It is recommended that the student maintain a field notebook. A two entry system is recommended. One section should contain a daily record. Here include a tabulation of data: 1. date; 2. time of day; 3. weather conditions, temperature, precipitation, etc.; 4. a list of species observed; and 5. notation of the precise habitat in which each species was observed.

[illegible] to important observations on the life history, migration, and ecology of birds.

It must be emphasized that field notes become valuable only if they are maintained continuously over a period of many years. These notes can be compared with the literature from time to time. The life history series by A. C. Bent listed at the end of Chapter 10 presents a summary of the literature which may serve as a starting point for literature comparison.

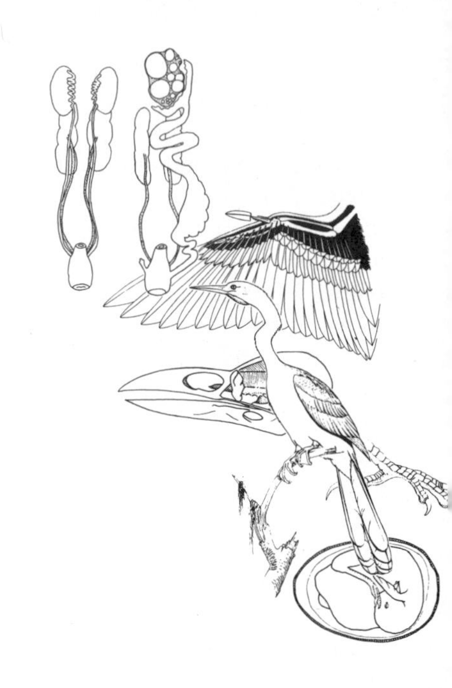

CHAPTER **8**

Bird Migration

Migration, the most distinctive phase of bird life, can be defined as the periodic movement to and from the breeding ground. Although birds migrate more than any other class of animals, migration is not restricted to birds. Eels, salmon, seals, and the monarch butterly are examples of other habitual migrants.

Aristotle, naturalist and philosopher of ancient Greece, recorded his observations on bird migration when he noted that cranes traveled from the steppes of Scythia to the marshes at the headwaters of the Nile and that other birds likewise passed to warmer regions to spend the winter. Aristotle was also responsible for some of the superstitions on migration, one of which, **hibernation**, persisted for many centuries. The idea of hibernation in birds was so prevalent that in 1878 Coues listed the titles of 182 papers dealing with the hibernation of swallows. Recent evidence has shown that the idea of birds hibernating is not to be discounted entirely, for there are some very recent records of Poor-wills (*Phalaenoptilus nuttallii*) that have been found in a torpid condition.

In December, 1946, Edmund C. Jaeger found a Poor-will resting in a shallow crypt on the wall of a canyon in the Chuckawalla Mountains of the Colorado Desert. A Poor-will, probably the same bird, was found in the same crypt in November, 1947, and was subsequently banded. This time Jaeger kept the bird under observation throughout the winter. He took rectal temperature readings and found the body temperature to be 64.4° F. to 67.6° F. in a bird whose body temperature when active is about 106° F. The bird was weighed four times from January 4, 1948, to January 14, 1948. During this time a gradual decline in weight was recorded from 45.61 grams to 44.56 grams. The same Poor-will (evidenced by a numbered aluminum leg band) returned to the same spot [illegible] are extremely active during the daytime and have a correspondingly high metabolic rate. A state of torpor enables these birds to survive on stored food through the night. Yet, hummingbirds are known to fly across the Gulf of Mexico, some 500 miles, in migration. This trip would seem to require more food than they can possibly store. These evidences of torpor in birds do not minimize the wonders of migration.

Aristotle also originated the **theory of transmutation** in which he believed that summer species become winter species, for he noted that summer birds disappeared and presently the winter residents occupied their areas. Many other supernatural powers were ascribed to birds to account for their disappearance in winter. Among them was the belief that birds flew to the moon. Some, who were able to accept migration on the part of the larger birds, accounted for migration of smaller ones by hitchhiking their ride with the larger ones.

It is apparent that the migratory habit enables a species to enjoy the summers of the northern latitudes while avoiding the severity of its winters. Migration makes it possible for birds to inhabit two different areas at seasons when each presents favorable environmental conditions. In the performance of its reproductive duties, every pair of birds requires a certain domain, the extent of which varies greatly in different species and in different individuals within the species, so that during the breeding season the total area required is far greater than at any other time. If all birds were to remain in the tropical or temperate regions there might be intolerable overcrowding during that season. By spring withdrawals to regions of cold winter climate, the migrants are assured of adequate space and ample food supply. Furthermore, the nonmigrating species, residents of the southern regions, are benefited by the withdrawal of the migrants. It cannot be said, however, that winter or summer areas are entirely unsuited to the requirements of every migrating species at other seasons. Some individuals of a species pass the winter in areas frequented only in summer by other individuals. The foremost cause for migrating is the depletion of food supply caused by the disappearance or hibernation of insects or by the mantle of snow or ice which prevents access to seeds or other forms of food on or close to the ground or submerged in the water. Decreased daylight possibly also materially restricts the ability of birds to obtain sufficient food supply at a time when the cold weather necessitates an increased quantity to maintain a high body temperature.

Migration has become a definite hereditary habit that recurs in annual cycles probably because of physiological stimuli. Many theories have been proposed to explain various aspects of the phenomenon. The **northern ancestral home theory** maintains that at one time nonmigratory birds inhabited the northern hemisphere, and ecological conditions (food supply and breeding requirements) were such as to permit them to remain throughout the year. (This is the condition in the tropics today, where most nesting species are nonmigratory.) Then the glacial ice fields advanced and forced the birds ahead of them until all were concentrated in more southern latitudes. As the ice cap gradually retreated each spring, the birds sought to return to their ancestral home, only to be driven south again with the approach of winter. This continued until the ice-covered area diminished, but the journeys became longer and longer until eventually the habit of migration was fixed.

The opposing **southern ancestral home theory** supposed that the ancestral home of all birds was in the tropics and that as birds tended toward overpopulation there was a constant effort to seek new breeding territory where competition was less keen. Species which moved to the north were stopped by the winter snows and were forced to return each winter. As the glacial ice caps retreated, greater breeding areas were made available, but winter continued to drive them south and again the habit became fixed.

A modern view favors the **theory of photoperiodism,** which holds as its major premise that quantity of light and length of day are the stimulating causes of migration. It is believed that light affects the endocrine system, possibly through the pineal body or the anterior pituitary. The affected organ stimulates the gonads to development, which in turn sets off a chain of physiological stimuli which cause the bird to sense that it is time to fly north to breed. In experiments with the Slate-colored

Junco (*Junco hyemalis*) it was found that increased light resulted in increased development of sex organs by the end of December, although the birds were exposed to outdoor temperatures as low as –44° F. The principle of photoperiodism is used by poultrymen to increase the production of eggs by supplementing the daylight hours with periods of artificial light.

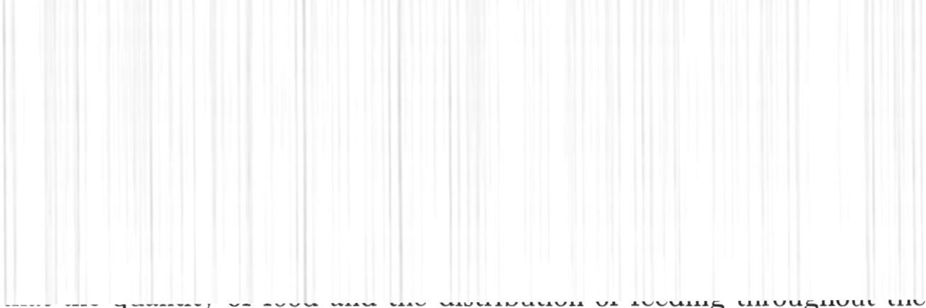

day are of great importance in prompting bird migration.

It is definitely known that many individuals leave a given point in the fall and return to that same point in the spring. Parents or progeny, rarely both, frequently return to the same tree, bush, or box. The trips taken by these birds may be over thousands of miles. Then how do these birds find their way back? Recent experiments on Homing Pigeons (*Columba livia*) have shown that when small magnets are tied to the underside of the wings of these birds they are unable to find their way back to the home cote. This fact was assumed to indicate that the birds are normally guided over unknown territory by the magnetic lines of force on the earth's crust. These lines, it would appear, serve to orient the bird so that he knows which way he wishes to fly. The experiments outlined are those of Dr. Henry Yeagley, Pennsylvania State College. Gordon (1948) repeated these experiments, however, and found that both experimental and control pigeons all returned to the home cote the same day. Griffin and Hock (1949) have shown that wild birds, when removed from a familiar territory, can return to the home area but that the return is by extended exploratory flights. They maintain that the birds simply wander about, more or less blindly, until they come upon landmarks which are familiar to them. This would imply that birds have a remarkable memory for landmarks and on their migrations they simply follow these landmarks. How do young birds, however, many of which migrate in groups separate from the adults, learn these landmarks?

Research by Gustav Kramer (1952) and others indicates that many species of birds may be able to "read the stars." Thus they may navigate, using celestial bodies to guide them, much the same as seafaring men have done for centuries. Kramer refers to this ability as the **astronomical analyser;** others call it **celestial orientation.** Our own experiments, using Kramer's methods, indicate that the State-colored Junco (*Junco hyemalis*) orients to the north-northeast while the sun is visible. It loses interest in direction while the sun is obscured by clouds. Other workers have found evidence of night time orientation in some species. These observations were made in a planetarium where the night sky could be reoriented at will to test responses.

The unerring certainty with which birds find their way over thousands of miles is admirable. Several general migration routes can be mapped on the basis of the findings of bird banders. These **migration routes** are lines of general advance or retreat; they are more or less theoretical in that they are concerned with species rather than individuals, and individuals may deviate from the regular channels frequently. Seacoasts, mountains, and river valleys serve to define the principal routes; thus the Atlantic coast, the Appalachian Mountains, the Mississippi Valley, the Rocky Mountains, and the Pacific coast loosely comprise the principal flyways. These bear many tributary routes and there are many lesser routes overland, some of which connect principal routes. They generally are funnel-shaped, or wide in the northern portion and narrow and well defined in the southern part. Birds which migrate south beyond the limits of the United States channel principally into Mexico and thence via the Isthmus of Panama to South America, or to South America via the islands of the West Indies. Recently there has been much controversy over whether or not many species and individuals fly directly over the Gulf of Mexico, but it is generally believed that most birds avoid that great body of water. It must be remembered that many birds do not retreat beyond continental North America.

The time at which migration occurs and the extent of the journeys are variable in different species and frequently vary considerably in different subspecies of a species. Spring migrations begin in February and continue into June, and fall migrations begin for some species in early July and continue on into the middle of winter, so that hardly a month passes in which there is no migratory activity. Daylight hours and night are about equally popular for the extended flights. Most smaller birds are nocturnal migrants, while most larger species fly during the daytime. Some species migrate only a comparatively few miles, while others travel all the way from the arctic regions to the antarctic. Common Crows (*Corvus brachyrhynchos*), Blue Jays (*Cyanocitta cristata*), Eastern Meadowlarks (*Sturnella magna*), and Song Sparrows (*Melospiza melodia*) migrate such short distances that the movement is hardly noticed. On the other hand the Arctic Tern (*Sterna paradisaea*) travels up to 11,000 miles from its breeding range to its antarctic winter home.

Birds have been classified according to their migratory habits. **Resident species** are those which spend their winters on the breeding range of the species. The Common Crow (*Corvus brachyrhynchos*) is present

Junco). **Transient visitants** are those that pass through a locality on their way to and from the breeding grounds. **Summer visitants** are those that make an unusual northward trip after the breeding season and before they are ready to fly south for the winter as does the American Egret (*Casmerodius albus*). (The summer residents are called summer visitants by some authors.) Birds that migrate farther south than usual

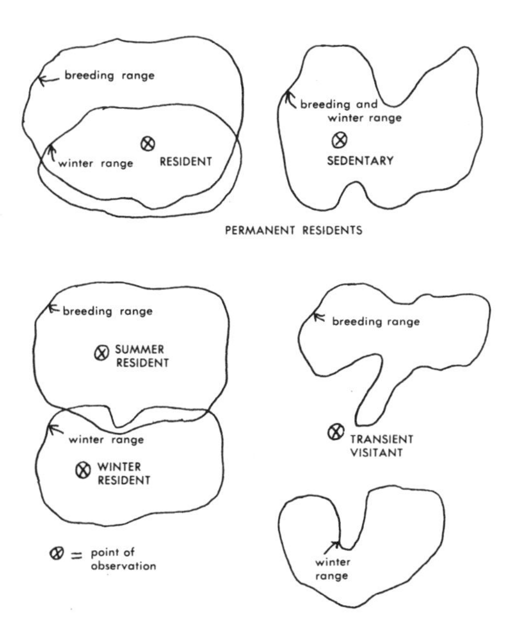

Figure 39. Diagrams illustrating the classification of migrants and nonmigrants according to their movements as viewed from a given point of observation.

and are observed only sporadically in winter in a given area are called **winter visitants**. The Snowy Owl (*Nyctea scandiaca*) generally is a permanent resident of the tundra, where lemmings are a major part of the Snowy Owl's diet. Lemmings have definite and distinct cyclic populations. When the population is low, food for the owl is scarce so it migrates south as far as South Carolina, Georgia, Louisiana, Texas, and California. For a graphic illustration of these range classifications see Figure **39**.

There is a general tendency for eastern species to extend their range westward, particularly in the north. The eastern race of the Chipping Sparrow (*Spizella passerina passerina*) and others have established breeding ranges to within twenty to a hundred miles of the Pacific Ocean. In the case of the Bobolink(*Dolichonyx oryzivorus*), a new extension of the breeding range and consequent change in migration route have occurred since the westward settlement of the United States. Since it is a bird of damp meadows, it was originally cut off from the western states by the intervening dry areas. With the appearance of irrigation ditches, however, small colonies of nesting Bobolinks have established themselves at various western points. This species migrates along the Atlantic coast and most continue into northern United States and southern Canada, but those which have moved west strike out across the United States to their western range. In the fall they head due east to the eastern coast and then move south with their north-ranging fellows.

The condition of the weather at any point is often thought to have little to do with the time of arrival of migratory birds. Temperatures recorded at the time of arrival of several common species show variations of 14° to 37° F. Movements started in January or February from the tropical region, where there is no marked climatic change, are in obedience to physiological promptings and have no relation to the prevailing weather conditions. Because they influence the water or food supply, however, weather conditions figure prominently. The advance of average temperature lines, known as **isotherms**, is found to coincide closely with the northward movement of certain species. The Canada Goose (*Branta canadensis*), for example, was found to travel north with the advance of the isotherm of 35° F. Examination of weather records over many years shows that there is actually little difference in the general trend of the weather from year to year. True, there are frequently more or less local variations which are sometimes quite extreme.

The origin of the bird is a major factor in considering the distances travelled in migration. Those birds that are of neotropical origin migrate back to South America or Central America, while those that had their origin elsewhere and arrived in the Americas via the Holarctic Region make shorter journeys. The family Parulidae, the Wood Warblers, are of strictly neotropical origin and nearly all of these species winter in Central or South America or in the West Indies. The Winter Wren (*Troglodytes troglodytes*), on the other hand, was at one time an immigrant

true, for the balance of nature is never a perfect one, rather it swings from high to low and vice versa.) Storms are probably the most potent factor in limiting the abundance of birds. The destruction of migrating birds when they strike lighthouses, tall bridge piers, monuments, tall buildings, or other aerial obstructions has been tremendous. Exhaustion cannot be said to be an important peril, although it may be more important than is known.

The study of migration by **banding** has come to be recognized as a very accurate and revealing method. Great numbers of birds are marked annually with numbered aluminum leg rings. When a banded bird is reported from a second locality, a definite fact is known concerning its movements, and a study of many such records develops a more complete understanding of the details of migration. Banding work in North America is conducted under the direction of the Fish and Wildlife Service of the Department of the Interior in cooperation with the National Parks Branch of the Canadian government. This practice was instituted in 1901 and was taken over by the federal government in 1920.

The migration of birds as it is known today had its origin in times so remote that nothing can be learned directly of the mode in which it began. The origin therefore can be interpreted only from existing conditions. The causes underlying migration are complex, but the mystery that formerly enveloped the periodic movements has largely been dispelled through the fairly complete information that is now available concerning the migration of most species of birds. Many things are still to be learned to clear away the uncertainties that continue to make migration one of the most fascinating subjects in the science of ornithology.

Bibliography and References

ALLEN, ARTHUR A., The Book of Bird Life, 2nd Edition. Princeton: D. Van Nostrand Co., pp. 133-149, 1961.

FARNER, DONALD S., The Annual Stimulus for Migration: Experimental and Physiologic Aspects. In Wolfson, Recent Studies in Avian Biology. Urbana: Univ. Illinois Press, pp. 198-237, 1955.

GORDON, DONALD A., Some Considerations of Bird Migration. *Science*, 108:705-711, 1948.

GRIFFIN, DONALD R., Bird Navigation. In Wolfson, Recent Studies in Avian Biology, Urbana: Univ. Illinois Press, pp. 154-197, 1955.

GRIFFIN, DONALD R. and RAYMOND J. HOCK, Experiments and Bird Migration. *Science*, 107:347-349, 1948.

GRIFFIN, DONALD R. and RAYMOND, J. HOCK, Airplane Observations of Homing Birds. *Ecology*, 30:176-198, 1949.

GRISCOM, LUDLOW, Modern Bird Study. Cambridge: Harvard Univ. Press, pp. 66-111, 1947.

JAEGER, EDMOND C., Does the Poor-will "Hibernate"? *Condor*, 50:45, 1948.

JAEGER, EDMUND C., Further Observations of the Hibernation of the Poor-Will. *Condor*, 51:105-109, 1949.

KIRKPATRICK, CHARLES M. and A. CARL LEOPOLD, The Role of Darkness in Sexual Activity of the Quail. *Science*, 116(3011):280-281, 1952.

KRAMER, GUSTAV, Experiments on Bird Orientation. *Ibis*, 94:265-285, 1952.

LINCOLN, FREDERICK C., Migration of Birds. U.S. Dept. Interior, *Fish and Wildlife Service Circ.* 16, 1950. (Reprint 1952 by Dover Publications, New York.)

LOWERY, GEORGE H., JR. and ROBERT J. NEWMAN, Direct Studies of Nocturnal Bird Migration. In Wolfson, Recent Studies in Avian Biology. Urbana: Univ. of Illinois Press, pp. 238-263, 1955.

MARSHALL, A. J., Biology and Comparative Physiology of Birds. Vol. II. New York: Academic Press, pp. 307-340, 1960.

PEARSON, OLIVER P., The Metabolism of Hummingbirds. *Condor*, 52:145-152, 1950.

WETMORE, ALEXANDER, The Migration of Birds. *Cambridge*: Harvard Univ. Press, 1926.

YEAGLEY, HENRY L., A Preliminary Study of a Physical Basis of Bird Navigation. *Jour. Applied Physics*, 18:1035-1063, 1947.

Exercise On Bird Migration

On the following outline maps indicate the migration routes used by the indicated species. Use arrows to indicate direction. Date early arrivals at locations along the route. Data on routes and arrival dates can be found in the life history series by Arthur Cleveland Bent listed at the end of Chapter 10, and in many other sources.

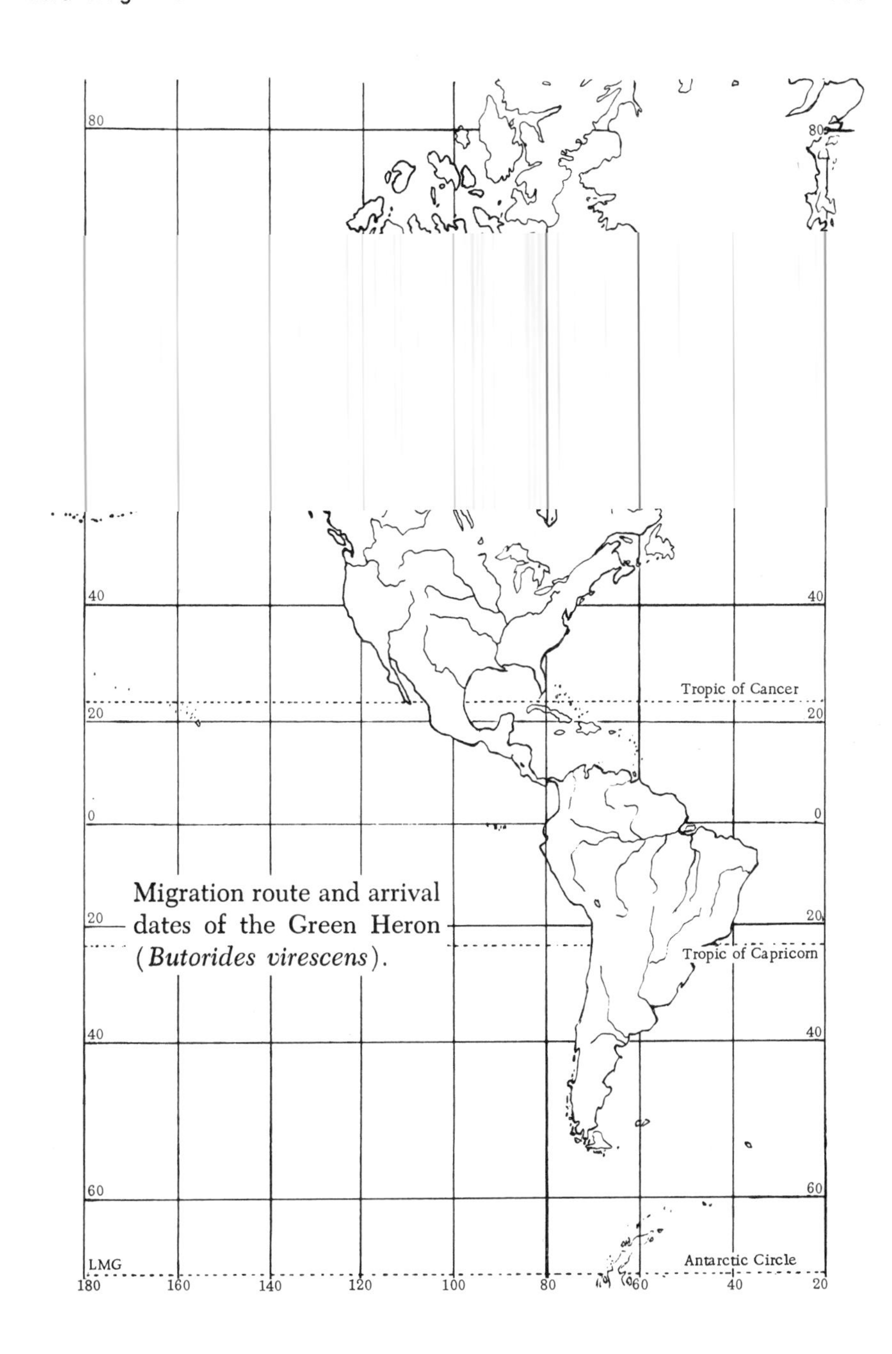

Migration route and arrival dates of the Green Heron (*Butorides virescens*).

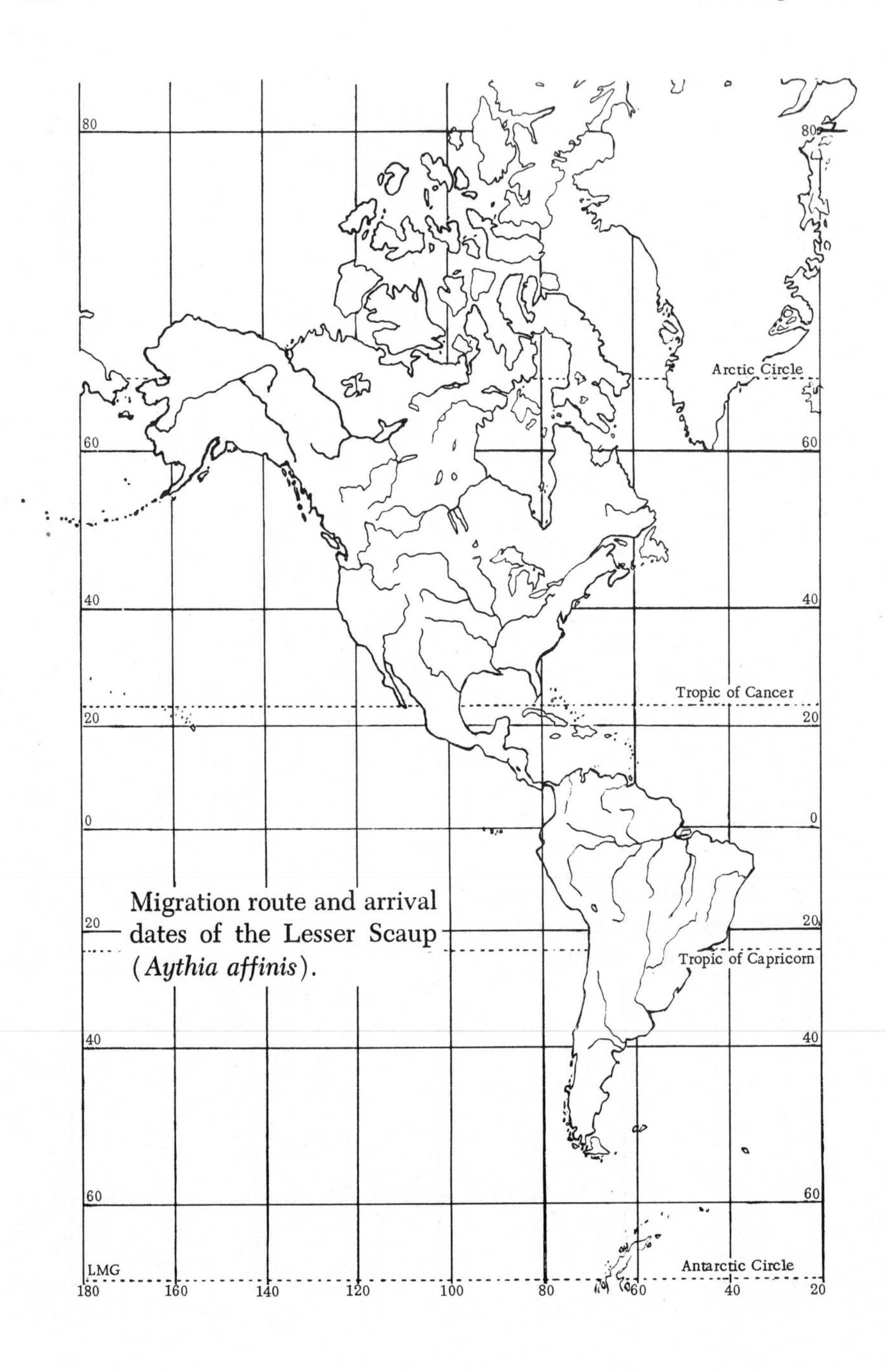

Migration route and arrival dates of the Lesser Scaup (*Aythia affinis*).

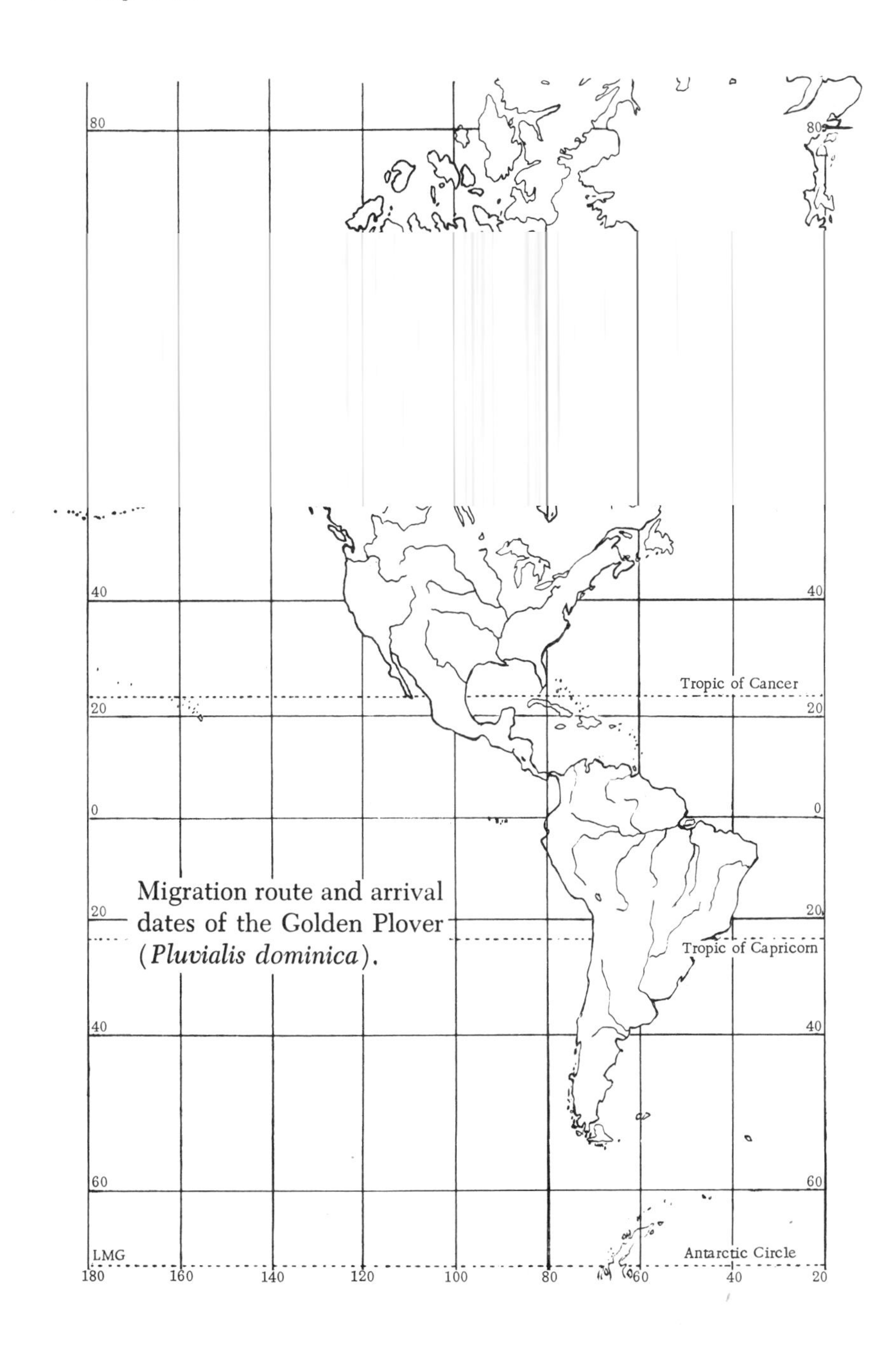

Migration route and arrival dates of the Golden Plover (*Pluvialis dominica*).

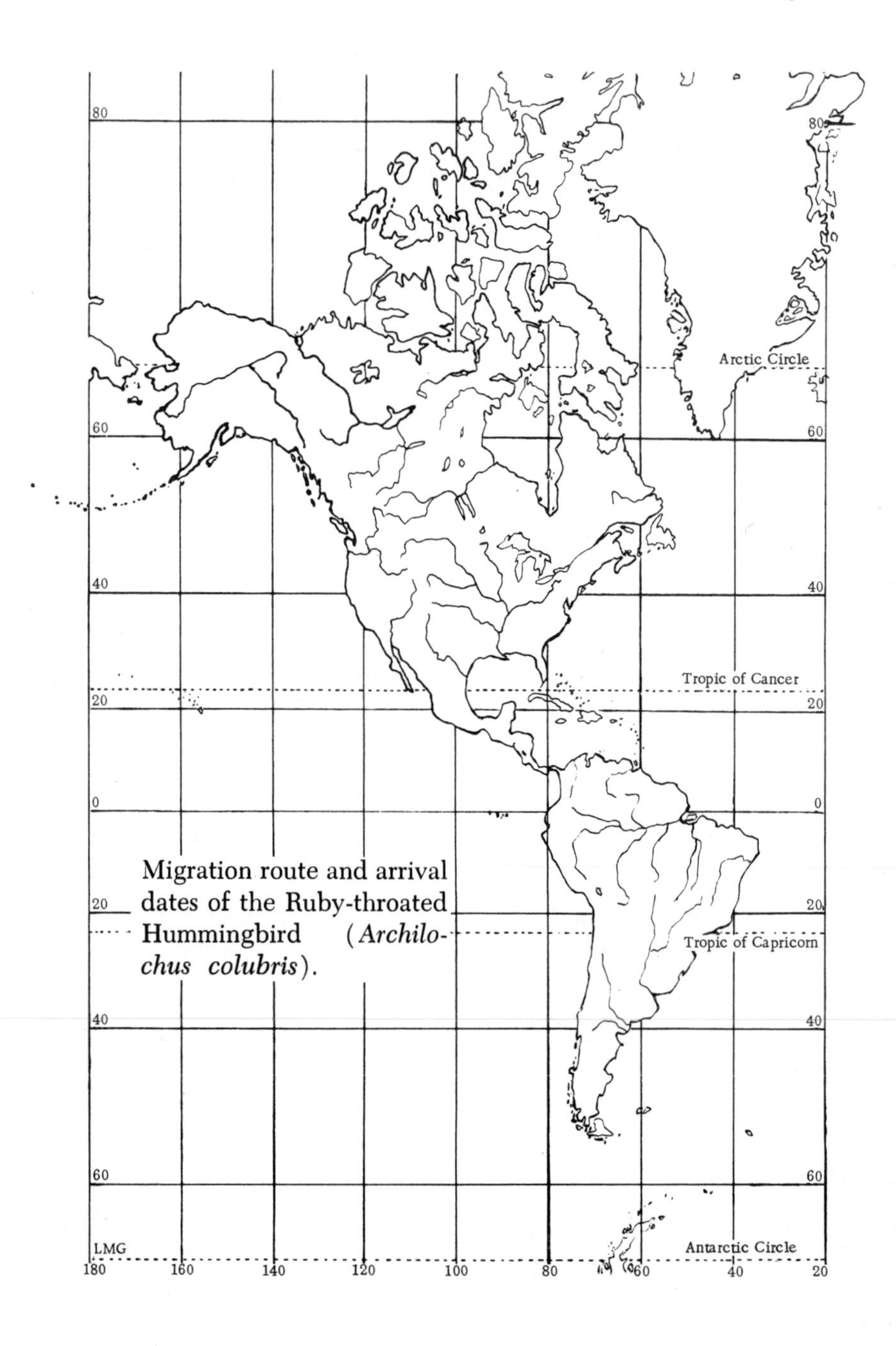

Migration route and arrival dates of the Ruby-throated Hummingbird (*Archilochus colubris*).

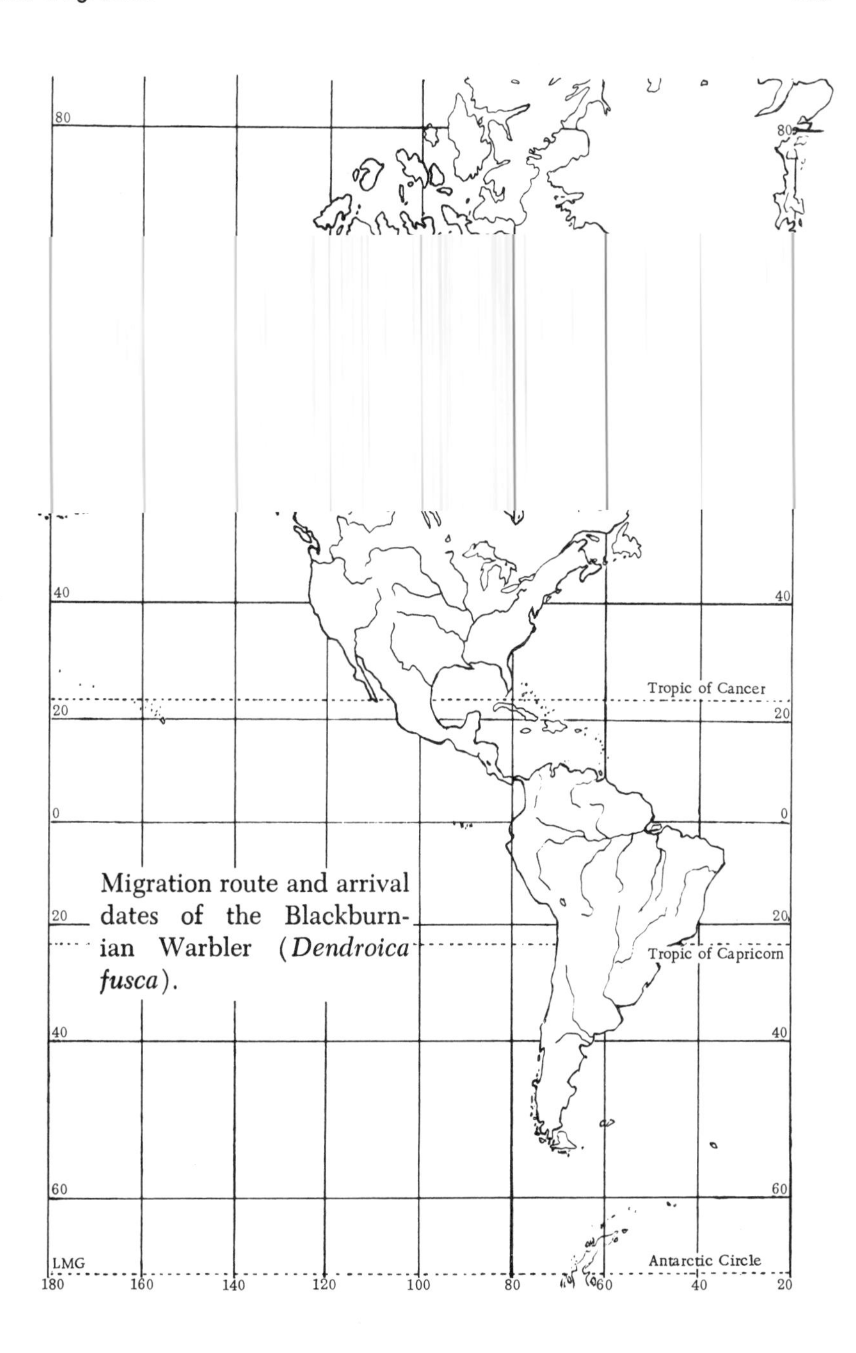

Migration route and arrival dates of the Blackburnian Warbler (*Dendroica fusca*).

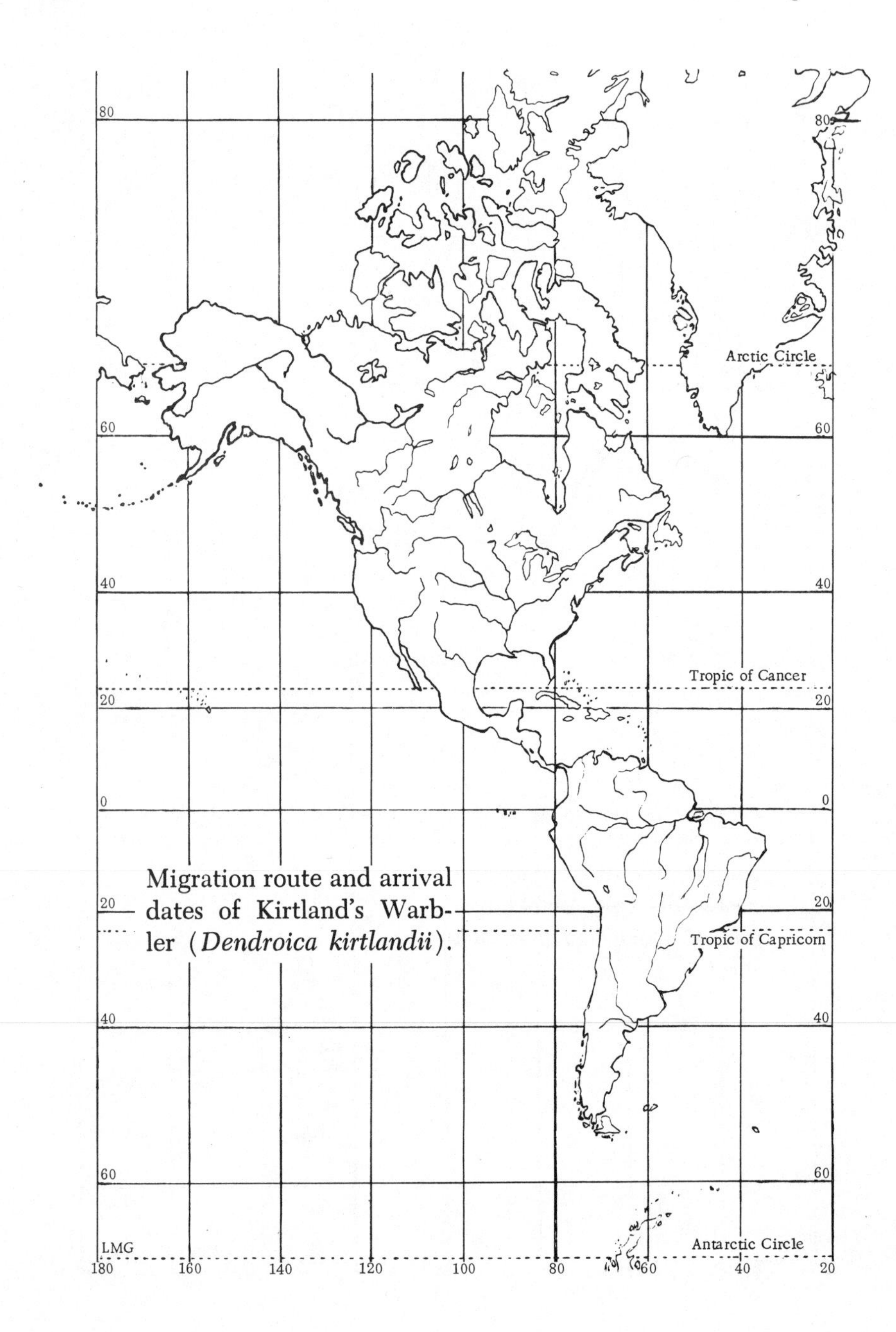

Migration route and arrival dates of Kirtland's Warbler (*Dendroica kirtlandii*).

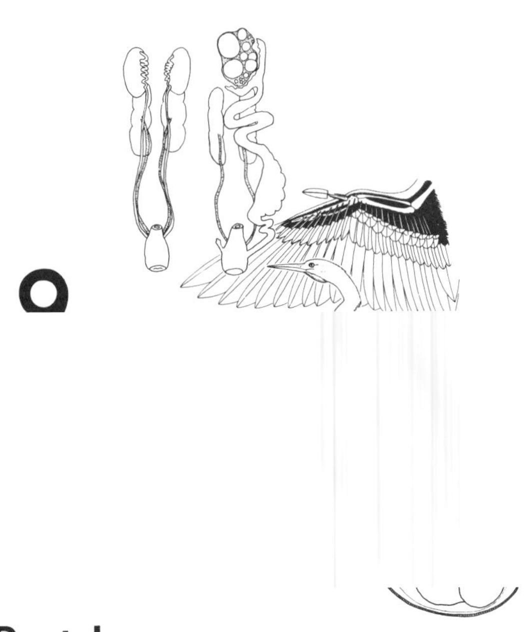

Life History - Part I

It has been said that ornithology is the most thoroughly studied and most thoroughly known of all the special sciences. Of all the phases of ornithology, life histories or life cycles are perhaps the least thoroughly known for the birds of the world. Little or no life history data have been published for most of the world's birds. In North America, north of Mexico, however, this phase of bird study is known to a greater or lesser degree for most species. For example, the eggs of every species of bird known to occur in North America, north of Mexico, have now been described. The last undescribed eggs, those of the Bristle-thighed Curlew (*Numenius tahitiensis*), were described by Allen and Kyllingstad in 1949. Nevertheless, there are many species in North America which have been studied little and there are no species about which nothing is left to be studied. Early ornithology was primarily descriptive, with many forms new to science described, and when most species were known the bird students turned to other phases among which life history studies have been prominent. Life history can be defined as a comprehensive study of the activities of a species from birth to death. It includes ecology, physiology, and all other phases involved in a species.

The winter ranges of birds need separate definition for each species. With many species the winter range is larger than the breeding range.

During their stay on the winter area the birds' activities might be classed principally as somatic, that is, the activities are concerned mainly with the maintenance of the individual. Some species wander about more or less solitarily, while others are gregarious. Palm Warblers (*Dendrocia palmarum*) and the Blue-gray Gnatcatchers (*Polioptila caerulea*) are solitary wintering birds. Red-winged Blackbirds (*Agelaius phoeniceus*) and Starlings (*Sturnus vulgaris*) are examples of gregarious birds during the winter season. Some gregarious species, like waterfowl (Family Anatidae), live in flocks of mixed sexes. The Red-winged Blackbirds live in flocks in which the sexes are separated, all males in a flock or all females in a flock. Little evidence of individual territory can be observed in such species in their wintering areas. The individuals seem to shift about within poorly defined limits. They feed and find roosting space during the daylight hours and roost at night.

With the approach of spring, migration (See Chapter 8) to the breeding range begins. Those species which are gregarious in their wintering habits generally migrate in rather tight, and often large, flocks. The migrating flocks are very conspicuous, and when they make their first appearance in spring it is difficult to miss them. Species which winter as solitary individuals migrate in various ways. Some forms congregate in the south and fly north in flocks of varying size. Others migrate as pairs and still others as single individuals. In the case of many species, such as the Robin (**Turdus migratorius**), adult males travel in loose flocks in advance of the females and younger birds. The adult females migrate in similar flocks but a few days behind the adult males. Then follow the first-year males, and last, the first-year females.

The time at which migrating begins varies among and within species. The distance between the wintering area and the breeding grounds, the speed at which the species flies, the time available on the breeding grounds for rearing a family, and the weather are among the factors which contribute to determining the departure time from the wintering area.

From a point of observation near the center of the range, the arrival of spring migrants at breeding range presents an interesting picture. The earliest arrivals are generally those which are transients and are en route to more northerly portions of the range. Furthermore, in many species the mature males, residents of northerly portions of the range, arrive first. The females of the northern part of the range may arrive with or before local resident males. Then follow the local resident females, and so on. Some stragglers, en route to points farther north, may arrive after the local resident birds. The arrival of the species occurs over several weeks, but local individuals of that species arrive within a relatively short time interval.

When the birds reach the particular spot in which they expect to spend the breeding season, a territory is established. **Territory** can be defined as the space claimed by one pair of birds of a species to rear a [illegible]

[illegible] to provide both a sufficient supply of food for the prospective family and a site for the nest. Other species nest in colonies which are in a particularly suitable environment and establish separate territories for feeding. Most species of herons and egrets (Family Ardeidae) nest in large colonies, usually in the tops of trees. The feeding territory for some of the pairs in the colony may be many miles from the nest. Actually, two territories are present here, one for nesting and another for providing the family with a food supply. Belted Kingfishers (*Megaceryle alcyon*) sometimes nest a mile or more from the feeding territory. These birds feed on small fishes. Usually the nest is built in a burrow in a gravel bank along the edge of a stream or lake. If no embankment is available the kingfisher seeks a suitable nesting site farther away from its feeding area.

Territories are generally laid out and claimed by the males. In the case of passerine birds this is usually accomplished by the male's selecting certain landmarks, such as posts, shrubs, branches of trees, etc. To each of these points the male makes regular short visits and from each of them he bursts forth in song. The landmarks are chosen so that they define the territory. The male makes regular short visits to each to proclaim to all others of his kind that the defined area is his personal possession. Once established, the territory is generally respected by other birds of that species. An occasional trespasser must be driven off. Invaders may be driven off by any one of several methods. The first effort by the owner is likely to be an increase in the frequency and volume of song. If song fails, the owner then may resort to **intimidation.** This is a procedure by which an attempt is made to repulse the intruder by showing ruffled feathers or by feigning attack. Feathers are arranged and **displayed** in such a way as to make the owner appear superior in size and color. If song and intimidation both fail to impress the intruder properly, a **fight** is likely to ensue. (See Figures 40, 41 and 42.)

If a second male intrudes upon the territory of the first for the purpose of claiming part of that territory for himself, he is less likely to be impressed by song or intimidation. The outcome of the fight that follows may determine the extent of alterations, if any, in the boundaries of the adjacent territories. If the intruder shows greater strength and endurance in the fight he may take over all or part of the territory. On the other hand, if the intruder is repulsed, he may be forced to retire without any additional property or he may retreat temporarily and later repeat the attempt to take possession of some of the area.

It is interesting to note that transients of the same species generally are permitted on the territory but other residents of the area are forced away. The male usually will permit all females into the territory. After a female has adopted the territory and the male as her own, however, she drives off the female intruders with the same vehemence as a male in driving off male trespassers.

Some birds show no evidence of territory establishment. Cliff Swallows (*Petrochelidon albifrons*) nest in large colonies with the flask- or retort-shaped nests built one against another. When approaching their nests, these birds may pause at the mouths of nests other than their own before they enter the proper nest. Such apparent violations of property rights go unchallenged. Furthermore, this species feeds in a communal manner and no feeding territory exists. Purple Martins (*Progne subis*) behave similarly. Other swallows (Family Hirundinidae) show little or no tendency to establish territories.

Upon arrival on the breeding ground, the female selects either its mate or the territory upon which it wishes to settle. Females of most species apparently select the territory which is to their liking, while the male that claims that territory is incidental. This is especially true of the passerine birds. Most birds are **monogamous**, that is, they have but one mate at a time. With many species the mate may be a different one each season. A few species, such as Canada Geese (*Branta canadensis*), are monogamous and mate for life. Some species are normally polygamous. **Polygamous** animals are those in which the male has more than one mate. Occasionally a few individuals of normally monogamous species may be polygamous. The male House Wren (*Troglodytes aedon*) has been known to have participated with two females through the nesting season. Normally House Wrens are monogamous. Here the male of one pair was possibly destroyed while the pair was preparing to nest so the widowed female enticed a neighboring male into her territory. The game birds (Order Galliformes) are polygamous birds. Male Turkeys, pheasants, grouse, and quail commonly surround themselves with a harem of two to ten or more females. A few species are **polyandrous**, that is, the female has more than one mate. House Sparrows

Figure 40. Display posture of the male Turkey, *Meleagris gallopavo*. Drawing by William C. Dilger.

best. Special structures, such as the ruffs of the Ruffed Grouse (*Bonasa umbellus*), the wattles of the Turkey (*Meleagris gallopavo*), the crest of the Cardinal (*Richmondena cardinalis*), and the horns of the Horned Lark (*Eremophila alpestris*) are used to full advantage. Some birds, such as grouse and Turkeys, hold their tail feathers in a fan shape, thus displaying appealing designs to the females. Other birds show off their powers of flight in difficult aerial evolutions. The American Woodcock (*Philohela minor*) courts his mate with a twittering call note while he performs a high spiraled flight followed by a plunge to the earth. The Horned Lark silently ascends to a height of several hundred feet. There he circles and sings a crude song for a minute or two, after which he plummets almost vertically to the ground. All this to impress his mate!

Song (see Chapter 11) and substitutes for song reach a peak during courtship. The Yellow-shafted Flicker (*Colaptes auratus*) may pound a tin roof with his bill to proclaim his affection. The drumming sound of the Ruffed Grouse, produced by whipping the curved stiff outer primaries through the air, is done for a similar purpose. Elaborate courtship dances by the Prairie Chicken (*Tympanuchus cupido*) function in intimidation and courtship. (See Figure 41.) During the breeding season the males assemble on a communal courting ground. Here they strut, display, fight, and utter loud booming love calls. The hens desirous of mating quietly put in an appearance, squat on the ground, and accept the male which won over all other rivals. After mating, the female leaves

Figure 41. Display posture of a male Sage Grouse, *Centrocercus urophasianus*. Drawing by William C. Dilger.

and other females approach the courting ground similarly. Two or three of the most superior males mate with most of the females.

The conclusion of the courtship period finds most birds paired. Presently they begin the task of nest-building. Generally the supervision of the construction of the nest is left to the female and the task is performed as rapidly as necessary to have it completed by the time the

Figure 42. Display posture of the male Redwinged Blackbird, *Agelaius phoeniceus*. Drawing by William C. Dilger.

spent at nest building and the amount of work done by the male or female vary with different species. In the case of hummingbirds (Family Trochilidae), most game birds (Order Galliformes), and others, the female does all of the nest building. On the other hand, male phalaropes (Family Phalaropodidae) build their nests with little or no help from the females. With most birds, both the male and female cooperate in nest building.

Nests are of diverse shapes and sizes. They are located in almost every conceivable situation. Many species nest on the **ground**. The Kildeer (*Charadrius vociferus*) lays its eggs in a crude nest which is merely a small depression in the ground and which bears no lining

Figure 43. The nest of a Killdeer . . . a simple depression on the ground.

materials. The Ring-necked Pheasant (*Phasianus colchicus*) lines its depression in the ground with grass, straw, and leaves. The nest of the Mallard (*Anas platyrhynchos*) is a simple depression lined with reeds, grasses, and leaves, plus many downy feathers which the female plucks from her breast. During incubation these feathers are also used to cover the eggs when the female leaves to feed. The Eastern Meadowlark (*Stumella magna*) and the Bobwhite (*Colinus virginianus*) arch grasses or other herbaceous plants over their nests so that they are well concealed.

Cavities provide nest sites for many species. Some species build their own excavations, while others utilize the abandoned cavities built by other birds or natural cavities. Bird houses fall into this category.

holes in which to build their nests. Larger natural cavities in trees provide a home for the eggs and young of the Screech Owl (*Otus asio*) and for the eggs of the Wood Duck (*Aix sponsa*). The Barn Owl (*Tyto alba*) might be called a cavity-nesting bird, for its eggs are laid in hollow trees, bird boxes, caves, barns, abandoned buildings, belfries, tunnels, or burrows in the ground.

Platform type nests are used by several species. Such nests generally are composed of sticks, piled so as to form a nearly flat upper surface, on which the eggs are laid. The Bald Eagle (*Haliaeetus leucocephalus*) uses large sticks usually placed high in a tall tree. Nests are used year after year and each season additions are made so that they sometimes reach tremendous proportions (one record was 10 feet in diameter and 20 feet high). The Osprey (*Pandion haliaetus*) builds a similar nest but places it in various places, among which are the tops of telephone poles. Mourning Doves (*Zenaidura macroura*) build fragile platform nests composed of only a very few twigs.

Most birds' nests are more or less **cup-shaped.** They are of several types and are classified according to the manner in which they are supported. **Statant** nests are those with rims standing upright and with support principally from below. The nest of the Robin (*Turdus migratorius*) is of this type. **Suspended** nests are those which are supported from the rims or sides. Those suspended nests which are supported mainly by adhesive substances from the sides are called **adherent.** Barn Swallows (*Hirundo rustica*) and Eastern Phoebes (*Sayornis phoebe*) build adherent nests. **Pensile** nests are those supported from the rims, such as those of the Red-eyed Vireo (*Vireo olivaceus*). Deeply cupped

Figure 44. The platform nest of the Bald Eagle, *Haliaeetus leucocephalus.*

Figure 45. The statant nest of the Robin, *Turdus migratorius.*

nests such as those of the Baltimore Oriole (*Icterus galbula*) are described as being **pendulous.**

Materials used in building nests vary with different species and to some extent within the species. Generally an outer layer of comparatively coarse material forms the rigid support and serves to attach the nest to the supporting structure. The coarse layer is lined with finer materials which are so molded that frequently there is space within the central cavity only for the eggs and one parent. After the young are half grown often there is insufficient space for all within the nest. Some of the nestlings are forced to perch on the rim. The materials used

Figure 46. The nest of a Cliff Swallow is attached from the sides. These adherent nests display some of the architectural ability of birds.

are generally to be found within or near the territory. Territories are selected, in part, for the nest materials available there.

The architectural ability of many species is admirable. The gourd- or retort-shaped nest of the Cliff Swallow (*Petrochelidon albifrons*), with its elongate tunnel entrance to the spherical main chamber, is a masterpiece in masonry. This species is gregarious, and the nests are frequently placed one above another, abode fashion, so that sometimes only the tunnels are evident. Many superlatives might be used to describe the meticulous care with which the Ruby-throated Hummingbird (*Archilochus colubris*) and the Blue-gray Gnatcatcher (*Polioptila caerulea*) build a knot-like nest and camouflage it with a covering of lichens. On the other extreme are such birds as the Razor-billed Auk (*Alca torda*), which builds no nest at all. The one egg laid by the razor-bill is deposited on a flat rock shelf of a cliff where it is inaccessible to potential enemies.

The life history of any species of bird is centered largely around [illegible]

tied up in the physiological stimuli which coordinate the breeding cycle of any species.

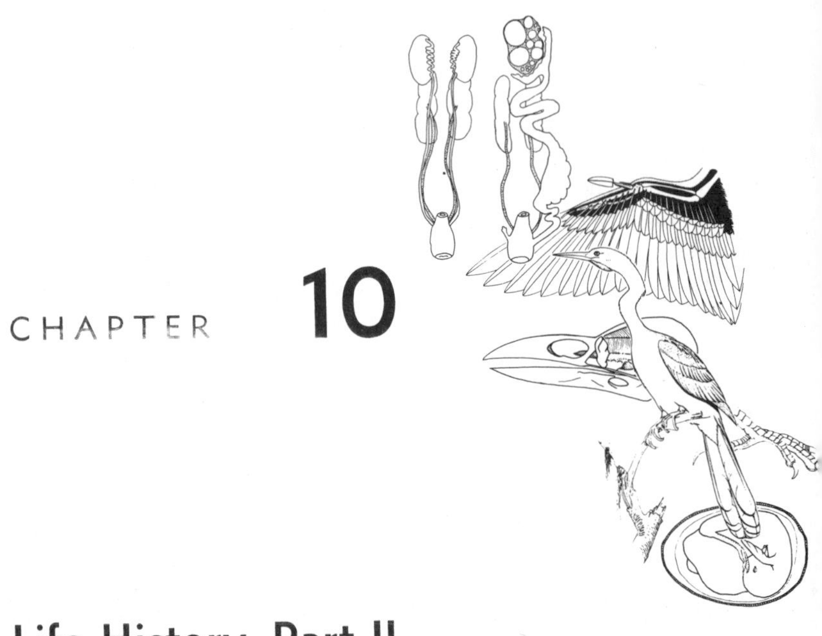

CHAPTER 10

Life History - Part II

Eggs of birds have appealed to collectors and ornithologists from early times. Oölogy, that branch of ornithology which treats specifically of the study of eggs, was at one time a very popular science. Private collections of birds' eggs were far more common than were collections of birds. Collecting of birds and of eggs is now prohibited, except by special permit, by the Migratory Bird Treaty Act.

The nest-building activities are so regulated that the nest is completed a day, more or less, before the first egg is to be laid. Eggs are laid at rather regular intervals, usually about one per day until the desired number is reached. The complete complement of eggs is known as a **clutch.** The clutch size is more or less constant within the species and is generally similar in related forms. Auks, albatrosses, and petrels lay one egg. Two is the normal number laid by most pigeons, doves, hummingbirds, and loons. Sandpipers produce a clutch of four, and most of the passerine species lay three to five eggs. Gallinaceous birds (pheasants, Turkeys, grouse, quail, etc.) produce a clutch of ten to fifteen or even twenty eggs. In general the number of eggs laid by any animal, including birds, corresponds rather closely with the rate of mortality of eggs, young, and adults of the species so that the clutch size is an indication of the rate of survival in that form. It should be noted that a species which has been introduced into a new range which presents favorable environmental conditions is not influenced by its normal limiting factors and it may increase its numbers very rapidly until a new limit is reached. This limit is the number of individuals of a species that an area can sustain. Actually the rate of increase is rapid for some time after the species becomes established and later the number fluctuates above and below the optimum. This is well

lay four or five eggs, while tropical thrushes lay only two or three. The number of eggs laid is apparently a response to physiological promptings which we frequently term "instinct." Some birds are indeterminate layers, that is they will continue to lay regularly as long as the clutch size is not reached, but most birds apparently are determinate layers and if a nest is disturbed it is abandoned and a new one is built and used.

The color of eggs is due to pigments deposited by glands associated with the shell glands of the lower region of the oviduct. One or all of the layers of the shell may be pigmented, and variation in color may result from the superimposition of pigments. The reptiles, from which the birds descended, lay white eggs, and early species of birds probably all laid white eggs too. Color is believed to be an adaptation which serves to protect the eggs from possible enemies as the birds departed from the reptilian habit of covering the eggs in their nests. Those eggs which are deposited in holes or cavities are usually white, and those which are laid in open situations are usually colored by pigments. Woodpeckers, owls, and kingfishers produce white eggs, while practically all birds that nest in open situations lay colored ones. The Mourning Dove (*Zenaidura macroura*) is a notable exception, for its white eggs are laid in a frail open platform nest. Both the male and the female participate in incubation, however, and the eggs are rarely exposed. Grebes also lay white or whitish eggs in open nests, but they generally cover them with nest material before leaving the nest. There is frequently a great deal of variation in the degree of pigmentation in eggs of a species, but they are, in general, specifically recognizable. The variations probably are caused by differences in the vigor of the reproductive system. Fully adult, vigorous birds lay eggs with heavier pigment, and the first eggs are more strongly pigmented than are those which are laid toward the completion of the clutch.

The size and shape of eggs is quite variable. In general the size of the egg is dependent upon the size of the species. There are, however, two categories to consider. Species which produce **precocial young,** that is, young which are active, feathered, and frequently capable of feeding

Figure 47. Spotted Sandpipers, *Actitis macularia,* precocial young shortly after hatching.

themselves shortly after hatching, lay eggs which are comparatively much larger than are those of birds which produce **altricial young** or young that are usually naked, or nearly so, and are helpless and completely dependent upon their parents. The eggs of precocial birds require a longer incubation period; hence more food material in the form of yolk and albumin is necessary and the eggs are larger. The eggs of the Red-winged Blackbird (*Agelaius phoeniceus*), an altricial bird, have only about one-fourth the capacity of those of the Killdeer (*Charadrius vociferus*), which is a precocial species of similar size. Size varies within the species and within the individual in about the same way that color varies, that is, vigorous adult birds lay larger eggs and they become somewhat smaller as more eggs are laid by an individual.

Figure 48. A newly hatched Eastern Bluebird (*Sialia sialis*), an altricial species.

The shape of eggs varies from almost spherical to greatly elongate. The shortest diameter of an egg is regulated by the calibre of the oviduct, thus increase or decrease in the size is caused largely by increasing or decreasing the length of the egg. The sandpipers produce pear-shaped or conical eggs; most owls lay nearly spherical eggs; but the eggs of most species are of the ovate type like those of the Domestic Fowl (*Gallus domesticus*).

In most species, when the female has laid the last egg of the clutch, the instinct to incubate is initiated, and generally within twenty-four hours that task is begun. **Incubation** involves keeping the eggs at a rather constant temperature and humidity while the embryo develops inside. It is a long and arduous task for the adults. Generally they sit very quietly and are always on the lookout for intruders. In some species incubation is performed entirely by the female, for example the Ruby-throated Hummingbird (*Archilochus colubris*) and the American Goldfinch (*Spinus tristis*). The male hummingbird abandons the female after courtship and mating and does none of the work connected with preparing for and rearing the young. The male goldfinch, however, feeds the female while she incubates the eggs and later he helps to feed the young. In many species both the male and female participate in incubating, but usually the female performs the greater portion of the work. The male Northern Phalarope (*Lobipes lobatus*) and the male Red Phalarope (*Phalaropus fulicarius*) take over the job of incubation and later care for the young, while the female does nothing but lay the eggs. In these species the females are more lavishly colored than the males. In most birds the reverse is true. Usually the male of the most brightly colored species do little or no incubating.

Hawks and owls begin incubating as soon as the first egg is laid. The remainder of the eggs in the clutch are laid, usually at two-day intervals, while the female incubates. The young thus hatch at the same intervals as those at which the eggs were deposited. Young hawks and owls in a nest show a distinct progression in size from small to large. This progression is often even more pronounced because the first-hatched, and hence the largest, young bird is stronger and more aggressive. The strongest of the young in the nest is the first to be fed and continues to eat until it is incapable of swallowing more food. The second largest bird receives the second largest quantity of food. And so the stages in the development of the young in a single nest become wider and wider. Survival of these young is similarly graded.

The megapodes (Order Galliformes, Family Megapodiidae) of the Australian Region and adjacent areas of the East Indies and the Philippines have a unique and apparently primitive system for incubating their eggs. These curious fowl-like birds (see Figure 49) deposit the eggs in the soil, in hot volcanic ashes, or in large mounds of decaying leaves and other forest litter. There the eggs incubate with the aid of the heat of the earth or the heat of decay. The eggs are not attended by the adult birds. The incubation period is well over 40 days and the young are very well developed at the time of hatching. They can fly soon after their feathers are dry. Young megapodes are never attended by their parents but are completely independent from the time they hatch.

The act of the young emerging from the egg is termed **hatching.** Hatching of the eggs occurs as a normal termination of the incubation period. To emerge from the shell, the embryo turns within the shell, and

Figure 49. A male megapode or mound-builder (*Catheturus lathami*) stands in front of the incubator mound of decaying vegetable matter. Drawing by William C. Dilger.

the **egg tooth,** which is located on the tip of the upper mandible of the young bird, cuts a groove around the large end of the egg shell. When this groove is sufficiently deep, the end of the shell breaks from the main body of the shell and the young bird begins to emerge. The young

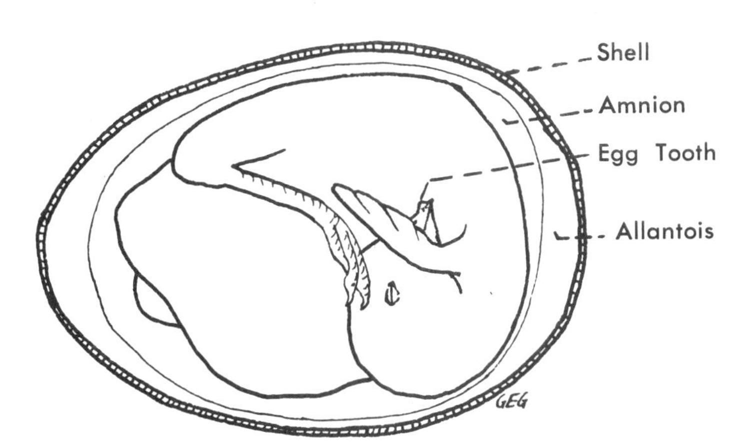

Figure 50. A nearly full term chick in the egg shell.

bird at the time of emerging from the shell is wet, for it was suspended in the amniotic fluid through most of its development. Within a few hours it dries off and the down feathers, if present, fluff out so that most of the body is covered. Figure 50 shows a nearly full-term embryo of the Domestic Fowl as it appears within the shell.

The time or duration of incubation varies with different species. The incubation period for the Domestic Fowl is 21 days; the period for the Ostrich is about 40 days; for the Eastern Bluebird (*Sialia sialis*) 12 days; for the Chipping Sparrow (*Spizella passerina*) 10 to 11 days. It should be noted that in general the more primitive birds bear precocial young, whereas the more highly evolved species produce young that are altricial. Therefore, the more primitive birds spend more time in incubation, while the higher forms spend comparatively more time rearing the young.

Care of the young in the nest is unnecessary with such precocial forms as the Ruffed Grouse (*Bonasa umbellus*) or the Killdeer (*Charadrius vociferus*) in which the young leave the nest soon after they emerge from the eggs. These young follow the female in the case of the grouse or both the male and the female in the case of the Killdeer. The adults do not feed these young but may help them find food until they are able to care for themselves. The young of ducks, geese, and swans are able to swim shortly after they are hatched. Some precocial forms are fed for a considerable time and sometimes until they are fully grown. Such is the case with gulls and terns, whose young generally stay in or near the nest for some time after hatching. Young gulls cannot swim well until they have attained the full juvenal plumage. When disturbed these birds may enter water and swim, but their feathers soon become water-logged and they are forced to return to land or drown. The downy young gulls can walk within a few hours after they emerge from the egg. Typically precocial birds leave the nest almost immediately upon hatching. Gulls and terns depart from the typical in that they normally remain in the nest for some time.

Altricial birds remain in the nest for some time after hatching and they usually have no, or only a sparse, covering of down feathers. Such young birds are called **nestlings,** while the young of precocial species are called **chicks.** There are a number of atypical altricial species that are well covered with down feathers at the time of hatching. Among this atypical group are the albatrosses, herons, hawks, owls, and goatsuckers and their relatives. This intermediate group produces young that stay in the nest, are fed by their parents, and are incapable of moving about for some time after hatching, but they are fully clothed with down feathers at hatching.

Many altricial birds are fed predigested food by their parents. This is true especially of the herbivorous forms, for the digestive enzymes of the young apparently are incapable of breaking down the plant materials. As these birds become larger, the food is given directly to the

pelicaniform birds eat fishes which are carried to them in the gular pouch of the parent, and the young place their heads into the mouth of the adult to pick out their meals. The quantity of food required by a growing bird is very great. When one considers that some species almost double their weight each day for the first several days it is easier to understand why great quantities of food are necessary. A growing Robin (*Turdus migratorius*) will eat up to 14 feet of earthworms a day.

As soon as the young birds emerge from their shells, the parents, especially the female, lose the instinct to incubate and it is replaced by an instinct to feed. The young are stimulated to open their mouths by some sort of **releaser signal** that is given by the adult. Generally all the young in the nest respond to the releaser, but it is apparent that the nestling which has the longest neck and the widest mouth is the first to be fed. If this individual is full and incapable of holding more food he is unable to swallow. The food is then lifted from his mouth and placed in that of the nestling with the second longest neck. If the second bird is unable to swallow the food, then it is placed in the mouth of the third, and so on. All the young beg for food, even though some may be so filled that they can contain no more!

Most species of birds practice **nest-sanitation** procedures. The excreta of the young of these birds are enclosed in a mucous *fecal sac* and these sacs are carried away from the nest by the parents. This is especially true with the passerine birds while the young are incapable of depositing their wastes outside the nest. Birds which feed fish to their young never carry the wastes away. Herons nest in colonies high in trees, and the alkaline defecated materials of the young often kill the trees after a period of a few years.

The changes of the young bird are many and great. Outstanding among these changes are those of the plumage. The precocial birds bear the **natal down** feathers at the time of hatching and altricial birds acquire these feathers soon after hatching. This is a loose-textured covering of fluffy down feathers which is lost by the **postnatal molt.** Molting is the process in which birds periodically shed and renew their plumage. The postnatal molt is complete but gradual as the down feathers are replaced by the feathers of the **juvenal plumage.** This is the first plumage to consist of contour feathers. In some species this is replaced, after being shed in the **postjuvenal molt,** by the **postjuvenal plumage.** The postjuvenal molt may or may not be complete. It is never complete in birds which produce a postjuvenal plumage. The juvenal or, in species in which it occurs, the postjuvenal plumage is followed by the **first winter plumage,** which is retained throughout the winter and is lost wholly or in part in the spring in the **prenuptial molt.** It is replaced by the **nuptial plumage,** which is retained throughout the breeding season. This is followed by the **second winter plumage** and then the **second nuptial plumage.** The third and fourth winter and nuptial plumages are distinguishable in a few species. When the plumages no longer are separable from the preceding year's plumage, or when there is no change from year to year in winter or nuptial plumages, the bird has acquired the adult plumage. The **adult nuptial plumage** is worn during the breeding season, and the **adult winter plumage** clothes the bird throughout the winter season. Adult plumages may be acquired at various times in various species from the first nuptial to the fourth winter plumages. The proposed new terms applying to these molts and plumages have been discussed in Chapter 2 (see page 20).

Altricial birds and those precocial birds that remain in the nest for some time after hatching attain the juvenal plumage before they leave the nest. The first winter plumage is generally born while the birds perform their fall migratory flight to the winter grounds. The molting of the feathers is a gradual process. As soon as the first plumes are lost their replacement is begun so that the body is always clothed with feathers. Waterfowl shed all the wing primaries at one time and are then incapable of flying until they are replaced.

Studies by Stoner (1939) on the temperature, growth, weight, and other phenomena of the Eastern Phoebe (*Sayornis phoebe*) reveal some of the great changes that occur with young and growing altricial birds. The body temperature of one bird taken at the age of four hours was

100.0° F. Temperature readings were taken at two- or three-day intervals and showed a steady increase to 106.6° F. on the fourteenth day. Weights measured at the same intervals ranged from 1.7 grams at age four hours to 18.3 grams at age 14 days. During the first two days the Phoebe nestling more than doubled its weight (1.7 grams to 3.7 grams). At the age of four days the same bird had almost quadrupled its initial

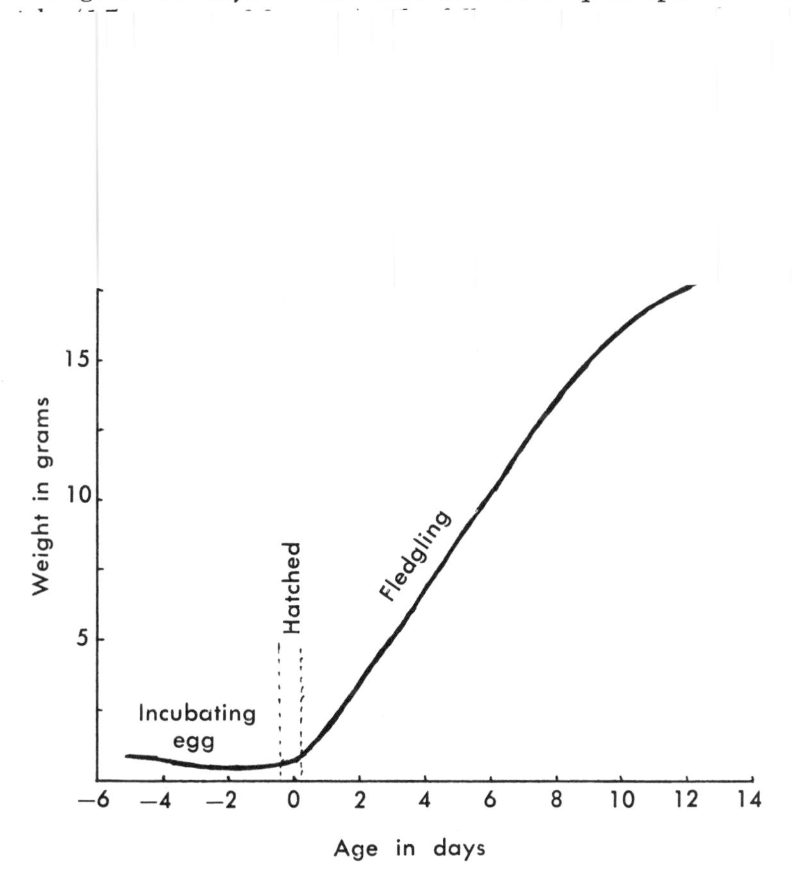

Figure 51. A growth curve of the Eastern Phoebe, *Sayornis phoebe*. Adapted from data by Stoner (1939).

from these data that the rate of increase is most rapid during the first few days and decreases with age. Feather growth in the young Phoebe was comparatively steady. The elongation of bones of the wings was most rapid toward the middle of the 14 day period.

While the foregoing data pertain to a single young Phoebe, Stoner's work indicates that these data are more or less typical of 20 young Phoebes studied. What is true of the Eastern Phoebe is not necessarily true of other species and may not be true of the Phoebe in a different part of the range. In general, however, the trends shown by these birds may be considered typical. More research of this kind is needed to gain good comparative data on growth and development in all species.

The departure from the nest by young altricial birds is an interesting and often critical part of their life cycle. As the nestlings near the full juvenal plumage they frequently climb to the rim or edge of the nest, where they stretch and exercise their wings. Most young are forced from the nest by starvation. When it is time for the actual departure, the adults approach the nest with food but refuse to go all the way to their offspring. Thus the hungry young birds are forced to move out to the parents if they wish to satisfy their appetites. This they invariably do. When they are disturbed, the nestlings may be forced out at a very early age. I have observed Rufous-sided Towhees (*Piplio erythropthalmus*) successfully calling the young from the nest one day after those young had opened their eyes! In this instance, I had set up a photography blind a few feet from the nest and was waiting inside for the adults to fed their progeny. Danger from predators is very great during the first days out of the nest. The young birds are comparatively slow and they react slowly to emergency situations. Death from accidents and from exposure is probably frequent during this critical period.

The young are generally fed by the adults for several days to several weeks after leaving the nest. The post-nesting parental care varies considerably in different species. There may also be much variation within the species. Those adults which produce a second brood during the same season desert the first brood early in order to have time to repeat the cycle. Young Brown-headed Cowbirds (*Molothrus ater*), which are reared by foster parents, demand a lot of post-nesting attention. Chipping sparrows (*Spizella passerina*) often continue to feed the parasitic Cowbirds long after their own young are left to manage their own ways. It is a peculiar sight when one observes a tiny "Chippy" feeding a juvenal cowbird which is more than twice its size. The fall migration to the winter range usually marks a definite end to parental care of the young.

The life history of every species has its own peculiarities, and much field research is necessary to complete our knowledge of this phase of ornithology. Many small incidents pertaining to some part of the behavior of an individual or a species, when properly recorded, may be a potential addition to our knowledge of that species. The precise ecological requirements of each species, actually a part of the life history, are probably not known for any species. It can be stated that there is no species about which nothing more is to be known. The field student should ever be on the alert in observing the behavior of birds. When one finds greater thrill in seeing a Robin do something new or unknown than

Jones Co., pp. 172-197, 1925. (Reprinted 1962, Dover Publications, New York.)

BENT, ARTHUR CLEVELAND, Life Histories of North American Birds. Washington: *U.S. National Museum Bulletins,* 1919-1958.

———. Diving Birds. *U.S.N.M. Bull.,* 107, 1919. (Reprinted 1946, Dodd, Mead & Co., New York.)

———. Gulls and Terns. *U.S.N.M. Bull.,* 113, 1921. (Reprinted 1947, Dodd, Mead & Co., New York.)

———. Petrels and Pelicans and Their Allies *U.S.N.M. Bull.,* 121, 1922.

———. Wild Fowl (part). *U.S.N.M. Bull.,* 126, 1923. (Reprinted 1951, Dover Pub., New York.)

———. Wild Fowl (part). *U.S.N.M. Bull.,* 130, 1925. (Reprinted 1951, Dover Pub., New York.)

———. Marsh Birds. *U.S.N.M., Bull.,* 135, 1927.

———. Shore Birds (part 1). *U.S.N.M. Bull.,* 142, 1927. (Reprinted 1962, Dover Pub., New York.)

———. Shore Birds (part 2). *U.S.N.M. Bull.,* 146, 1929. (Reprinted 1962, Dover Pub., New York.)

———. Gallinaceous Birds, *U.S.N.M. Bull.,* 162, 1932. (Reprinted 1963, Dover Pub., New York.)

———. Birds of Prey (part 1). *U.S.N.M. Bull.,* 167, 1937. (Reprinted 1961, Dover Pub., New York.)

———. Birds of Prey (part 2). *U.S.N.M. Bull.,* 170, 1938. (Reprinted 1961, Dover Pub., New York.)

———. Woodpeckers, *U.S.N.M. Bull.,* 174, 1939.

———. Cuckoos, Goatsuckers, Hummingbirds and Their Allies. *U.S.N.M. Bull.,* 176, 1940.

———. Flycatchers, Larks, Swallows, and Their Allies. *U.S.N.M. Bull.,* 179, 1942.

———. Jays, Crows, and Titmice, *U.S.N.M. Bull.,* 191, 1947.

———. Nuthatches, Wrens, Thrashers, and Their Allies. *U.S.N.M. Bull.,* 195, 1948.

———. Thrushes, Kinglets, and Their Allies. *U.S.N.M. Bull.*, 196, 1949.
———. Wagtails, Shrikes, Vireos, and Their Allies. *U.S.N.M. Bull.*, 197, 1950.
———. Wood Warblers, *U.S.N.M. Bull.*, 203, 1953.
———. Blackbirds, Orioles, Tanagers, and Allies. *U.S.N.M. Bull.*, 211, 1958.
DELACOUR, JEAN and ERNST MAYR, Birds of the Philippines, New York: Macmillan Company, pp. 52-53, 1946.
NICE, MARGARET MORSE, Studies in the Life History of the Song Sparrow, I. *Trans. Linn. Soc. N.Y.*, 4:1-247, 1937.
———. Studies in the Life History of the Song Sparrow, II. *Trans. Linn. Soc. N.Y.*, 6:1-328, 1943.
PALMER, RALPH S., Handbook of North American Birds, Vol. 1, Loons through Flamingos. New Haven, Conn.: Yale Univ. Press, 1962.
STONER, DAYTON, Temperature, Growth and Other Studies on the Eastern Phoebe. *N.Y. State Mus. Circ.*, 22, 1939.

EXERCISE ON LIFE HISTORY

From the literature, including ornithological journals, prepare outlines of the life histories of the following bird species:

1. Brown Pelican, *Pelecanus occidentalis.*
2. Wood Duck *Aix sponsa.*
3. Spotted Sandpiper, *Actitis macularia.*
4. Parasitic Jaeger, *Stercorarius parasiticus.*
5. Barn Owl, *Tyto alba.*
6. Pileated Woodpecker, *Dryocopus pileatus.*
7. Yellow Warbler, *Dendroica petechia.*
8. Brown-headed Cowbird, *Molothrus ater.*

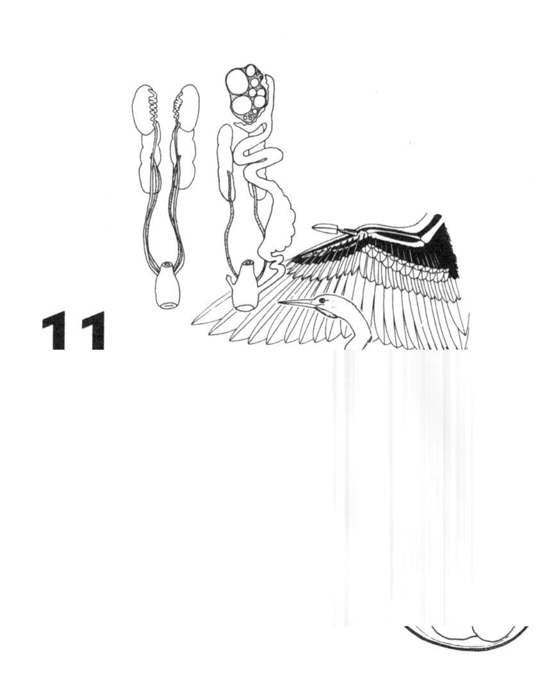

11

Bird Song

The most melodious sounds in nature are produced by birds. Many invertebrates such as grasshoppers, katydids, crickets, cicadas, and many vertebrates such as frogs, toads, and many mammals, produce sounds that can be called song. Few of these approach the quality of the musical tones produced by many birds. Not all birds sing. In general the more highly specialized or more highly evolved birds have more elaborate songs than the more primitive birds.

Most bird sounds, and all true songs, are produced by the bird's vocal organ, the syrinx. (See Figure 16.) Air, passed back and forth over the membranes of the syrinx, produces vibrations. These vibrations initiate waves of sound which can be modified in various ways in the trachea, pharynx, and oral cavity. The tongue apparently plays little, if any, part in modifying the sounds. The syringeal muscles, by contracting to produce tensions on the several sound producing membranes of the syrinx, regulate the rate at which the syringeal membranes vibrate. Thus these muscles are responsible for the pitch of the sounds.

Not all sounds which originate from birds are classed as song. **Song** is a vocal utterance, usually confined to the male, produced principally at times of territory establishment, courtship, and mating. Song is not always melodious nor is it confined to the passerine or song birds, although it is within this group that song is most highly developed. The clacking or rasping sound produced by the Common Grackle (*Quiscalus quiscula*) is harsh and unpleasing to the ear but it is a song. The crow of a Domestic Rooster (*Gallus domesticus*) is not musically impressive but it is a true song. On the other hand the *cluck* of a domestic fowl is known as a **call note** and is not properly called a song. Call notes are used for various purposes. The adults frequently utter a call note when they approach the nest, and the young respond with their calls. Such sounds apparently serve as identifying notes or function to serve notice of presence. Other call notes are used as signals of distress, hunger, fear, contentment, etc.

The origin of song in birds is a subject upon which one could speculate at great length. The Family Fringillidae (sparrows, finches, cardinals, grosbeaks, etc.) demonstrates how song may have developed from call notes. The Chipping Sparrow (*Spizella passerina*) utters a call note that is more or less typical of fringillids. It is a simple *chip* with short staccato enunciation. The Chipping Sparrow's song is composed of many of these short chipping notes, run together in a legato rendition. The Field Sparrow's (*Spizella pusilla*) song consists of three or four long whistled notes followed by an increasingly rapid series of shorter whistled *chips* so that toward the end of the song they form a definite trill. Most of this song stays close to a single high whistled pitch, but toward the end it rises or falls until it fades out. The song of the Cardinal (*Richmondena cardinalis*) consists of highly modified chipping notes which are slurred either up or down. They start slowly but increase gradually in speed until the slurred *chips* are hardly separable at the end of the song. The Song Sparrow's (*Melospiza melodia*) song has evolved far beyond the stage where *chips* are identifiable in most of the song, but the simple and typical call note has been retained.

Any sound is a result of vibrations which are transmitted by waves through some medium such as air. The pitch of any sound is determined by its wave length, or, more specifically, there is a different wave length for each pitch of sound. Sounds of all pitches travel at the same speed; hence there may be several waves occurring in a high or short wave length pitch, while only one occurs in a sound of low pitch. The pitch or highness or lowness of a sound then can be described in terms of waves or **cylces per second** (c.p.s.). The highest note on a piano keyboard has a frequency of 4096, or it produces 4096 cycles per second. The lowest note on the piano keyboard is 27 c.p.c. The human ear can normally hear sounds between 20 c.p.s. and 16,000 c.p.s. With these figures available for comparison, let us look at the vibration frequency of some bird songs.

The Eastern Phoebe (*Sayornis phoebe*) song is rendered at about 4300 cycles per second. The frequency of the Robin's (*Turdus migratorius*) song averages about 2800 c.p.s. with a recorded low of 2200 c.p.s. and a high of approximately 3300 c.p.s. The Starling (*Sturnus vulgaris*) ranges between 1100 and 8225; the Song Sparrow (*Melospiza melodia*) between 1900 and 7700; the Red-winged Blackbird (*Agelaius phoeni-*

Each species of bird that sings has a distinctive song which differs in at least some slight respect from the songs of all other species. The field ornithologist should learn to identify birds, especially the more common ones, by their songs. Frequently song may reveal the presence of species which otherwise would be overlooked by the field observer. A census of breeding birds in an area is most easily accomplished by locating and counting singing males. To make such a census, prepare a grid map of the area to be covered, then systematically walk over the area and plot, by entering an arrow on the map, the direction from which a song is heard. The same singing male may be heard from several locations, thus an extension of the arrows should narrow the source of the song down to a small plot which should more or less define the territory of that male. The number of breeding birds of any singing species therefore can be determined without actually ever seeing the birds. Several repeats of the census will more precisely define the territories. Figure 52 shows such a grid as it might appear at the end of a census. This system, or a modification of it, is useful in locating the nests of birds.

The usefulness of a knowledge of bird songs is apparent to anyone who would do serious studies in field ornithology. Learning songs is a task which ordinarily cannot be accomplished in one or two years but rather requires repeated attention over many years. It shall be our purpose here to demonstrate some methods that can be used in recording the songs and calls of birds so that they can be referred to at times other than when hearing them in the field.

The English language is very inadequate when it comes to describing bird sounds. The surest way of committing a song to memory is

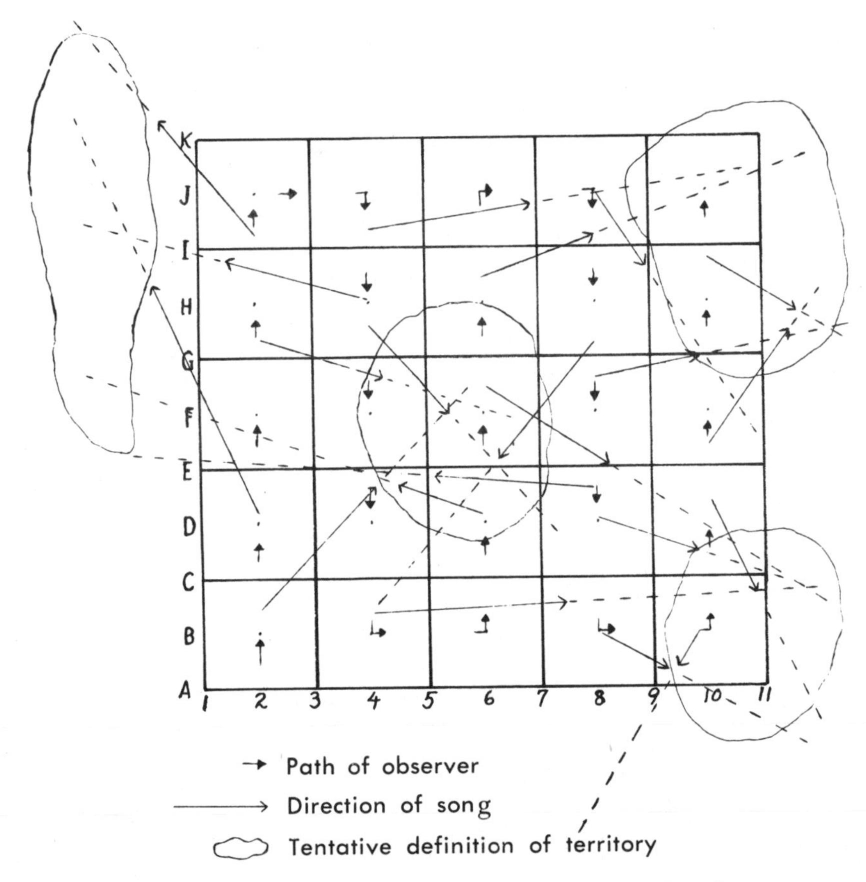

Figure 52. Plan for executing a breeding bird census based on singing males (see text).

through repetition. This may be easy with a few species which breed near the student's home, for in such instances the song is repeated frequently throughout much of the breeding season. It is difficult, however, to learn, through repetition, the songs of transient species whose songs may be heard for only a week or so each spring. Learning to imitate songs is extremely helpful if it is possible, but many songs are so intricate that neither the human voice nor whistle is capable of accurate rendition. If one can imitate it frequently, the song of a species may soon become permanently fixed in memory. I have heard the song of the Olive-sided Flycatcher (*Nuttallornis borealis*) on only two occasions, both of which were several years ago in northern Michigan, but if I were to hear one of these birds singing his whistled *"Hic! three beers!"* now, I would immediately recognize it. This particular song I found easy to imitate, so I carried it with me until now I remember it well.

The Wood Pewee (*Contopus virens*) sings *pee-a-wee* with the first syllable high pitched, then the lower *ah,* followed by the trailed-out and higher-pitched *wee.* Notice that both these birds sing their names. Many other species are named for their songs. Among them are Bobwhite, Killdeer, Chuck-will's-widow, Whip-poor-will, Flicker, Chickadee, Veery, and Dickcissel.

The use of catch phrases is especially helpful in learning some bird songs. The *Hic! three beers!* (some say: *"Hip! Three Cheers!"*) of the Olive-sided Flycatcher is an example which will appeal to the memory. Other examples of catch phrases include the *drink your teaeee* of the Rufous-sided Towhee, the ascending *I am lazy* song of the Black-throated Blue Warbler, and the *please please please ta meetcha* of the Chestnut-sided Warbler.

The value of the use of phonetic syllables or phrases may be greater if some method is employed to represent variations in pitch. Lines, short strokes, circles, etc. can be used to show such variations. The lines can be placed above or below a permanent line on field notebook paper at such a height that it represents the pitch above or below a certain standard you have established. This line can then waver up or down as the pitch of the song moves high or low. Volume of the song can be represented by the thickness of the line and variations in volume by variations in thickness. Breaks in the song are represented by breaks in the line. The following examples illustrate this method:

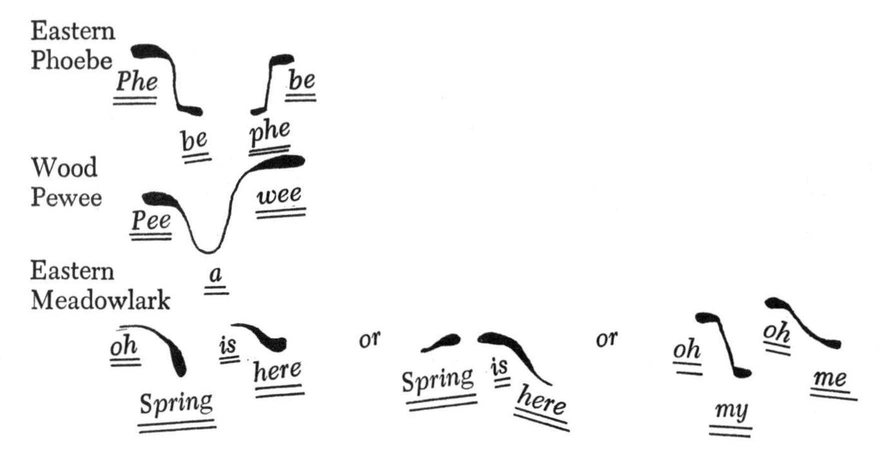

Trills can be represented by waved or undulating lines as demonstrated by the call of the Common Tern (*Sterna hirundo*) or the song of the Upland Plover (*Bartramia longicauda*).

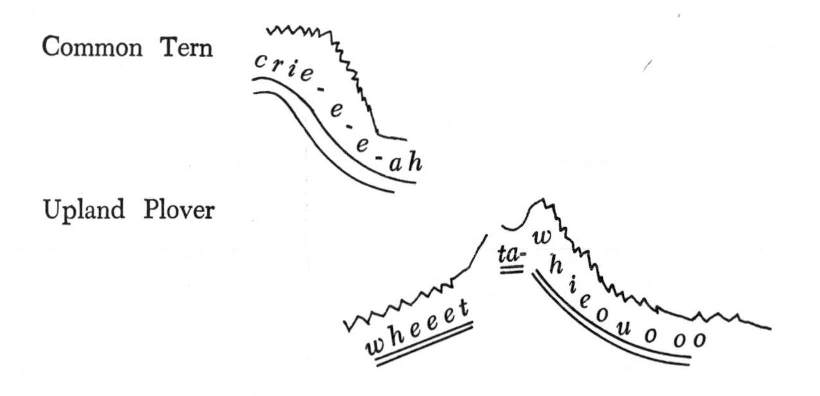

Songs which have rising and falling pitches, so that the starting pitch is repeated, can be represented by circles or spiralled lines. The song of the Veery (*Hylocichla fuscescens*), for example, might be represented thus:

Veery

'turee-aree-aree-aree-aree

For those who are musically talented, still another method is suggested. The notes of the songs of birds generally are not equal to the tones and halftones of the musician but they usually fall close to them and rather accurate renditions in pitch, rhythm, and meter are possible for many species. F. Schuyler Mathews' *Field Book of Wild Birds and Their Music* presents the musical notations of many bird songs. The

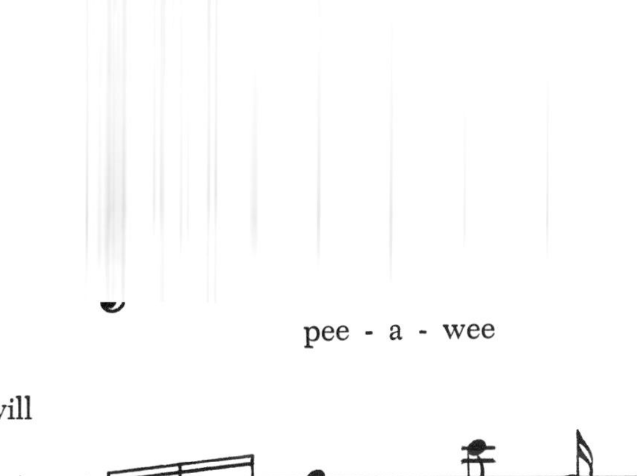

Whip-poor-will

whip-poor - will

The Albert R. Brand Bird Song Foundation of the Laboratory of Ornithology, Cornell University, Ithaca, N. Y. (and numerous other sources), has published recordings of a number of bird songs. These discs can be of considerable aid in learning songs, for they can be played over and over again. The volumes of Brand and other records are listed in the bibliography at the end of this chapter. The development of easily operated tape recorders has proved very helpful to bird-song students. They are being used advantageously by many students. In most cases additional amplification is necessary, but some songs can be recorded without additional equipment. A parabolic reflector, when properly directed, enhances the value of a tape recorder. It reflects sound waves to the focal point where a microphone picks up the concentrated sounds, which thus can be transmitted to the tape recorder. The reflected waves provide sound concentration; therefore volume is increased. Tape recordings, like disc recordings, can be played repeatedly; thus learning the recorded songs may be simplified.

Most bird songs have a quality similar to that of the human whistle. Anyone who is willing to practice and master the imitation of a few bird songs may find great enjoyment in "calling" a bird to within a few feet of himself. Many species respond to imitated calls or songs. Apparently they react in this manner for the purpose of driving a supposed intruder from their territory. Men, more than women, will find enjoyment in imitating birds, for men generally have greater ability at whistling.

Bibliography and References

Allen, Arthur A., The Book of Bird Life. Princeton: D. Van Nostrand Co., pp. 342-348, 1961.

Allen, Francis H., The Evolution of Bird Song. *Auk*, 36:528-536, 1919.

Armstrong, Edward A., A Study of Bird Song. London, England and Fair Lawn, N.J.: Oxford Univ. Press, 1963.

Borror, Donald J. and Carl R. Reese, The Analysis of Bird Songs by Means of a Vibralyzer. *Wilson Bull.*, 65:271-276, 1953.

Brand, Albert R., A Method for the Intensive Study of Bird Song. *Auk*, 52:40-52, 1935.

Brand, Albert R., Vibration Frequencies of Passerine Bird Song. *Auk*, 55:263-268, 1938.

Lanyon, W. E. and W. N. Tavolga (Editors), Animal Sounds and Communication. Washington: Publication No. 7, Am. Inst. Biol. Sci., 1960. (Includes a 12" L.P. Record edited by Peter Paul Kellogg.)

Matthews, F. Schuyler, Field Book of Wild Birds and Their Music. New York: G. P. Putnam's Sons, 1921.

Saunders, Aretas A., Bird Song. *N.Y. State Museum Handbook* 7., 1929.

Saunders, Aretas A., A Guide to Bird Songs. New York: Doubleday & Co., 1959.

Recordings of Bird Song

Cornell Laboratory of Ornithology — Peter Paul Kellogg and Arthur A. Allen

American Bird Songs, Vol. I and II.
A Field Guide to Bird Songs.
A Field Guide to Western Bird Songs.
A Day at Flores Moradas (Venezuela).
An Evening in Sapsucker Woods.
Bird Songs in Your Garden.
Bird Songs from the Tropics (Venezuela) (by Paul Schwartz).
Mexican Bird Songs.
Music and Bird Songs.
Songbirds of America.
Sound Guide to North American Waterfowl.
Voices of African Birds.

Federation of Ontario Naturalists – William W. H. Gunn
A Day in Algonquin Park.
Birds of the Forest.
Finches.
Prairie Spring.
Songs of Spring.
Thrushes, Wrens and Mockingbirds.

those you hear in the field.

2. Use the suggested systems (or devise you own system) to record and learn the songs of birds in the field. Pay particular attention to learning the more common species in your area. Continuation of this exercise will enable you to learn the songs of most species over a period of several years of conscientious effort.

CHAPTER 12

The Economic Value of Birds

A complete and fair treatment of the economic value of birds is extremely difficult. For each species some beneficial and some injurious traits can be found. A flycatcher which feeds on a single honeybee, if observed by the beekeeper, may condemn the entire species in the mind of the beekeeper and in the minds of many people to whom the beekeeper speaks. That single honeybee might comprise only 0.01 percent of a month's flycatcher diet and the remaining 99.99 percent could consist of injurious insects, yet the bird is condemned. The old saying that "a little learning is a dangerous thing" is well exemplified in the attitude of many humans toward many species of birds. It can be said that most species of birds have such little effect upon the economic interests of man that they are neither beneficial nor injurious. For the thousands of bird students, however, even these are beneficial, for they provide additional outdoor enjoyment.

Some birds are valuable because they provide man directly with useful materials. Those birds whose feathers are used to adorn ladies' hats by the millinery industry; those whose eggs or flesh are eaten; those which leave deposits of excreta called **guano;** those whose feathers are used in pillows, or in fishermen's flies, or on arrows, or on badminton "birds," and those whose feathers are used for feather paintings and for other ornamental purposes contribute directly to man's economy.

Most economic values of birds are indirect. Whether beneficial or injurious, these indirect values are concerned primarily with food habits. Those birds which feed upon injurious insects, rodents, and weed seeds generally are acclaimed beneficial, while those which feed upon game animals, domestic animals, and cultivated grains and fruits are injurious. These generalizations can be variously modified. For example, an Eastern

many individuals must be sacrificed in order to get significant data. These must be collected under all possible conditions in order that the data will be valid. Obviously, a Robin (*Turdus migratorius*) collected deep in a forest would show no traits that are detrimental to the interests of a farmer. Food habits of owls are more easily studied. These birds prey upon small mammals and other small vertebrates and upon larger insects. Most of the undigestible parts of this food are regurgitated in the form of **pellets.** Skulls and other bones, hair, feathers, insect legs or wings, and the like can be identified easily from these pellets. Thus many samples of the diet of a single owl can be analyzed without harming the owl. Such food habit data are available for many species of American birds primarily through the efforts of the former Bureau of Biological Survey of the United States Department of Agriculture and later through the United States Fish and Wildlife Service of the Department of the Interior.

The following account is a general summary of the economic value of birds. Each order of birds is briefly discussed and some of the more outstanding beneficial or injurious attributes are mentioned. A serious and honest attempt has been made to be entirely impartial so that the reader can determine relative values for himself.

The ostriches (Struthioniformes) have been partially domesticated, and their large eggs are used as food by man. The plumes are used extensively in the millinery industry. In the wild, their food habits are extremely varied and might be considered both beneficial and detrimental to man's interests. The kiwis (Apterygiformes) are valuable for their bizarre characters alone. Their food consists principally of earthworms, insects, mollusks, and similar small animals. Penguins (Sphenisciformes) are harvested for their oil. They also produce valuable deposits of guano on some of the subantarctic islands. Fish comprise their principal food supply. In the Antarctic region, their range is principally in an area where the penguins do not conflict with man's interests.

The food of grebes (Podicipediformes) is a mixture of aquatic insects, crustaceans, and fish. The fish are mostly species of little economic value but nothing prevents them from eating other species. The loons (Gaviiformes) may also destroy some important edible fish, but loons are not abundant and as a whole they cannot be said to be seriously harmful. The albatrosses, petrels, and their allies (Procellariiformes) are marine species, and while they live largely on fish they are not harmful to the interests of man. The pelicans, boobies, cormorants, and their allies (Pelecaniformes) are also largely fish eaters and are claimed by some to be destructive. One species, a cormorant, is domesticated in China and Japan and is used to catch fish. The herons, egrets, bitterns, storks, ibises, flamingos, and their relatives (Ciconiiformes) have diverse feeding habits. Most species live in the vicinity of water, where they feed on insects, crustaceans, mollusks, reptiles, fish, mice, shrews, frogs, and the like. The plumes of some species have been used in the millinery trade, but this practice is now prohibited by federal law in the United States. The prohibitive legislation was brought about as a result of the near extinction of the Snowy Egret (*Leucophoyx thula*).

The value of the ducks, geese, and swans (Anseriformes) needs hardly be mentioned. They comprise the largest group of game animals in the world. In America, the mergansers (although on the game list) are not generally hunted, for they are largely fish eaters and their flesh is not particularly palatable. Feathers, plucked by the several species of eider to use in the nest, are much in demand. Eider down is used in making sleeping bags, bedding, and arctic clothing. The peoples of northern Europe, Asia, and America often expend much effort in encouraging eider to breed in their area. Feathers plucked from a dead bird are inferior to those plucked by the duck itself and available at the nest. Many varieties of domesticated ducks and geese have been bred. These provide man with feathers, eggs, and flesh.

The vultures, eagles, hawks, and their allies (Falconiformes) are a much disputed group with respect to their relations to man. Vultures are carrion eaters and as such they perform a valuable service in clearing the landscape of dead animal matter. Most of the hawks and eagles are predators. Their prey consists of insects, rodents, rabbits, and other small mammals, amphibians, reptiles, birds, including domestic fowl, and fish. The Osprey (*Pandion haliaetus*) feeds on fish which it catches in its talons from near the surface of a body of water. Its catch is sometimes forced from the osprey and taken by the Bald Eagle (*Haliaeetus leucocephalus*). The accipiters will take game birds and poultry together with small birds, small mammals, and some insects. It is generally believed that diseased game animals form a considerable part of the diet of some hawks. These predators thus serve well in

[illegible]

caillie Grouse, the Hungarian Partridge, and the Chukar Partridge.

The rails, gallinules, coots, cranes and their relatives are a group with diverse feeding habits, but most feed on invertebrate animals or plant materials and none can be said to be destructive. Several of these birds are considered game species and are hunted in various areas. In Cuba, the Limpkin (*Aramus guarauna*) is comparatively tame and is killed and used as food by some of the inhabitants. The snipe, woodcocks, sandpipers, plovers, gulls, terns, auks, and their allies (Charadriiformes) are commonly known as shore birds. Many are hunted as game; some, like the gulls, serve as important scavengers particularly around coastal cities. Few of the species can be said to be injurious and most are very beneficial. The Black-backed Gull (*Larus marinus*) destroys the eggs of other birds to supplement its scavenged diet. The pigeons and doves (Columbiformes) are principally seed eaters and are generally considered game species. The Rock Dove (*Columba livia*) has been domesticated, and many breeds have been developed for homing, racing, and show. The flesh of pigeons, particularly that of the young or squabs, is eaten extensively by man. The cuckoos, anis, and Roadrunner (Cuculiformes) are largely beneficial. The Black-billed Cuckoo (*Coccyzus erythropthalmus*) and the Yellow-billed Cuckoo (*C. americanus*) are almost the only birds in North America that relish the hairy caterpillars which defoliate many cultivated plants. The Roadrunner (*Geococcyx californianus*) has been damned for eating the eggs of quail, which may make up some part of his diet; this species devours almost anything, including such supposedly unpalatable items as tarantulas, scorpions, and lizards.

Owls (Strigiformes), like the hawks, are predators, and their prey consists largely of rodents. Only one species, the Great Horned Owl (*Bubo virginianus*), can be said to be destructive; it will take poultry and game birds if they are easily accessible. The Barn Owl (*Tyto alba*) feeds almost entirely on rats and mice. It has been claimed that a family of seven young Barn Owls requires over 100 rats and other small mammals daily. The goatsuckers (Caprimulgiformes) that occur in North America are essentially insectivorous. It might be pointed out that not all insects are injurious to the interests of man and birds do not usually discriminate among good, bad, or indifferent insects. The swifts and hummingbirds (Apodiformes) are also largely insectivorous. Some of the hummingbirds feed on the nectar of flowers.

Belted Kingfishers (*Megaceryle alcyon*), the only representatives of the order Coraciiformes in most of the United States and Canada, feed principally on fish. They have been condemned by fishermen, for they do take occasional game fish, but a recent study pointed out that they take only small individuals, thus allowing more food and space for the remaining fish to grow to game size. It has been definitely shown that in many situations an overpopulation of fish results in a dwindled food supply and a subsequent reduction in the size of the fish. Predators, then, have a definite place in the control of populations of prey species.

Woodpeckers, the only North American representatives of the order Piciformes, are largely insectivorous. They frequently feed upon scale insects and bark boring insects which are not a part of the diet of other animals. Many of these insects are very harmful to trees. The Yellow-shafted Flicker (*Colaptes auratus*) is one of few North American species that feeds extensively on ants. The Yellow-bellied Sapsucker (*Sphyrapicus varius*) may cause serious damage to trees, including fruit trees, by girdling them with their drillings. This species drills small holes through the bark of trees, thus causing them to "bleed." The bird then makes rather regular rounds of his series of drillings and feeds on the sap which collects at the wounds of the trees. It has been reported that when the sap ferments the sapsucker may become intoxicated, whereupon he may be very erratic. This species is not a common one, that is, nowhere is there a large population of sapsuckers. The Pileated Woodpecker (*Dryocopus pileatus*) has become something of a pest in north-central Pennsylvania. Here the pressure of a dense population apparently has caused many individuals to drill nest cavities in utility poles.

The large order Passeriformes is one of diverse forms with feeding habits that vary as greatly. Some may destroy some fruit and grain, but the small quantity of cultivated fruits appropriated by these birds is generally negligible. Most species can be classed as insect eaters or weed seed eaters. A few species have been attacked for obnoxious habits. Among them are the crows and jays, which may eat seeds of farm crops or the mature crop, and the grackles and some other icterids, which do some damage in grain fields. Crows and jays are truly om-

in our cities, where they frequently become quite messy. The shrikes are predaceous and take small mammals, birds, reptiles, amphibians, and insects. These birds are considered beneficial, for the number of gophers, mice, and grasshoppers they take far outweighs the more detrimental parts of their diet.

A treatment of the economic value of birds would be incomplete without mention of conservation practices such as game management. Americans spend millions of dollars annually for licenses which permit them to hunt game birds and mammals. These funds are used to study and propagate the game species so that their continued existence will be insured. In order that a game species be preserved, its normal habits and habitat requirements must be known so that it can be regulated or propagated as necessary. Supplementary propagation may ease the pressure on those more hardy individuals that were reared in the wild, but the expense involved is great and the whole program should be eliminated as soon as wild stock becomes sufficiently abundant. The propagation of Ring-necked Pheasants (*Phasianus colchicus*) is fairly successful, for when released they are wild and can apparently manage fairly well on their own. This species is not native. Other introductions are being considered to provide more game and to relieve the kill of native forms.

Another phase of game management, that of predator control, has been given much attention. The use of **bounties** has been tried and found lacking. Pennsylvania has a bounty on the Goshawk (*Accipiter gentilis*), which is a rather heavy predator on poultry and game birds and is probably the most destructive of the hawks and owls. In 1929, bounty fees were paid on 80 Goshawks, while eight years later 1,090 fees were paid by the Pennsylvania Game Commission. The thousands of dollars could have been far more profitably spent on a study of the Goshawk's habits, habitat, and range, after which professional exterminators would be far less expensive and far more efficient. Most states are beginning to realize the folly of the bounty system and are making studies through which they hope to find measures for control of undesirable forms. It is unfortunate that many bounty seekers are unable to distinguish between useful and harmful species because numerous beneficial predators are uselessly destroyed.

The following paragraphs by Dr. C. Hart Merriam are quoted from Chapman's *Handbook of Birds of Eastern North America.* Merriam's analysis of bounties, made in 1886, still rings true in principle. Furthermore, the analysis demonstrates, in terms of dollars and cents, something of the total value of birds.

"On the 23rd of June, 1885, the Legislature of Pennsylvania passed an act known as the 'scalp act,' ostensibly 'for the benefit of agriculture,' which provides a bounty of fifty cents each on Hawks, Owls, weasels and minks killed within the limits of the State, and a fee of twenty cents to the notary or justice taking affidavit.

"By virtue of this act about $90,000 has been paid in bounties during the year and a half that has elapsed since the law went into effect. This represents the destruction of at least 128,571 of the above mentioned animals, most of which were Hawks and Owls.

"Granting that 5,000 chickens are killed annually in Pennsylvania by Hawks and Owls, and that they are worth twenty-five cents each (a liberal estimate in view of the fact that a large portion of them are killed when very young), the total loss would be $1,250, and the poultry killed in a year and a half would be worth $1,875. Hence it appears that during the past eighteen months the State of Pennsylvania has expended $90,000 to save its farmers a loss of $1,875. But this estimate by no means represents the actual loss to the farmer and the taxpayer of the State. It is within bounds to say that in the course of a year every Hawk and Owl destroys at least a thousand mice or their equivalent in insects, and that each mouse or its equivalent so destroyed would cause a loss of two cents per annum. Therefore, omitting all reference to the enormous increase in the numbers of these noxious animals when Nature's means of holding them in check has been removed, the lowest possible estimate of the value to the farmer of each Hawk, Owl, and weasel would be $20 a year, or $30 in a year and a half.

"Hence, in addition to the $90,000 actually expended by the State in destroying 128,571 of its benefactors, it has incurred a loss to its agricultural interests of at least $3,857,130, or a total loss of $3,947,130 in a year and a half, which is at the rate of $2,631,420 per annum. In other words, the State has thrown away $2,105 for every dollar saved! And even this does not represent fairly the full loss, for the slaughter of such a vast number of predaceous birds and mammals is almost certain to be followed by a correspondingly enormous increase in the num-

Horned Owl (*Bubo virginianus*).

Birds play a very important role in the control of insect pests. The insects form the earth's largest faunal constituent and without control they would dominate the earth in a very short time. Actually, parasites, diseases, adverse weather, and other insects play the greatest part in insect control, but the part played by birds is far from negligible. The role of birds in the "balance of nature" is an important one which should not be disturbed by man, at least not before thorough study and experiment. If a species is found undesirable it should not be killed to the point of extinction but rather its natural enemies should be encouraged or some other control measure should be exercised. An exotic species should not be introduced without first carefully testing to find out how it will respond to a new environment and what its effects will be on the native species with which it will compete.

Perhaps the greatest value of birds is an esthetic one. The pleasure derived by bird watchers, the sport of hunting game, the mental challenges provided by such phenomena as migration by themselves make birds worth while. In some parts of the world, game birds provide a major portion of the native food supply, but domestication of a few species has replaced this in most areas. More and more people are coming to realize the value of getting out of doors after a dreary week at the factory, shop, or office, and bird hunting with binoculars, camera, or gun has been found to be a pleasant avocation.

The Common Stork (*Ciconia ciconia*) of Europe is perhaps the most utilitarian species of bird. It acts as a scavenger in the towns of Europe, where it is permitted to nest on the tops of roofs and chimneys. And do we not owe our presence here to its existence?

Bibliography and References

ALLEN, ARTHUR A., The Book of Bird Life. Princeton, N.J.: D. Van Nostrand Co., pp. 240-265, 1961.

BEAL, F. E. L., Some Common Birds Useful to the Farmer. *USFWS Conservation Bull.*, 18, 1942.

BEAL, F. E. L., W. L. McATEE, and E. R. KALMBACH, Common Birds of Southeastern United States in Relation to Agriculture. *U.S.F.W.S. Conservation Bull.*, 15, 1941.

CHAPMAN, FRANK M., Handbook of Birds of Eastern North America, Second Rev. Ed. New York: D. Appleton-Century Co., pp. 105-110, 1940.

ERRINGTON, PAUL L., Predation and Vertebrate Populations. *Quart. Rev. Biol.*, 21:144-177; 221-245, 1946.

LACK, DAVID, Competition for Food by Birds of Prey. *Jour. Animal Ecol.*, 15:123-129, 1946.

LACK, DAVID, The Natural Regulation of Animal Numbers. London: Oxford Univ. Press, 1954.

McATEE, W. L. and F. E. L. BEAL, Some Common Game, Aquatic, and Rapacious Birds in Relation to Man. *USDA Farmer's Bull.*, 497, 1924.

McATEE, W. L., Usefulness of Birds on the Farm. *USDA Farmer's Bull.*, 1682, 1931.

MAY, JOHN RICHARD, The Hawks of North America. Nat. Assn. Audubon Soc., New York, 1935.

PALMER, E. LAWRENCE, Fieldbook of Natural History. New York: McGraw-Hill Book Co., pp. 475-586, 1949.

SWEETMAN, HARVEY L., The Principles of Biological Control. Dubuque, Iowa: Wm. C. Brown Company Publishers, pp. 383-389, 1958.

VANTYNE, JOSSELYN and ANDREW J. BERGER, Fundamentals of Ornithology. New York: John Wiley & Sons, pp. 237-264, 1959.

See Also BENT, ARTHUR CLEVELAND, Life Histories of North American Birds. *U.S. Nat. Mus. Bulletins*, listed at end of Chapter 10.

EXERCISES IN ECONOMIC ORNITHOLOGY

1. Analyze the contents of an owl pellet. Most pellets will contain skeletal material of small rodents. Skulls of these are rather easily identified by the literature. See Burt, William Henry, and Richard Philip Grossenheider, 1952 *A Field Guide to the Mammals*. Houghton Mifflin Co., Boston (illustrates skulls on pp. 152-169), and Glass, B.P., 1951 *A Key to the Skulls of North American Mammals,* Burgess Publ. Co., Minneapolis.

2. If available, analyze the "stomach" contents of any bird.

3. From the literature, prepare a list of food materials utilized by any hawk or owl or the Belted Kingfisher. Discuss the impact of this bird on the ecology of prey populations.

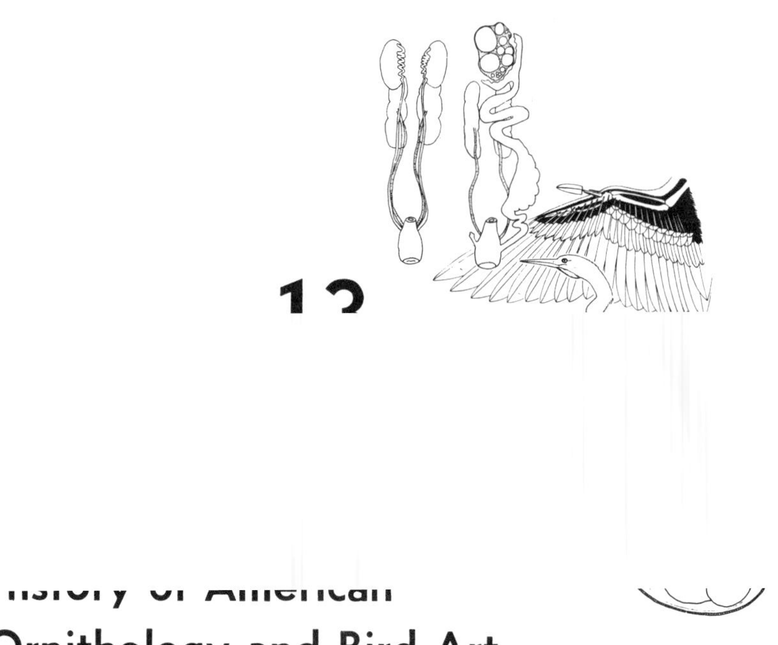

12

History of American Ornithology and Bird Art

The name Audubon almost automatically comes to mind when birds are mentioned. Audubon's fame has become so widespread that few people realize there were other men who played important roles in the development of the science of ornithology in America. The records of early work in American bird study are available for the most part only in the libraries and museums of Europe. A recent and very excellent publication, *The History of American Ornithology Before Audubon,* by Elsa Guerdrum Allen, has made available innumerable accounts of the early ornithological works in the Western Hemisphere.

The Indians of Mexico and the Mayas of Yucatan recorded replicas of the Great Horned Owl on wood and stone. Doubtless the Red Men of the whole of North America knew a great deal about birds, for many species were hunted for food. Feathers, claws, and bills were used as ornaments. Chiefs robed themselves in feather fabrics. Medicine men invented potions of owls' eyes and the gizzards of geese. The primitive Indians, however, apparently never studied birds in a systematic manner. American ornithology, therefore, did not begin until the Europeans invaded the Western Hemisphere. It was shown by Chapman (1896) that had it not been for birds, Columbus might never have discovered America. He apparently crossed the course of birds which passed Bermuda on their migratory flight from the North American mainland to the West Indies or South America. As a result Columbus changed his course to the southwest, thus decreasing his distance to land by about 200 miles. Perhaps the mutinous sailors of his ships would not have tolerated the extra 200 miles west which would have put the famous navigator ashore at northern Florida.

Although he described and named some 200 species of North American birds (Audubon named only 33 species), Carolus von Linné (Lin naeus) never set foot upon American soil. His descriptions were based on specimens sent to him from the colonies. Linnaeus described some species from the rather crude paintings of Mark Catesby. Catesby produced the first notable publication on American birds in his *The Natural History of Carolina, Florida, and the Bahama Islands,* which was published in 1731. He was an Englishman who traveled in America between 1710 and 1719 and again between 1722 and 1726. His volumes included many rather crudely drawn illustrations, some of which were in color. He did not consider himself an artist, for he said of himself "I was not bred a painter and I hope some faults in perspective and other niceties may (therefore) be more readily excused." Catesby was the first American ornithologist of note and he has been called "the founder of American ornithology." He was preceded by many lesser students, some of whom are of historical interest.

As far as is known, Jaques Le Moyne was the earliest bird artist to depict American birds in their native land. He was chosen by the French Admiral Gaspard Coligny "to make an accurate description and map of the country and drawings of all curious objects." Accordingly, he was part of the second French expedition to North America in 1564. His bird drawing was apparently restricted to several figures of wild turkeys on a painting which depicts life at Fort Caroline, near what is now Beaufort, South Carolina. It was there that the French, under the leadership of Captain Jean Ribault, initiated a colony in 1562. The colony was subsequently destroyed by a Spanish massacre, and only a handful of men, including Le Moyne, escaped.

John White, the grandfather of Virginia Dare, who was the first person of the white race born in America, was chosen by Queen Elizabeth for the express purpose of studying and painting the aborigines and "natural products" of this country. He was governor of Sir Walter Raleigh's ill-fated colony at Roanoke in 1587 but was persuaded to return to England by dissatisfied colonists. He had made a previous voyage to America in 1585, when he painted several of the native birds. Among his bird paintings is one of the flicker. The description of this bird by Linnaeus was based on a description by Mark Catesby. It is therefore evident that the flicker was known and pictured almost 150 years before it was scientifically described. In all probability, John White was the first to produce colored paintings of American birds.

Many casual and superficial accounts of American birds can be found in the reports of English colonists at Jamestown, Virginia. Captain John Smith, who headed the Jamestown colony, which was founded in 1607, [illegible] with Alexander Wilson, who, with Audubon, was a contemporary. Abbot came to America in 1776 and lived in Georgia until 1839 and possibly until 1845, according to Bassett (1938).

William Bartram (1739-1823), the son of John Bartram, who was a famous American botanist, was hailed by Elliot Coues as the starting point of "a distinctly American school of ornithology." The younger Bartram was a keen and accurate observer of birds and pioneered in bird migration studies. He stood alone in his time when he maintained that swallows did not hibernate. Bartram's influence on American ornithology was even greater because of his influence on other American and continental scientists. Alexander Wilson was spurred on to his accomplishments largely through Bartram's encouragement. Bartram was the first native born ornithologist to work in America.

Alexander Wilson's *American Ornithology, or the Natural History of the Birds of the United States,* an eight-volume, rather comprehensive work, was the first real ornithological treatise on the birds of America. The first volume appeared in 1808 and the last was published in 1814, a year after the author died. These volumes treated life history, largely habits, together with detailed descriptions and carefully executed water-color illustrations.

Wilson, often referred to as the father of American ornithology, was born at Paisley, Scotland, where he learned the weaver's trade. He had a flair for song and published a volume of poems in 1790. For writing a tepid satire on a Paisley notable, he was jailed and later forced to burn the composition publicly at Paisley Cross. Upon his release from prison in 1794, he came to Newcastle, Delaware, and became a schoolmaster. While teaching in several Pennsylvania towns he became acquainted with William Bartram, the famous Philadelphia natural historian, who encouraged him in his ornithological pursuits. His painstaking research has not been given the acclaim it justly deserves because his work was soon succeeded by that of Audubon.

The early part of the nineteenth century brought a number of naturalists to the United States, and many of them settled in or near Philadelphia. Charles Lucien Bonaparte wrote *American Ornithology or the Natural History of the Birds Inhabiting the United States, Not Given by Wilson,* a supplement to Wilson's work, which was published in four volumes from 1825 to 1833. George Ord, a friend and benefactor of Wilson's, published a three-volume edition of Wilson's *American Ornithology* in 1828. Thomas Nuttall wrote the first of the handbooks of ornithology, *Manual of the Ornithology of the United States and Canada,* in 1832 - 1834. Titian Peale reported on some western birds which he studied while with Long's expedition to the Rocky Mountains. John Cassin wrote the volume on birds which was part of the United States government report on survey and exploration for a railway route to the Pacific coast. The many scientists in the Philadelphia area at this time organized the Academy of Natural Sciences, the first of the museums of natural history in the United States. John Cassin was in charge of the growing collection of birds at the Academy of Natural Sciences in Philadelphia.

John James Audubon, born in what is now Haiti and educated in France, came upon the American scene in 1798. He was sent to this country by his father to manage one of his estates near Philadelphia. In 1808 he married Lucy Bakewell, daughter of an English neighbor, and shortly moved to Kentucky and later to Louisiana. Back in Philadelphia he was one of the many interested in matters of science, and there he lost interest in matters of business. At making a living he was an early failure. He was forced to paint portraits and teach dancing and fencing to support himself and his family. All the while he gathered notes and specimens of birds for what was to be a most stupendous undertaking in ornithology. He travelled widely and in 1842 he settled down in New York (then outside but now within the city limits), where he spent the remainder of his life. His first volume of the elephant folio of bird portraits appeared in 1827. The four volumes of *Birds of America,* containing 435 plates of bird paintings, were all published by 1838. His descriptive text, *Ornithological Biography, or an Account of the Habits of the Birds of the United States of America,* in five volumes appeared from 1831 to 1839. Audubon was not a trained scientist, but he was a keen observer with a fluid ability for imparting his knowledge to others through his writing. His life is well recorded in numerous biographies. Only 190 copies of his elephant folio of plates were published. Of this number about 80 remained in this country. Many of the existing sets have been broken and individual plates have been sold, for they are now collectors' items.

The nineteenth century brought many great ornithologists and consequently many great contributions to the science. Spencer F. Baird was appointed assistant secretary to the Smithsonian Institution in 1850 and set about establishing a natural history section in that museum, which was founded through the bequeathed funds of James Smithson, an Englishman. Baird later became Secretary of the Smithsonian Institution and Director of the United States National Museum. Under him, the collection there became one of the finest in the world. He was succeeded by Robert Ridgeway, whose *The Birds of North and Middle America* has been regarded as a standard in North American nomenclature. He did not succeed in finishing that monumental work but it is being continued by Dr. Herbert Friedmann at the present time. Dr. Alexander Wetmore followed Ridgeway as Secretary of the Smithsonian Institution, a directorial position. Wetmore's work on birds of South and Central America, his work on fossil birds, and his work in taxonomy are world famous. He retired from the secretaryship in 1952.

Frank M. Chapman became associate curator of ornithology and mammalogy at the American Museum of Natural History in New York City in 1888. He contributed much to our knowledge of birds. Although most of his research was concerned with South American forms, his *Handbook of Birds of Eastern North America*, first published in 1895 and revised in 1912 and 1932, is the latest and finest of the manuals of ornithology up to the present time. He did much to popularize the study of birds, and several of his books met with great acclaim.

Elliot Coues contributed much in his *Key to North American Birds*, the first edition of which appeared in 1872. The introduction of this work, some 230 pages, treats of general ornithology and the anatomy of birds.

In 1883, the American Ornithologists Union was formed for "the advancement of its members in Ornithological Science; the publication of a journal of Ornithology and other works relating to that science; the acquisition of a library; and the care and collection of materials relating to the above objects." In 1886 the Committee on Classification and Nomenclature published the first edition of *The Code of Nomenclature and Check-list of North American Birds.* This useful work, now in its fifth edition and generally known as the *A.O.U. Check-list,* is highly regarded by taxonomists everywhere. The fifth edition was published in 1957. The checklist bears the names, synonyms, and ranges of all species and subspecies that are recognized by the Committee on Classification and Nomenclature in the area including Lower California, the United States, Canada, Alaska, and east to and including Greenland. Supplements to the checklist are published in *The Auk,* which is the official periodical of the A.O.U. *The Auk* is now in its 81st volume (1964). This journal is published quarterly (January, April, July, and October).

Two other bird societies of major importance in America are The Wilson Ornithological Society and The Cooper Ornithological Society. The Wilson Society was founded in 1888. It publishes *The Wilson Bulletin,* which appears quarterly (March, June, September, and December) and is in its 76th volume (1964). The Cooper Ornithological Society, founded in 1893, publishes *The Condor,* which appears bimonthly and is now in its 66th volume (1964). The Cooper Society and its publication are concerned primarily with ornithological events on the Pacific Coast. *The Auk, The Wilson Bulletin,* and *The Condor* are free to members of the sponsoring organization who pay dues equal to the subscription price.

In the latter part of the nineteenth century and in the early twentieth century many advances in ornithology were accomplished. The science changed from one that was primarily descriptive to a science of natural history. More and more men began to record notes on nesting or breeding behavior, courtship, interspecific relations, ecology, and other phases of life history. Birds came under the protection of state and federal statutes. The Audubon Society was organized and with it bird study became a popular pastime instead of a cold descriptive science.

In 1919 Arthur Cleveland Bent published the first of a long series of life histories of North American birds which are being continued at the present time. His twentieth volume appeared (posthumously) in 1958, and there are more volumes to be published to complete the series. His works include an accumulation of facts gleaned from the literature and from personal observation by the author and many collaborators. Bent died in 1954, but he selected a committee, headed by Wendell Taber, to complete the project.

include T. M. Shortt, R. Bruce Horsfall, Roger Tory Peterson, Francis Lee Jaques, Earl L. Poole, Walter A. Weber, and Don Eckelberry. The younger generation is very ably represented by William C. Dilger, a Cornell University professor, who may reach or possibly surpass the perfection of Fuertes.

The early history of American ornithology is slowly coming to light. It has been interesting and colorful. More recent work in the science of birds is abundant, comprehensive, and rather thorough. So popular has bird study become that it is probably the best understood of all the special sciences and is understood, at least in part, by more people than any other similar science.

Bibliography and References

Allen, Elsa G., Some Sixteenth Century Paintings of American Birds. *Auk,* 53:17-21, 1936.

Allen, Elsa G., Jaques Le Moyne, First Zoological Artist in America. *Auk,* 55:106-111, 1938.

Allen, Elsa G., A Third Set of John Abbot Bird Drawings. *Auk,* 59:563-571, 1942.

Allen, Elsa G., The History of American Ornithology Before Audubon. *Trans. Am. Phil. Soc.,* Vol. 41, pt. 3, 1951.

Bassett, Anna Stowell, Some Georgia Records of John Abbott, Naturalist. *Auk,* 55:244-254, 1938.

Chapman, Frank M., The Ornithology of Columbus' First Voyage. Papers Presented to the World's Congress on Ornithology. Chicago, pp. 181-185, 1896.

Chapman, Frank M., In Memoriam: Louis Agassiz Fuertes. *Auk,* 45:1-26, 1928.

FAXON, WALTER, John Abbot's Drawings of the Birds of Georgia. *Auk*, 13:204-214, 1896.

RHOADS, SAMUEL N., More Light on Audubon's Folio "Birds of America." *Auk*, 33:130-132, 1916.

RHOADS, SAMUEL N., Georgia's Rarities Further Discovered in a Second American Portfolio of John Abbot's Bird Plates. *Auk*, 35:271-286, 1918.

SAGE, JOHN H., An Historic Letter. *Auk*, 12:359-362, 1895.

STONE, WITMER, Some Unpublished Letters of Alexander Wilson and John Abbot. *Auk*, 23:361-368, 1906.

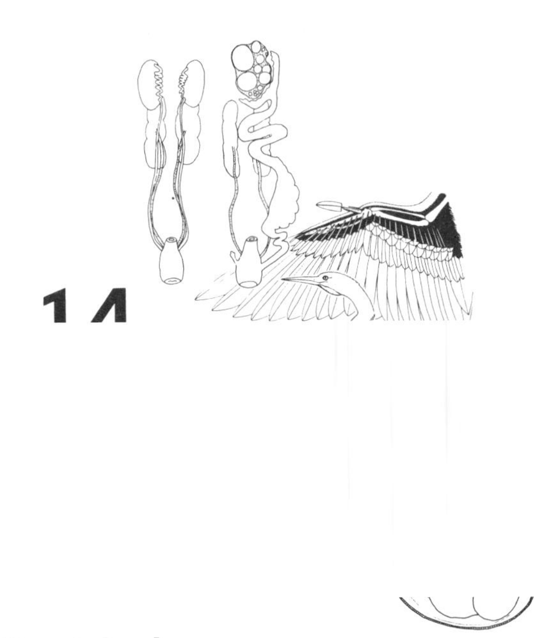

14 Methods in Ornithology

Many methods have been developed for studying birds. Some recent publications review those methods. It will be our purpose to outline some of the more common and popular systems. Before one can undertake a comprehensive ornithological investigation capably he must be familiar not only with most of the birds he will encounter but also with many of the other forms of life. If he is recording an observation of a nest, he will want to record the species of bird that built the nest, the species of tree or shrub in which the nest is situated, the height of the nest above the ground, the kind of materials used in building, and many other pertinent data. The bird student must be ingenious, for every circumstance will present problems of its own. Scaling trees and falling from them, tramping in marshes in waist-deep mud and water, and tearing clothes on barbed-wire fences are all common experiences to the ornithologist.

Methods in field identification are as varied as the interests of field observers. For those bird students who go afield only for the thrill of seeing a goodly number of birds the methods may be quite simple. These persons perhaps could make a real contribution, however, by putting forth a little more effort in the form of seeking out diverse habitats and keeping records. While it is possible to attract some birds to convenient locations, it generally is necessary to go out in search of them. To see all of the birds that one can see in a certain area it is necessary to penetrate every habitat situation in that area – swamps, marshes, islands in rivers, valleys, mountains, forests, fields, and any other conceivable type of environment. Further, it is necessary to look everywhere from the surface of land or water to as high as the eye can penetrate. At first it is well to travel with a competent observer from whom much can be gained and who can help the beginner lest his identifications be too hasty and hence inaccurate.

Field glasses or binoculars of fairly good quality are desirable though not absolutely essential. A field checklist of the local avifauna is a help in making easy and speedy recordings of species seen. No trips in the field should be made without a small pocket notebook in which should be noted the date, locality, habitat-type, weather conditions, time of day, and approximate temperature, plus any data on the activities or abundance of some or all species. Even the most commonplace activities should be noted, at least until it is definitely known that those facts are firmly established in the literature. A good field guide, such as Peterson's *A Field Guide to the Birds* or his *Field Guide to Western Birds* for students west of the 100th meridian is indispensable. Field clothing should be practical, comfortable, and of a neutral color. Canvas gym shoes are generally the most practical foot covering, for while they do not prevent wet feet, they do allow for quick drying.

The only way to learn the birds of an area is to take bird walks. It should be pointed out that many beginners are apt to see things that they want to see rather than what is actually present. It is peculiar how one often sees the most unusual bird in an area a day or two after he learns that it is rare there. Be cautious in making observations and do not record anything until you are convinced that you could not be mistaken. It generally is recommended that any observer call upon one or two other competent ornithologists to confirm the identification of any rare or unusual bird. Needless to say, this should be done as soon as possible after the bird in question is first observed. Keep in mind that there is no harm in listing a bird as unidentified. There is great value in field observations, but inaccurate observations will cast doubt upon any records you may accumulate.

As soon as possible after a field trip the ornithologist should transfer his records to a permanent form. The checklists can serve as permanent records, but other notes are bound to be sketchy and unless they are clarified may mean nothing after a month or a year or more. A good system for recording such notes utilizes a loose-leaf notebook in which a page is devoted to each species. After the trip simply record the pertinent data for each species that was seen. Such a notebook should be arranged in taxonomic sequence to facilitate the location of the notes on a particular species. Notes should include items such as date, time of day, weather conditions, temperature, and precise locality of each species observed. Common birds which are frequently encountered may be recorded as widespread and common, whereas less common species [illegible]

the term **abundant** applies where every available habitat of suitable type in a given area is occupied by as many individuals of a species as can be sustained in the given area. The other terms are purely relative.

Notes can and should include additional data which may substantiate present knowledge or add to it. Your notes, plus those of other local ornithologists, may provide important source materials for a paper on the avifauna of your area. Such local avifauna lists are recognized as important, for when considered collectively they provide a great deal of information on the general distribution of birds and the factors which control their distribution. Discussions of local avifaunas made up a large percentage of the contents of the early American ornithological journals. They declined in popularity several decades ago but are now again considered important.

Any manuscript prepared for publication must be typewritten, with lines double-spaced. It must be on good quality standard size (8½ x 11 inches) bond paper. The left-hand margin should be one and one-half inches wide and the right-hand margin about one or one and one-fourth inches. Manuscripts should not be folded. All words which are to be *italicized* should be underscored. Except in bibliographies, abbreviations should be avoided. Numbers below 10 should be written, but figures should be used for 10 and above except when the number begins a sentence. Use figures only in page numbers, plate numbers, in the text of tables, etc. For style of writing it is suggested that the prospective author consult the works of other authors in the journal to which the article is to be submitted for publication. Any article accepted for publication will be returned to the author prior to actual publication for the author's approval of the editor's changes, additions, or deletions.

One of the best ways to learn the habits of species is by photographing them. Bird photography involves many special techniques and the individual's ingenuity may be greatly taxed. First, a word of caution! One is likely to be carried away with tremendous enthusiasm in photographing birds, and it is a rather expensive hobby. Birds are comparatively small creatures, thus expensive equipment is necessary to produce a photograph that will be worth showing. Furthermore, there are many expert and professional photographers, and it is difficult to sell pictures even though quite a sizeable market exists. Still further, the percentage of acceptable photos of birds is very low; therefore the cost of film and processing can be quite burdensome.

The best equipment for bird photography varies with the results desired. For black-and-white still pictures a large-sized reflex type camera is best. For color transparencies the cost of the film prohibits the use of a large camera and a 35-millimeter camera is most desirable. Motion picture photography is somewhat easier but more expensive. With motion pictures there need be less concern for composition, for the movements of the bird attract attention while many other factors may go unnoticed. No matter what the desired results may be, single-lens reflex-type camera is best. This is a camera in which the subject is viewed through the same lens through which the light passes to make the recording on the film. It involves a ground glass viewer, which enables one to compose well, for the factor of parallax (the displacement of an object when viewed from two or more different places) need not be considered since viewing and photographing are accomplished through the same lens.

A steady and rugged tripod is essential, for generally a photograph of a bird must be taken comparatively slowly to compensate for little or poor light on the subject or to allow greater depth of field. Birds have a habit of staying in shaded places where a maximum amount of light is not available. A telephoto lens or other accessory lenses are necessary, for the image of the bird must be large enough on the film to be seen.

The most important requisite for successful photography is patience; however, a knowledge of the habits of birds is essential before patience is necessary. Some of this knowledge may be gained during unsuccessful attempts at photographing. To get a picture, the photographer must get within rather close range of the bird, and since birds are wary, it is necessary that one hide himself from the bird's view. An **observation blind** (see Figure 53) is generally the best device for secluding one's self

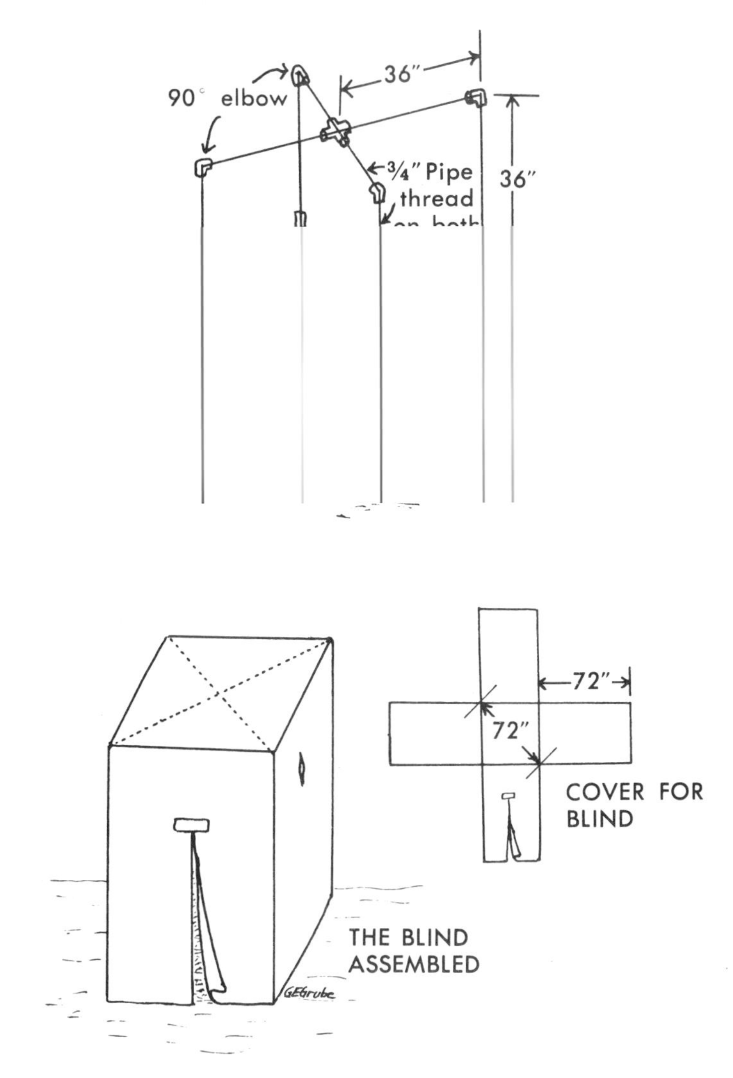

Figure 53. Plan for making and assembling a portable blind for observing and photographing birds.

from the view of the bird. The blind may consist of anything from a sizeable packing case to a frame over which a canvas, burlap, or other suitable covering is placed. Generally, a collapsible blind is most useful; this is a frame assembled from iron pipes (one-half or three-fourths inch) over which a prepared covering can be secured. To photograph birds high in trees it is necessary to have a tower upon which the blind can be placed or a platform built in the tree above which the blind can be suspended.

Setting up the blind will disturb most species and it generally is advisable to set it up one or two days in advance of entering with the cameras. When one reapproaches the blind he again disturbs the birds and they frequently will not come to the nest or other location for some time. The waiting time can de decreased if an extra person accompanies the photographer to the blind and shortly walks away, thus giving the bird a feeling of greater security. It is evident that most species cannot count; therefore the photographer who remains in the blind will not be suspected.

Sometimes it is advisable to use decoys. In migration season, especially during spring, ducks might be attracted to within photographing distance when they see a flock of decoys which have been set out several yards from a blind. The blind will be less obvious if it is covered with reeds, cattails, or other suitable vegetation. In the fall, ducks are similarly lured to hunter's blinds and therefore photography is both dangerous and difficult. The male Ruffed Grouse (*Bonasa umbellus*) will attempt to drive away another male from his territory, so if a mounted male grouse is placed in a territory known to harbor grouse a photograph can be taken. The male grouse can also be photographed at his drumming log, a spot from which he declares territory and courts his harem. Every species and almost every individual will present problems of its own. Given good equipment and the ability to operate it, the success of the photographer is entirely dependent upon his patience and resourcefulness.

Recent advances in recording and analyzing bird song have been numerous and rapid. The Laboratory of Ornithology and the Albert R. Brand Bird Song Foundation at Cornell University have been pioneers in this field. There, in 1929, Dr. Arthur A. Allen assisted Fox Movietone in taking, on sound motion picture film, the first recording of wild birds in the natural state. Since then wire recorders and now tape recorders have replaced the movie film. The perfection of the small portable tape recorder and the use of a relatively simple parabolic reflector with microphone and amplifier have placed bird song recording within the range of possibility of any ornithologist.

A microphone placed at the focal point of a parabolic reflector picks up the sound waves. They are then fed through an amplifier and recorded on cellulose tape. The parabolic reflector can be aimed in the direction of the source of the song; thus it is possible to have the apparatus placed some distance away from the bird. Sounds caught by the reflector are reflected to, and hence concentrated on, a point at which the microphone is placed. It therefore is no longer necessary to laboriously rig a microphone a foot or so from the song perch of a bird.

Once recorded, the song can be transferred to discs for permanent keeping or can be kept on tape. A song can be thoroughly analyzed

this method.

The **banding** of birds has provided much of what we know about the migration and other movements of the avian tribe. By placing aluminum leg bands on a bird and recording the necessary data, a chain of investigation is initiated that may continue for several years over the whole Western Hemisphere. A bird banded in Maine might be trapped by a bander a few months later in Maryland and then in Florida and it could be found dead in Venezuela three or four months after it was originally banded. Such an incident is unlikely, but many accumulated records enable ornithologists to trace general patterns of migration for each species.

Banding is permitted only under license by the Fish and Wildlife Service of the United States Department of the Interior. The present system provides that only one person in an area is issued a permit; that individual may then allow as many collaborators as he sees fit. Thus all records for that area are channelled through the licensed bander. You can find out whether or not a bander is situated in your area, and get his name and address, by writing to the Bird-banding Office, Section of Distribution and Migration of Birds, Patuxent Research Refuge, Laurel, Maryland. In Canada, the information can be obtained by writing to the Chief, Dominion Wildlife Service, Ottawa, Ontario.

Bird banding had its origin in Europe and was introduced into the New World early in the twentieth century. In 1920 all banding activities were centralized and the responsibility for directing and recording all undertakings in the Western Hemisphere was taken over by the Bureau of Biological Survey of the United States Department of Agri-

Figure 54. A game management agent attaches a band to the leg of a duck. Photograph by Rex Gary Schmidt, U.S. Fish and Wildlife Service.

culture. This bureau was later transferred to the Department of the Interior under a new name, the Fish and Wildlife Service, with which the responsibility for handling the banding program now rests. Some six million birds of over 600 species have now been banded by thousands of collaborators in the United States and Canada.

Methods in banding are numerous and diverse. Most individual birds are captured in traps, especially during the migration seasons. Baited with food, the traps are of various designs and are harmless to the birds provided they are regularly attended. Since license by the Fish and Wildlife Service is necessary in order that the student may be permitted to band birds, and since that agency provides many specific suggestions to collaborators, it shall not be our purpose to discuss them here.

Cooperators in the banding program receive no compensation save the thrill of participating in what is perhaps the largest scientific experiment ever undertaken. Persons applying for permits must be 18 years of age or over; they must be able to produce vouchers from three recog-

[illegible]

number and may be at right angles to the serial number. If the bird is alive, read and carefully record the number, and release the bird without removing the band. If dead, remove the band from the bird's leg, flatten it out, fasten it to your letter with cellulose tape, and forward it with your name, your address, and the date and exact location at which the bird was observed. This information should be sent to the Bird-banding Office at the Laurel, Maryland, address. All such letters will be acknowledged. You will be informed as to the name of the bird and the date and place banded.

UNITED STATES DEPARTMENT OF THE INTERIOR
FISH AND WILDLIFE SERVICE
BUREAU OF SPORT FISHERIES AND WILDLIFE
PATUXENT WILDLIFE RESEARCH CENTER
LAUREL, MARYLAND

POSTAGE AND FEES PAID
U.S. DEPARTMENT OF THE INTERIOR

Thank you for your communication regarding bird band number 591 - 41722. Our information on the original banding is given below.

G E GRUBE
STATE COLLEGE
LOCK HAVEN PA

SPECIES EVENING GROSBEAK
BANDED IN PENNSYLVANIA
BANDED AT 40° 40′ N. LATITUDE 077° 50′ W. LONGITUDE
DATE 12 30 61 (MONTH DAY YEAR)

Figure 55. Bird banding report form from U.S. Fish and Wildlife Service received in response to sending band from dead bird to them.

In addition to providing invaluable data on migration, banding makes possible the study of individual birds. One interesting sidelight to the program is the answer, in part at least, to the question of longevity in birds. A Red-winged Blackbird (*Agelaius phoeniceus*) banded in New York was shot 14 years later in North Carolina. The bird known to have lived the longest in the wild in North America was a Caspian Tern (*Hydroprogne caspia*) banded on an island in Lake Michigan on July 19, 1925, and shot in Ohio on August 19, 1951, 26 years after banding.

It may sometimes be valuable for the ornithologist to make collections. Most species of birds and their eggs are protected by law, and it is permissible to collect them only after necessary federal and state permits have been secured. Private collections are frowned upon, but frequently an association can be made with an educational institution, school, college, or museum, where specimens can be deposited. Birds found dead in the field, on highways, or around tall buildings or bridges can be skinned and made into study skins without much difficulty. The use of borax has largely replaced the arsenic compounds that were used a few decades ago. The author has found it difficult but not impossible to follow written instructions on how to skin a bird. Chapman, *Handbook of Birds of Eastern North America,* presents such an outline on pages 16-21. If it is possible, arrange to look over the shoulder of an experienced preparator while he is at work. Chapman also quotes Bendire's instructions for preparing eggs for the collection.

Indiscriminate collecting is rightfully forbidden; any collecting should be for a good purpose. Nests may be collected freely after they have been used by their builders. Some nests, such as the pendant vireo's, should be taken with the supporting branches; with others that frequently is impossible. Nests can be stored in padded cigar or shoe boxes so that they will not be mutilated in handling.

In all cases any material that is collected should include complete data with the material as well as in a catalog where the specimen is identified by a number. All collected items should bear notation of the date collected, the exact location where found, the collector's name, the preparator's name if other than the collector, and whenever possible, the sex. It generally is recommended that the color of soft parts be listed together with the weight in grams and the size of the gonads. Eggs generally are marked with the AOU Check-list number of the species, which is then recorded in a catalog where the full data are listed.

The study of bird populations by censusing has become an important phase of ornithology. A **population** of birds can be defined as the total number of individuals found in a given area. It has been found that populations generally vary and fluctuations can be considered as indices to the ecological requirements of birds. Changes of seasons, climatic conditions, disease, predation, and seral changes in a community are among the factors which cause fluctuations in populations. Many species of animals, grouse for example, exhibit cyclic population

[illegible]

standardization of procedure in recent years. Census by direct counting generally is possible only in restricted areas and then only for one or at most a few species. Colonial-breeding birds, and birds of very restricted habitat, can be counted directly and sometimes quite easily. Sample censusing of a strip or plot permits the approximation of the total population in a large area. A strip census is accomplished by counting all the birds, or all singing males, in a strip of measured width through the entire area. A method for plot censusing is outlined in Chapter 11 (pages 135-136).

A discussion of methods for each specific phase of ornithology could comprise a series of volumes. It has not been the intent or the purpose of this chapter to provide all tedious details. The student who wishes to pursue the subject farther in some specific line is referred to the bibliography, where he can get at least a preliminary acquaintance with his specific needs. Furthermore, published papers on the problem or a closely related one generally discuss the methods employed in the pursuit of the research. The student who wishes to engage in any specific research therefore should thoroughly examine the literature which relates to his problem before undertaking the work.

A brief annotated list of problems appears in Appendix B of this volume.

Bibliography and References

Allen, Arthur A., The Book of Bird Life. Princeton, N.J.: D. Van Nostrand Co., pp. 269-288, 309-359, 1961.

Baldwin, S. Prentiss, Harry C. Oberholser and Leonard G. Worley, Measurement of Birds. Sci. Pub. Cleveland Museum of Nat. Hist. Vol. II, 1931.

BRECKENRIDGE, W. J., A Bird Census Method. *Wilson Bull.*, 47:195-197, 1935.

CHAPMAN, FRANK M., Handbook of Birds of Eastern North America. New York: D. Appleton-Century Co., pp. 9-26, 1931.

HEADSTROM, RICHARD, Birds nests — A Field Guide. New York: Ives Washburn, 1949.

HICKEY, JOSEPH J., A Guide to Bird Watching. Cambridge: Oxford Univ. Press, 1943.

KENDEIGH, S. C., Measurement of Bird Populations. *Ecol. Monographs,* 14:67-106, 1944.

LOW, SETH H., Bird Banding. *USFWS Leaflet* WL-235, 1951.

LOW, SETH H., Banding with Mist Nets. *Bird-Banding,* 28:115-128, 1957.

MOYER, JOHN W., Practical Taxidermy. New York: Ronald Press, 1953.

PETTINGILL, OLIN SEWALL, JR., A Guide to Bird Finding East of the Mississippi. New York: Oxford Univ. Press, 1951.

PETTINGILL, OLIN SEWALL, JR., A Guide to Bird Finding West of the Mississippi. New York: Oxford Univ. Press, 1953.

PETTINGILL, OLIN SEWALL, JR., A Laboratory and Field Manual of Ornithology, 3rd Edition. Minneapolis: Burgess Pub. Co., pp. 207-226, 298-331, 1956.

SAUNDERS, ARETAS, A., A Guide to Bird Song. Garden City, N.Y.: Doubleday & Co., pp. 3-18, 1951.

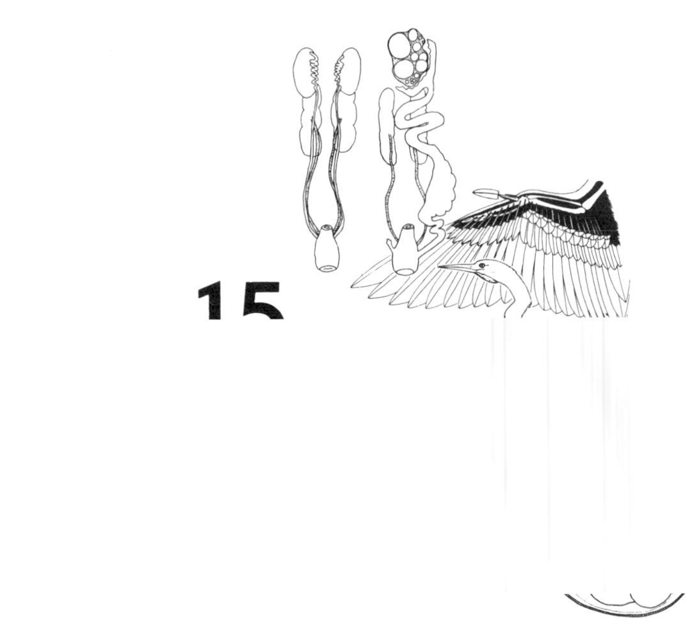

15

Attracting Birds

The greatest incentive and the greatest reward for attracting birds is personal enjoyment. The activity, songs, and beauty of wild birds bring life, charm, and color into the neighborhood. Aside from esthetic values there are numerous economic values. Certainly an area with an abundance of birds will have fewer insects and weed seeds than a birdless area. Pugnacious species like martins, mockingbirds, and grackles are said to be of considerable aid in driving away crows and hawks that might prey on poultry or on other wild birds. Attracting birds may prove rewarding in many other ways. The photographer's task may be simplified; the serious student may find a ready supply of experimental animals close at hand; the bird-watcher may delight in a variety of species with a minimum of effort.

Certain handicaps involved in bird attraction must be mentioned. The artificial assemblage of overpopulations may be detrimental to the birds themselves. Concentrations of populations expose the birds to the hazard of disease transmission. This is especially common whenever birds are enticed to feed on trays or on the ground where they may be exposed to the droppings of other birds. Another drawback to attracting birds is that in a restricted area there may be assembled more individuals than the natural food resources will support. In this event any cessation or interruption of feeding may be detrimental either to the birds, if in winter, or to crops of neighboring fields and gardens, if in summer. The planting of natural food plants also may have some ill effects. Unless a variety of plants are set out so that a more or less continuous food supply is available, the birds may prove detrimental to crops.

One of the simplest ways to attract birds is to use winter feeding stations. Species which may thus be lured into a desired area can be divided into two general groups: those which normally feed on insects, like the woodpeckers, kinglets, nuthatches, and creepers, and those which normally feed on seeds, such as the members of the finch or sparrow family (Fringillidae). For the former group, suet or beef fat generally is recommended. This can be placed in a wire enclosure and should be nailed or otherwise attached to a tree or stump to prevent crows or squirrels from carrying away large chunks. Nut meats, peanuts, peanut butter, doughnuts, and other fatty foods are also highly suited to most insectivorous birds. For seed-eating species, almost any kind of grain is suitable. "Chick-feed" is the most convenient and least expensive. Sunflower seeds are relished by most granivorous birds as well as many insectivorous ones. Grains, nut meats, and the like can be placed on the ground, or on window shelves, or anywhere on any design of feeder. In areas where snows of considerable depth are likely it is well to have a roof over one or several of the feeders.

Feeding is most rewarding if it is started early in the fall so that passing and arriving migrants can find the food before they establish the normal and natural routes which they follow in search of their winter food supply. Once started, feeding should be continued without interruption throughout the winter months.

The best design for a nut or grain feeder is one in which a narrow and shallow tray forms the base of a small bin in which a quantity of the foodstuffs can be placed. This type, illustrated in Figure 56, has two distinct advantages. First, it requires less attention, and second, its narrow tray minimizes the possibility of birds' leaving their droppings on the tray, thus reducing the hazard of disease transmission at the feeding station.

During the migration season, and throughout other seasons as well, birds are attracted to water. Water lures are most effective if so arranged that water drips slowly into a small pool. It seems that glittering reflections of light cast from the broken surface of the water in a pool are like a magnet to passing birds. Migrating wood warblers, which never visit feeding stations, are frequently attracted to such pools. Bird baths also are valuable attracting structures.

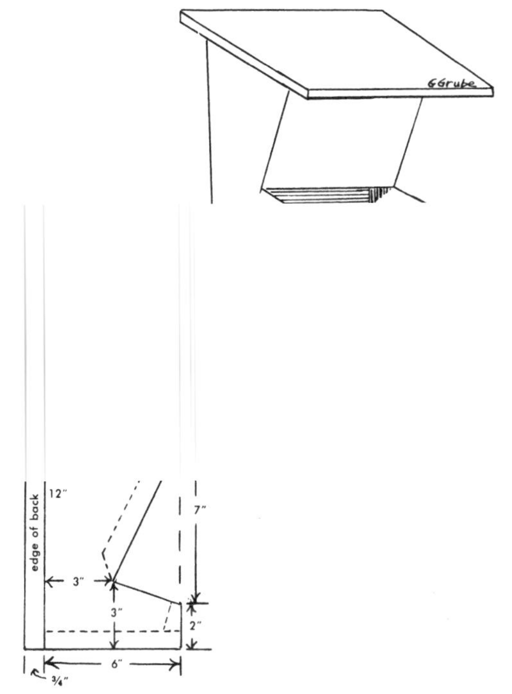

Figure 56. A feeder for supplying small grains in winter feeding of birds. The width may vary from eight to twelve or more inches.

Bird houses serve to attract cavity-nesting species such as woodpeckers, nuthatches, chickadees, wrens, martins, Tree Swallows, and Bluebirds. Some 15 to 20 species of North American birds have been known to utilize these man-made nesting sites. Robins, Eastern Phoebes, and Barn Swallows may be induced to use shelters which are left open at the sides. The best materials to use in constructing bird boxes are slabs of wood with the bark adhering, weathered boards, worn shingles, or asphaltum roofing paper. Smoothly planed boards and paint, while more attractive to humans, are not as readily accepted by birds. Gourds with an entrance hole cut into a side are very acceptable.

Dimensions of houses and the size of entrance holes vary with the species for which they are intended. It is recommended that no box be smaller than 3½ x 3½ x 6 inches inside measurements, and it is better to make them somewhat larger, even for the diminutive wrens. The most acceptable general size which will attract a maximum number of species is 4 x 4 x 9 inches inside with the long axis in the vertical position. The opening should be cut about two inches from the top. Recommended hole diameters are: 1⅛ inches for wrens and chickadees; 1¼ inches for nuthatches and titmice; 1½ inches for Bluebirds, Downy Woodpeckers, Crested Flycatchers, and Tree Swallows; 2 inches for Red-headed and Hairy Woodpeckers; 2½ inches for flickers, martins, and Saw-whet Owls; 3 inches for Screech Owls, and Sparrow Hawks; and 4½ inches for Barn Owls and Wood Ducks. For species requiring a hole diameter diameter of greater than 1½ inches a correspondingly larger sized box is necessary. A Wood Duck box, for example, should be approximately 10 x 10 x 24 inches inside. Martins require apartment type houses with 10 to 30 compartments, each of which should be six to eight inches square and about eight inches high. The holes to the compartments should be placed near the bottom, because martins, unlike other cavity nesting species, like to see outside while they are incubating their eggs.

Bird houses should be placed in relatively cleared situations, away from shrubs or thick branches of trees. Natural nesting cavities of birds are almost invariably in sunlight or light shade. Generally a pole should be erected. It should be placed from five to 20 feet above the ground and should be no closer than about 25 feet from the next one, particularly if adjacent houses are intended for the same species. It is possible to have a flicker and a bluebird nest in adjacent houses which are placed only a few feet apart and on the same tree or pole. Houses for owls, nuthatches, and woodpeckers should be placed at least 12 to 15 feet above the ground for best results.

Bird boxes should be constructed in such a way that the top or bottom or one of the sides can be removed easily in order that they can be cleaned out at the end of each nesting season. Placing nesting material in the house is of no avail; however, placing twigs, horsehair, feathers, or chips near the houses, on the ground, or on a fence post or the like may serve as an added attraction. Woodpeckers build no nest and therefore ground cork or coarse sawdust should be placed to a depth of about one-half inch in boxes intended for them. This will prevent the eggs from rolling about and being broken. A layer of sawdust will do no harm in other boxes, although it is not necessary.

Plantings of trees, shrubs, vines, and herbs are as important in attracting birds as are winter feeding and providing nesting boxes. The plantings may take the form of elaborate landscaping, but simpler plantings are just as effective. No matter how elaborate the planting may be, there should always be open spaces which allow plenty of light to reach the plants. Light permits greater growth, more luxuriant foliage and hence greater forage surface for insects, and more abundant fruiting. Thus more food is provided both directly and indirectly. In addition to providing food, plantings serve as nesting and roosting sites for many species of birds. A variety of trees, shrubs, and vines arranged both in relatively open situations and in occasional tangles affords attraction

of a proper variety of fruiting plants will provide food throughout most of the year.

Seed-eating birds can be attracted by plantings of grains and grasses such as millet, buckwheat, clover, corn, sorghum, sunflower, barnyard grass, and many others. The plants can be seeded along fence rows or in patches where they may remain unmolested throughout the winter following their season of growth.

Planting of flowering plants, particularly those which have a tubular corolla, may be extremely rewarding in attracting hummingbirds. These diminutive creatures feed upon the nectar of flowers. They seem to prefer those flowers that are red, orange, or purple in color. Jewelweed and trumpetvine are popular favorites. Artificial feeding of hummingbirds can be accomplished by supplying sirup in small bottles or vials. At first it may be necessary to draw their attention to the sirup with a brightly colored flower, real or imitation. After the habit is established the sirup will be visited regularly without added enticement. A saturated aqueous solution of ordinary cane sugar seems to be preferred. Solutions of honey and other sirups also are readily accepted.

Game birds and waterfowl may be attracted by planting to augment the food supply and to provide adequate cover. These birds and their welfare are the concern of numerous federal and state publications. Students who are interested in game species will find a considerable literature and frequently personal guidance available for their project by appealing to the local, state, or federal conservation or game officials.

Attracting birds, particularly through feeding operations, is frequently accompanied by the response of hordes of House Sparrows and Starlings. These birds serve a very useful purpose initially, for they are the first to discover the new source of food. In turn they attract other species and thus the project can be launched with expectations of quick results. The House Sparrows and Starlings generally become unwelcome guests, and their elimination or control may be found necessary. The safest way to remove undesirables is by live trapping. Traps such as are used in banding operations can be used to take the birds, and the pests can be destroyed. Individuals of desirable species can be released.

The number of birds inhabiting an area may be increased manyfold by bird-attracting methods. Experience has demonstrated that efforts to attract birds are rewarded by decrease in the number of insect pests, by a decrease in noxious weeds, and by innumerable esthetic pleasures that accompany the sprightly songsters.

Bibliography and References

ALLEN, ARTHUR A., The Book of Bird Life. Princeton, N. J.: D. Van Nostrand Co., pp. 289-308, 1961.

BAKER, JOHN H., Editor, The Audubon Guide to Attracting Birds. Garden City, N. Y.: Doubleday & Co., 1941.

GRANGE, W. B., Feeding Wildlife in Winter. *USDA Farmer's Bull.*, 1783. 1937.

KALMBACH, E. R., English Sparrow Control. *USDA Leaflet*, 61, 1930.

KALMBACH, E. R., Suggestions for Combating Objectionable Roosts of Birds with Special Reference to Those of Starlings. *U.S.F.W.S. Leaflet*, 172, 1940.

KALMBACH, E. R. and W. L. MCATEE, Homes for Birds. *U.S.D.A. Farmer's Bull.*, 1456, 1926.

MCATEE, W. L., Attracting Birds. *USDI Consv. Bull.*, 1, 1940.

MCATEE, W. L., Plants Useful in Upland Wildlife Management. *USDI Consv. Bull.*, 7, 1941.

MCATEE, W. L., Propagation of Aquatic Game Birds. *USDI Consv. Bull.*, 29, 1942.

MCATEE, W. L., Homes for Birds. *USDI Consv. Bull.*, 14 (Reprint), 1957.

MCELROY, THOMAS P., JR., The New Handbook of Attracting Birds. New York: Alfred A. Knopf, 1960.

MARTIN, A. C. and F. M. UHLER, Food of Game Ducks in United States and Canada. *USFWS Research Report* 30. (Reprint of *USDA Tech. Bull.*, 634, 1939), 1951.

SAWYER, E. J., Bird Houses, Baths, and Feeding Shelters. How to Make and Where to Place Them, 4th Ed. *Cranbrook Inst. Sci. Bull.*, 1, Bloomfield Hills, Mich., 1944.

SEDAM, JOHN B. and C. C. FREEBURN, Food and Cover for Farm Wildlife. *Harrisburg: Pa. Game News,* Special Issue No. 6, 1953.

TERRES, JOHN K., Songbirds in Your Garden. New York: Thomas Y. Crowell Co., 1953.

EXERCISE ON ATTRACTING BIRDS

1. Prepare a plan for planting a plot with annuals, shrubs, trees, and other plants designed to attract a maximum variety of species of

APPENDIX A

An Illustrated Key to the Orders and Families of Birds of America North of Mexico

A. KEY TO THE ORDERS

Orders of birds are based on internal anatomy for the most part, so the keys, which are designed for use on study skins, must necessarily be artificial. Bird skins frequently become worn and broken from continuous use or from improper handling of the skin. **Never force wings or toes to look at them.** If a character is not plainly visible try to find out whether that particular bird has or lacks that character without mutilating the skin. Frequently the skin may be extremely valuable in that it may be difficult to replace. If properly used, skins will survive many years of use; therefore use them with care.

1. Feet webbed 2
   Feet not webbed 7
2. All four toes joined in web (Fig. 57) .... **PELECANIFORMES** (IV)

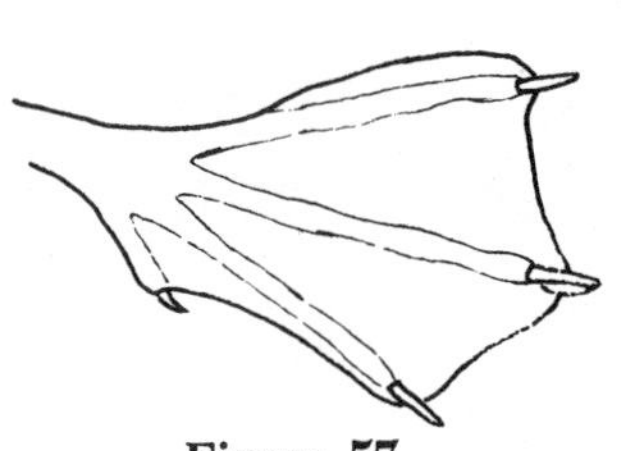

Figure 57

Only front toes joined in web (Fig. 58) 3

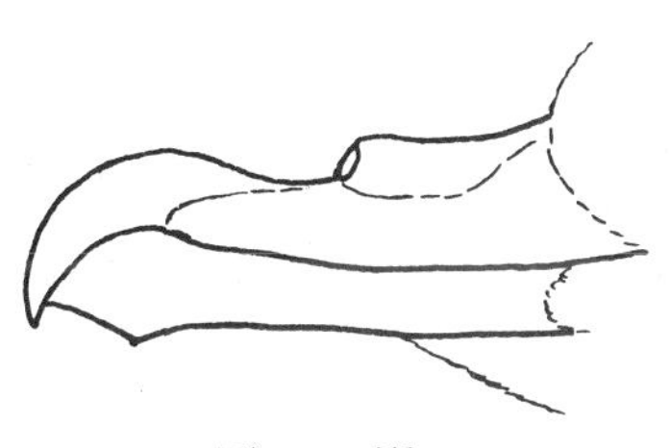

Figure 59

Nostrils not as above 4

4. Bill broader than high away from proximus (lamellate or spatulate) or abruptly bent downward 5

   Bill not as above 6

5. Bill decurved or abruptly bent downward, legs long .... **CICONIIFORMES** (in part) (V)

   Bill more or less straight with nail-like hook at tip of upper mandible (Fig. 60) .... **ANSERIFORMES** (VI)

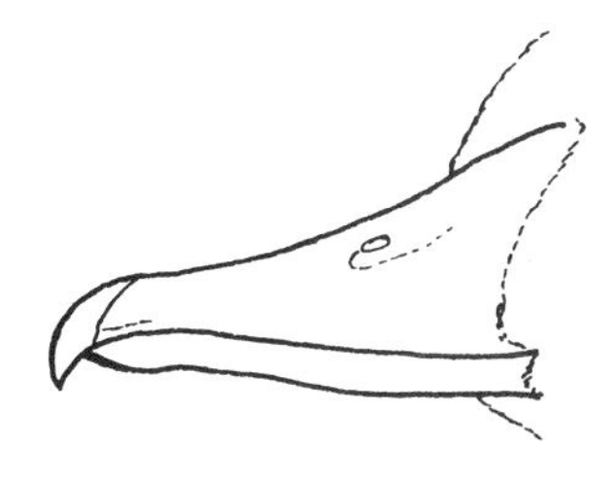

Figure 60

6. Bill straight, sharply pointed; pelvic appendages inserted far behind middle of body .... **GAVIIFORMES** (I)
   Legs not inserted as above, or if so bill not pointed, usually sulcate (Fig. 61) .... **CHARADRIIFORMES** (in part) (X)

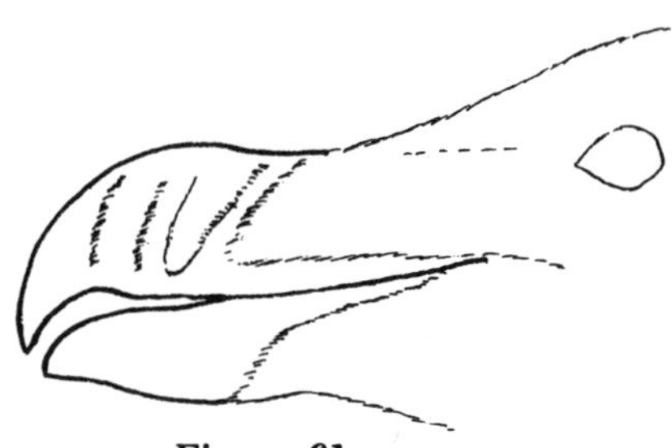

Figure 61

7. Toes three in number 8
   Toes four 9
8. Toes, two front, one back .... **PICIFORMES** (in part) (XIX)
   Toes, three directed forward .... **CHARADRIIFORMES** (in part) (X)
9. Toes lobed and with flattened nails .... (Fig 62) .... **PODICIPEDIFORMES** (II)

Figure 62

   Not as above 10
10. Toes, two directed front, two back 11
    Toes, three forward, one back 14
11. Bill toothed; heterodactyl .... (Figs. 63 and 64) .... **TROGONIFORMES** (XVII)

Figure 63

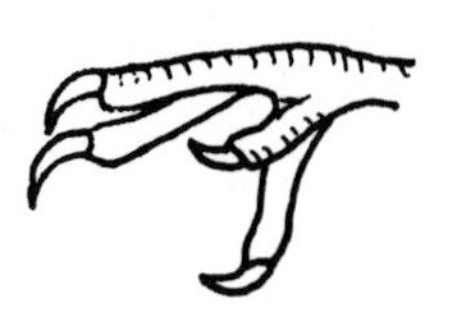

Figure 64

Bill not toothed; zygodactyl 12

12. Bill with cere and hooked ....
(Fig. 65) .... **PSITTACIFORMES** (XII)

Bill without cere and not hooked 13

13. Bill chisel-like; retrices usually stiff ....
(Fig 66) .... **PICIFORMES** (in part) **(XIX)**

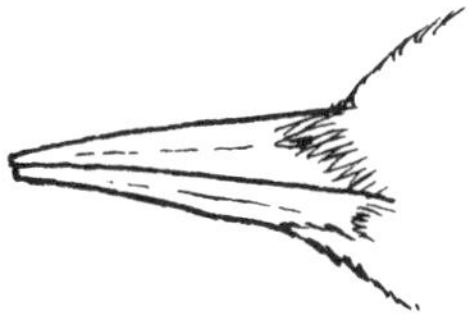

Figure 66

Bill not as above, retrices long and always soft ....
.... **CUCULIFORMES** (XIII)

14. Toes joined at base; head proportionately large
(Fig. 67) .... **CORACIIFORMES** (XVIII)

Figure 67

Not as above 15

15. Feet raptorial, (strong and with large hooked nails) 16
Feet not raptorial 17

16. Facial disc; eyes directed forward ....
.... **STRIGIFORMES** (XIV)

Eyes directed laterad ....
....FALCONIFORMES (in part) (VII)

17. Head entirely bare or bare in part (note lores) 18
Head completely feathered 21

18. Head entirely bare 19
Lores bare, rest of head feathered entirely or in part
(Fig 68) ....CICONIFORMES (in part) (V)

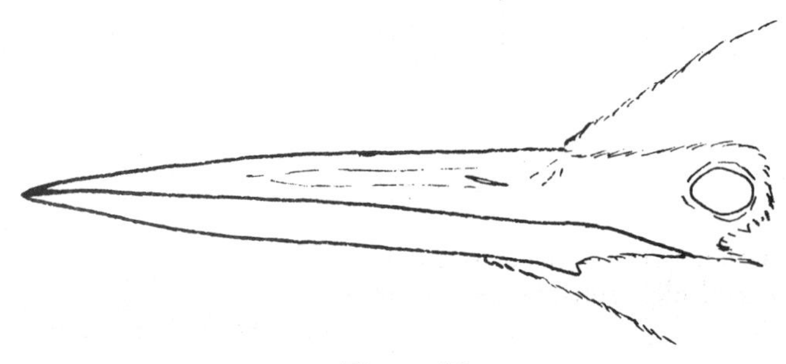

Figure 68

19. Hallux incumbent (on the same level as the front toes)........
....CICONIFORMES (in part) (V)
Hallux elevated 20

20. Nostrils perforate; plumage black ....
....FALCONIFORMES (in part) (VII)
Nostrils imperforate; feet adapted for scratching
(Fig. 69) ....GALLIFORMES (in part) (VIII)

Figure 69

21. Toes lobed 22
Toes not lobed 23

22. Nail flattened 9
Nail not flattened, toes long, wings short ....
....GRUIFORMES (in part) (IX)

23. Feet small, weak; wings long, pointed 24
    Without above combination of characters 25
24. Middle toe nail pectinate; bill short
    (Fig. 70) .... **CAPRIMULGIFORMES** (XV)

25. Bill with operculum (Fig. 71) .... **COLUMBIFORMES** (XI)

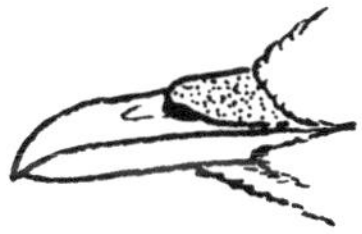

Figure 71

    Bill without operculum 26
26. Hallux incumbent; hallux with claw as long as or longer than middle front toe without claw; 12 rectrices
    (Fig. 72) .... **PASSERIFORMES** (XX)

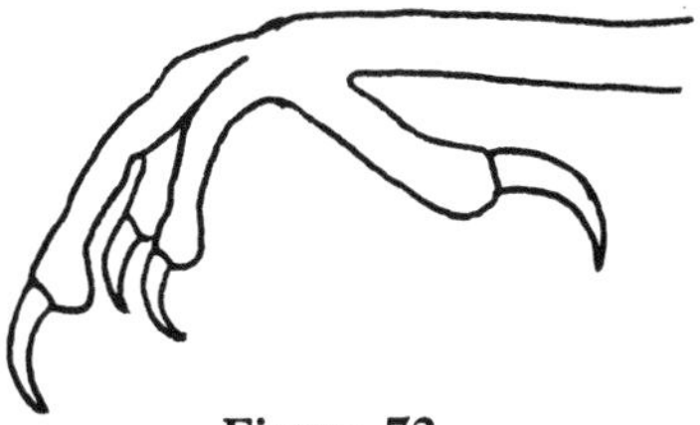

Figure 72

    Hallux elevated; rectrices variable 27
27. Bill short and stout, culmen decurved; primaries stiff and usually curved; tarsi feathered or bare and scutellate; feet strong and adapted for scratching ....
    .... **GALLIFORMES** (in part) (VIII)
    Without above combination of characters 28

28. Hallux always short; wings pointed (except in Jacanidae where carpal spur is present); bill straight, slender, often soft .... **CHARADRIIFORMES** (in part) (X)
Hallux variable; wings rounded; bill variable, short and stout to long and slender and sometimes decurved .... **GRUIFORMES** (in part) (IX)

B. KEY TO THE FAMILIES OF BIRDS OF AMERICA NORTH OF MEXICO

I ORDER GAVIIFORMES – Loons.
Bill straight, pointed; feet webbed; tail short, stiff; length 24 to 38 inches.
One family .... **GAVIIDAE** (Loons)

II ORDER **PODICIPEDIFORMES** – Grebes.
Bill straight, compressed, usually pointed; feet lobed; nails flattened; tail rudimentary; length 7.5 to 26 inches.
One family .... **PODICIPEDIDAE** (Grebes)

III ORDER PROCELLARIIFORMES – Tube-nosed swimmers.
Nostrils opening through tubes; bill variable; feet webbed, hallux rudimentary or absent; wings long, narrow; length 6 to 48 inches. Four families, 3 reach North America's shores.

1. Nostril tubes apparently combined into one tube without a septum (Fig. 73) .... **HYDROBATIDAE** (Storm Petrels).

Figure 73

Nostril tubes separated 2

2. Nostril tubes separated by culmen (Fig. 74) .... **DIOMEDEIDAE** (Albatrosses).

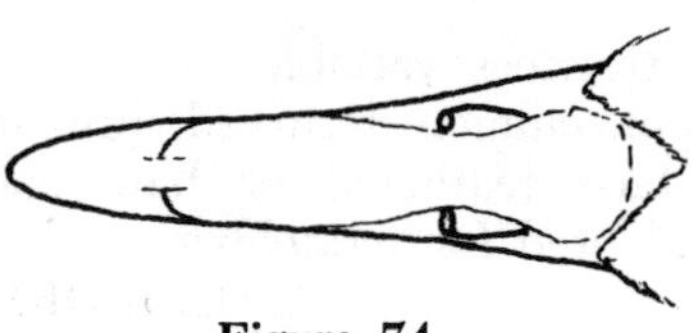

Figure 74

Nostril tubes together but separated by a septum........ ....**PROCELLARIIDAE** (Shearwaters and Fulmars).

IV ORDER PELECANIFORMES – Totipalmate Swimmers. Bill with more or less conspicuous gular pouch; feet totipalmate. Six families, all reach North America.

1. Bill hooked 2

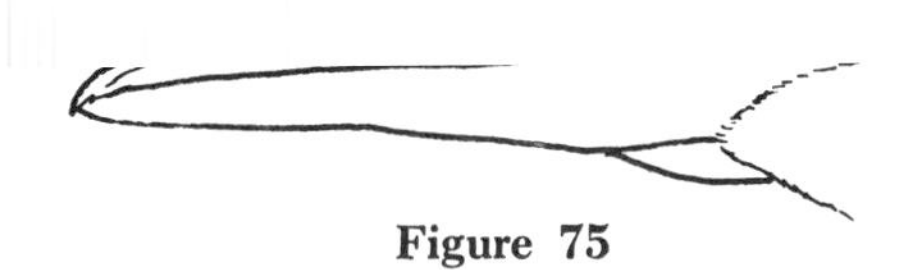

Figure 75

Bill not depressed; gular pouch moderate to small; tail long 3

3. Tail deeply forked ....**FREGATIDAE** (Frigate-birds or Man-o'-war-birds).
   Tail long, rounded ....**PHALACROCORACIDAE** (Cormorants).
4. Bill straight but slightly decurved at tip, tomium not serrate, but maxilla notched near proximus (Fig. 76) ....**SULIDAE** (Boobies, Gannets).

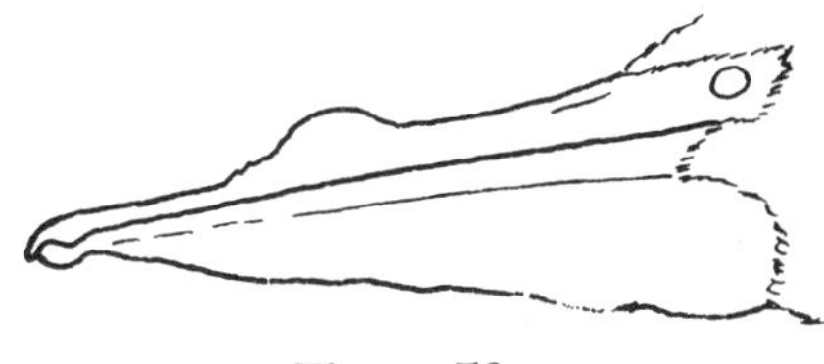

Figure 76

Bill straight, or slightly decurved, tomium serrate.......... 5

5. Bill with tomium finely serrate; neck long, slender; tail long, rounded ....**ANHINGIDAE** (Anhinga or Water Turkey).

Tail with middle feathers greatly elongate; bill conspicuously serrate ....
.................................**PHAETHONTIDAE** (Tropic-birds).

V ORDER CICONIIFORMES – Long-legged Wading Birds.
Bill and feet variable; length 10 to 60 inches. Seven families, 4 reach North America.

1. Bill bent abruptly downward; toes webbed ....
............................**PHOENICOPTERIDAE** (Flamingos).
Not as above 2
2. Bill straight, pointed; toes long, hallux incumbent, middle claw pectinate (Fig. 77) ....
....................................**ARDEIDAE** (Herons & Bitterns).

Figure 77

Bill variable, without above combination of characters.... 3
3. Bill cylindrical and decurved, or flattened and spatulate; nostrils open in long nasal grooves; toes webbed at base only ....
...........**THRESKIORNITHIDAE** (Ibises & Spoonbills).
Bill long, tapering, pointed, straight or curved, no nasal groove, feet not webbed.......................................
..................**CICONIIDAE** (Storks & Wood Ibises).

VI ORDER ANSERIFORMES – Screamers, Ducks, Geese, Swans.
Bill broad and fluting or narrow and serrated or fowl like (Family Anhimidae); toes webbed; length 14 to 60 inches.
Two families, 1 in North America.......................................
....**ANATIDAE** (Ducks, Geese & Swans).

C. KEY TO SUBFAMILIES OF ANATIDAE

1. Neck longer than body, lores bare ....
....**CYGNINAE** (Swans).
Not as above 2
2. Tarsus completely reticulate 3
Tarsus scutellate in front 4

3. Wings rounded, smaller, not over 20 inches in length ....**DENDROCYGNINAE** (Tree Ducks).
   Wings pointed, more than 20 inches in length ....**ANSERINAE** (Geese).
4. Rectrices narrow and stiff with short coverts ....**OXYURINAE** (Ruddy Ducks).
   Rectrices normal, coverts of normal length 5

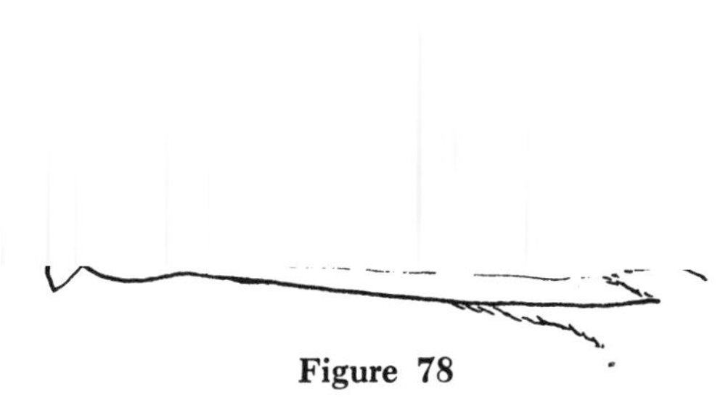

Figure 78

6. Hallux lobed; no speculum (an iridescent patch of wing coverts). (Fig. 79) ....**AYTHYINAE** (Diving Ducks).

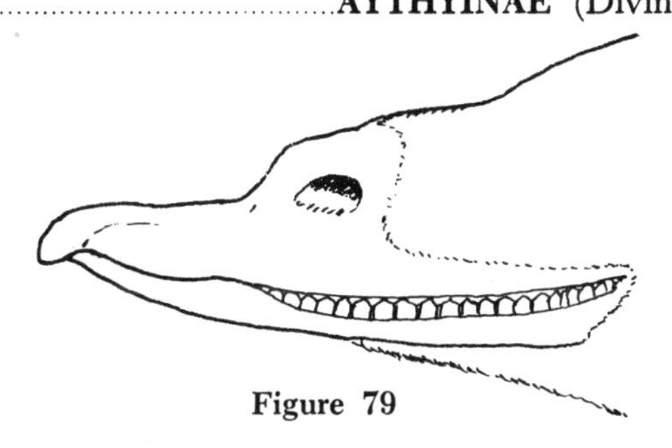

Figure 79

   Hallux not lobed; speculum usually present (Fig. 80) ....**ANATINAE** (Dabbling Ducks).

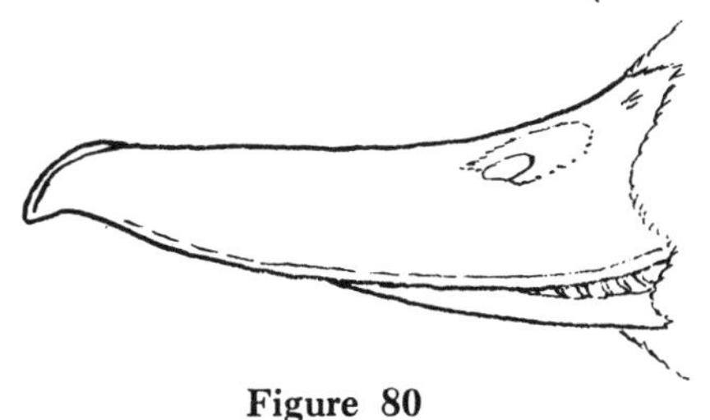

Figure 80

VII ORDER FALCONIFORMES – Hawks, Falcons, Vultures, etc.
Feet raptorial; bill strong, hooked; length 5 to 50 inches. Five families, 4 in North America; one, the **Pandionidae,** is included here in **Accipitridae.**

1. Head bare (Fig. 81) .... **CATHARTIDAE** (New World Vultures).

Figure 81

Head not bare 2

2. Front of tarsus reticulate; maxilla toothed; nostrils usually circular; wings pointed (Fig. 82).. **FALCONIDAE** (Falcons and Caracaras).

Figure 82

Without above combination of characters; tarsus usually scutellate or feathered; nostrils, oval-shaped; wings more or less rounded (Fig. 83) .... **ACCIPITRIDAE** (Hawks, Harriers, Osprey).

Figure 83

VIII ORDER GALLIFORMES – Gallinaceous Birds
Generally heavy-bodied birds; length 6 to 60 inches. Seven families, 4 in North America.

1. Head bare; large birds .... **MELEAGRIDIDAE** (Turkeys).
   Head not bare 2
2. Hallux not elevated; tail long, rounded

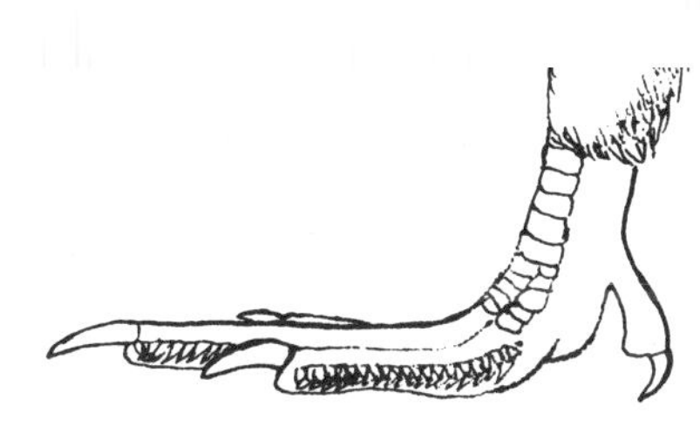

Figure 84

Tarsi naked (Fig. 85) .... **PHASIANIDAE** (Pheasants, Partridges, Quail).

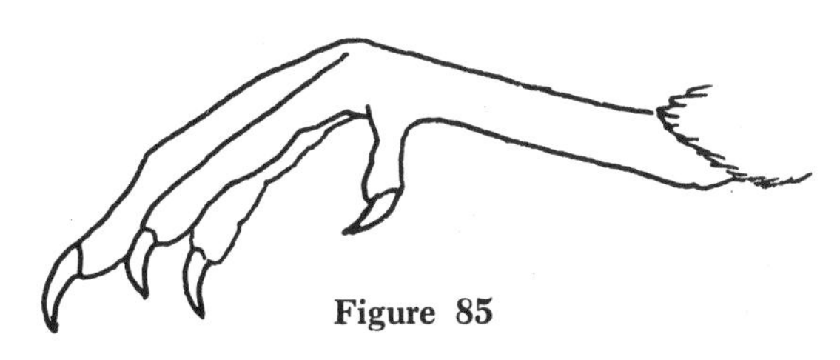

Figure 85

IX ORDER GRUIFORMES – Rails, Cranes, Limpkins, etc.
A group with diverse characters; length 5 to 54 inches. Thirteen families, three in North America.

1. Bill slightly decurved; outer primaries narrow; mottled brown birds, 25 inches long .... **ARAMIDAE** (Limpkins).
   Bill variable; without above combination of characters 2

2. Bill straight; feet not webbed nor lobed; wings with some secondaries longer than primaries (Fig. 86) .... **GRUIDAE** (Cranes).

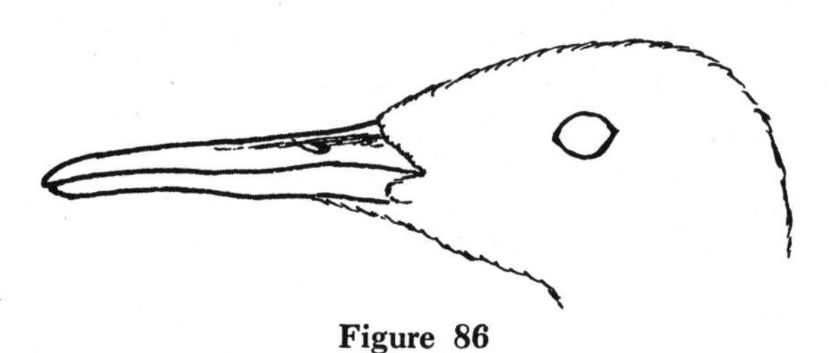

Figure 86

Bill variable; toes partially webbed or lobed; wings short (Fig. 87) ....**RALLIDAE** (Rails, Gallinules, Coots).

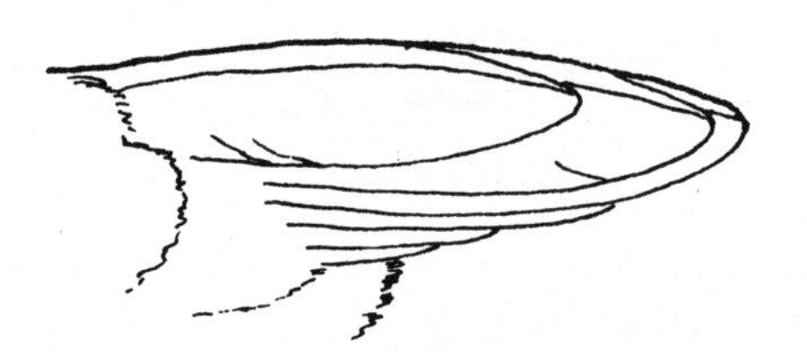

Figure 87

X ORDER CHARADRIIFORMES – Shore Birds

A group with diverse characters; generally drably garbed birds; length 5 to 30 inches. Sixteen families, ten in North America.

1. Long-legged shore or upland birds; bill slender; wings long, flat, pointed; tertails long; toes may or may not be webbed; usually less than 12 inches long 6
   Moderate to short-legged water birds; bill strong, high or sharply pointed; wings long or short; front toes webbed 2
2. Bill compressed 3
   Bill not compressed 4
3. Lower mandible longer than upper ....**RHYNCHOPIDAE** (Skimmers).
   Lower and upper mandibles equally long (Fig. 88) ....**HAEMATOPODIDAE** (Oyster-catchers).

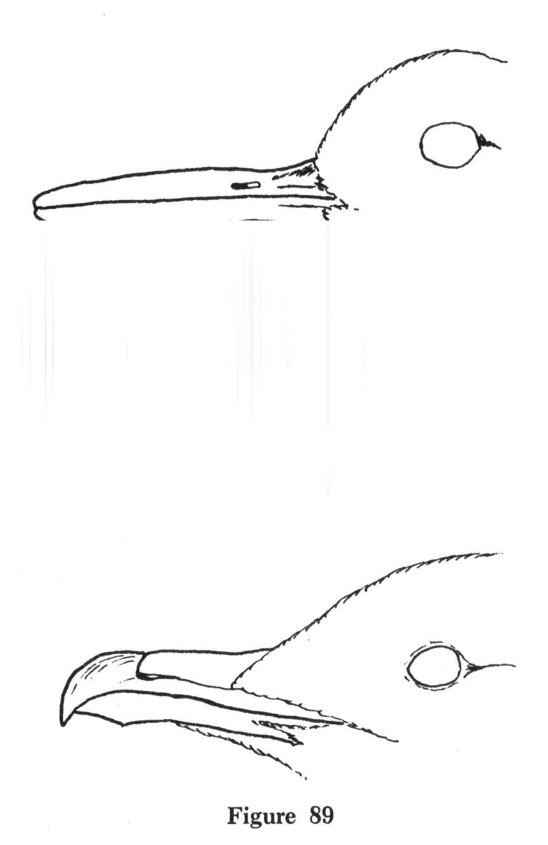

Figure 89

5. Wings long; hallux present (Fig. 90) ....
....LARIDAE (Gulls & Terns).
Wings short, hallux usually lacking, bill variable from

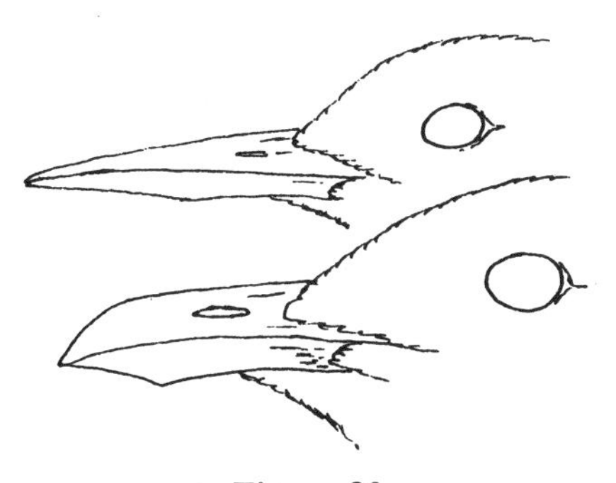

Figure 90

short and pointed to sulcate (Fig. 91)..............................
..............................**ALCIDAE** (Auks, Murres, Puffins).

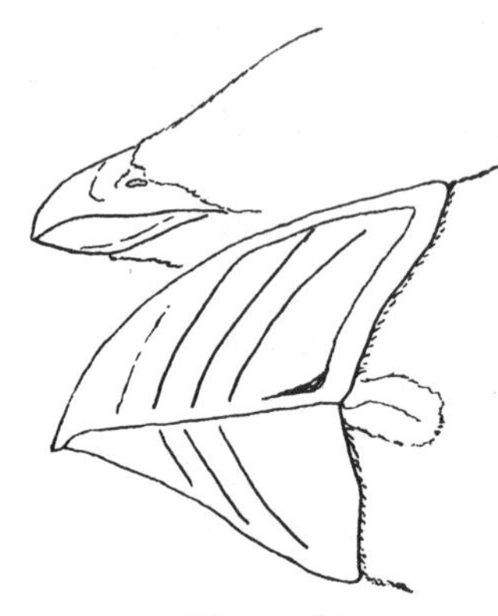

Figure 91

6. Carpal spur present; claw of hallux greatly elongate (Fig .92) ....**JACANIDAE** (Jacanas).

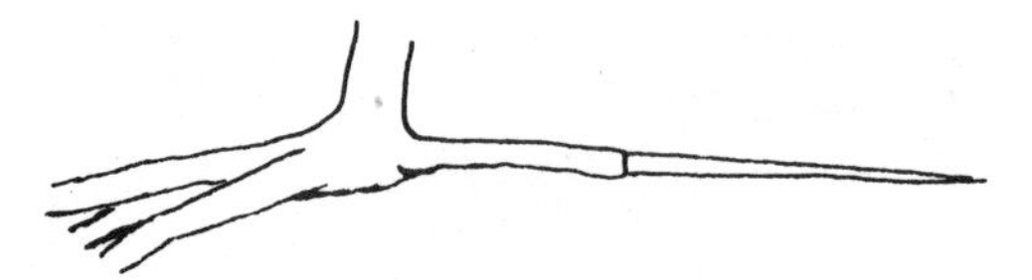

Figure 92

Not as above 7

7. Bill moderate, swollen at tip or constricted near base and tapering to a point; tarsi usually reticulate in front; hallux lacking or reduced in size (Fig. 93)...............
........**CHARADRIIDAE** (Plovers, Kildeer, Turnstones).

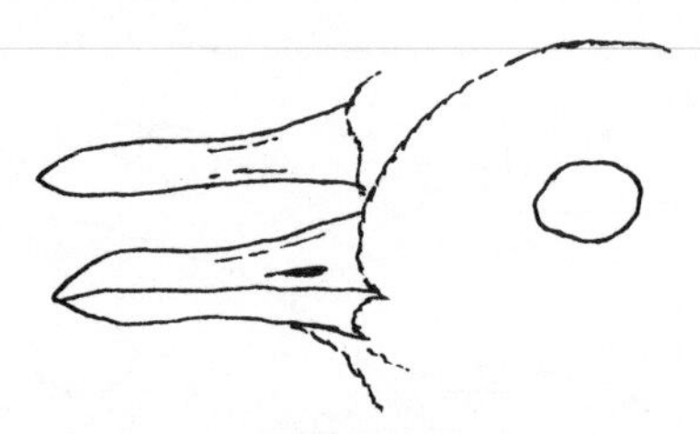

Figure 93

Not with above combination of characters 8

8. Bill slender, pliable and depressed, straight, decurved, or recurved; toes not lobed, hallux present except in

one species (Sanderling) where tarsus is scutellate. (On study skins the pliable character of the bill is not evident as such but the bill will lack the glossy appearance of hard bills. (Fig. 94)..
SCOLOPACIDAE (Snipe, Woodcock, Sandpipers, etc.)

9. Bill slender, recurved, or straight; toes webbed at base or lobed 10
Bills compressed ....
........................**HAEMATOPODIDAE** (Oyster-catchers).
10. Legs moderately long; toes lobed or without membranes......................**PHALAROPODIDAE** (Phalaropes).
Legs long; toes webbed at base; bill long, slender and recurved (Fig. 95) ....
................**RECURVIROSTRIDAE** (Stilts and Avocets).

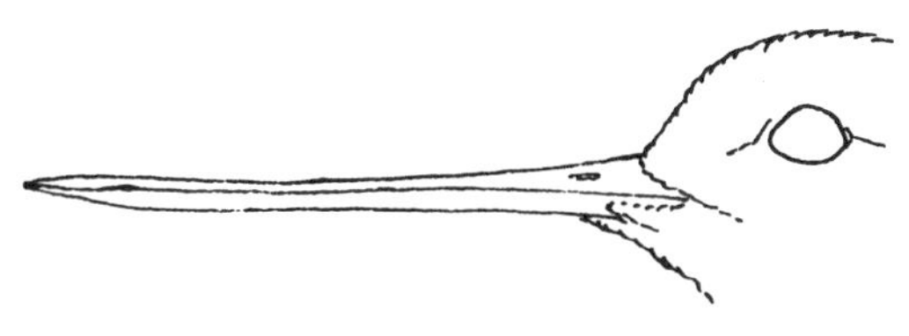

Figure 95

XI ORDER COLUMBIFORMES – Pigeons, Doves and Sand Grouse.
Bill fowl like (Sand Grouse) or swollen at tip; membraneous operculum at base of bill; feet weak and with four toes on same level; length 6 to 34 inches.
Two families, 1 in North America ....
....**COLUMBIDAE** (Pigeons & Doves).

XII ORDER PSITTACIFORMES – Parrots, Lories, and Macaws.
Bill strong and hooked; feet zygodactyl; length 5 to 36 inches.
One family ....**PSITTACIDAE.**

XIII ORDER CUCULIFORMES – Cuckoos, Anis and Plantain-eaters.
Bill slender, decurved (carinate in Anis); feet zygodactyl; length 5 to 24 inches.
Two families, 1 in North America .... **CUCULIDAE** (Cuckoos, Anis).

XIV ORDER STRIGIFORMES – Owls
Birds with a facial disk; bill strong and hooked; feet strong, length 6 to 30 inches. Two families.

1. Middle claw serrate (Fig. 96a) .... **TYTONIDAE** (Barn Owls).
   Middle claw not serrate (Fig. 96b) .... **STRIGIDAE** (Typical Owls).

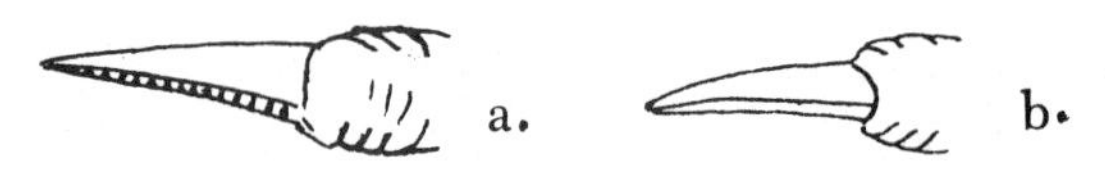

Figure 96

XV ORDER CAPRIMULGIFORMES – Goatsuckers, Frogmouths, Oil Birds, etc.
Neutrally colored birds with weak feet; bill wide and gape large; length 7 to 21 inches.
Five families, one in North America .... **CAPRIMULGIDAE** (Goatsuckers).

XVI ORDER APODIFORMES – Swifts and Hummingbirds
Sooty colored or iridescent birds with weak feet; length 2 to 13 inches. Three families, two in North America.

1. Bill flat, plumage sooty brown (Fig. 97a) .... **APODIDAE** (Swifts).
   Bill long, slender; plumage usually iridescent (Fig. 97b) .... **TROCHILIDAE** (Hummingbirds).

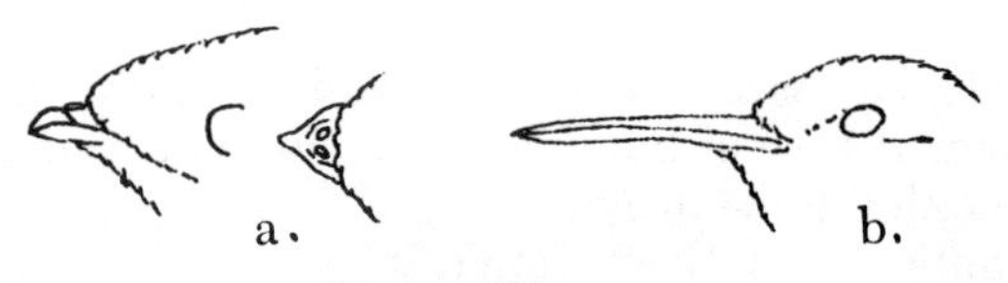

Figure 97

XVII ORDER TROGONIFORMES – Trogons
Feet heterodactyl; bill short, stout and hooked; length 9 to 15 inches.
One family .... **TROGONIDAE.**

XVIII ORDER CORACIIFORMES – Kingfishers, Todies, Motmots, Rollers, Hornbills, etc.
A variable group usually with large head and bill; length 3 to 63 inches.
Nine families, one in North America ....ALCEDINIDAE (Kingfishers).

twenty-six in North America.

1. Back of tarsus rounded or toes partially syndactyl; bill variable (Fig. 98a) 2
   Back of tarsus ridged; toes never syndactyl; bill variable (Fig. 98b) 4

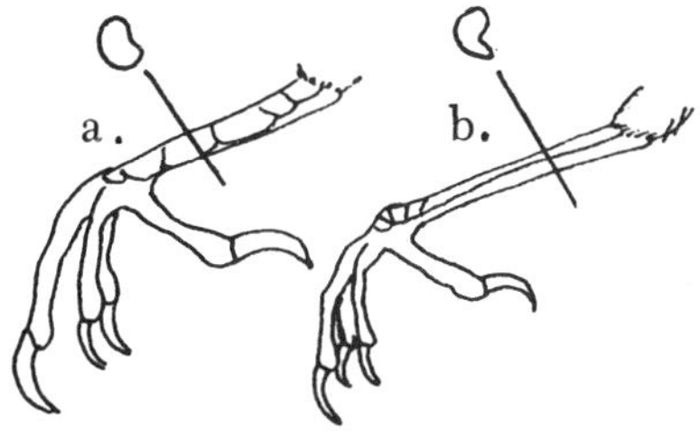

Figure 98

2. Bill notched or short and stout 3
   Bill flattened, triangular as seen from above (Fig. 99) ....TYRANNIDAE (Tyrant Flycatchers).

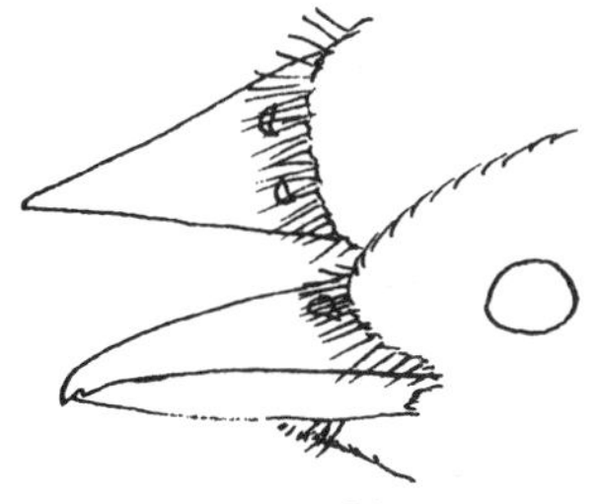

Figure 99

3. Bill notched; toes syndactyl; hind claw normal .... **COTINGIDAE** (Cotingas).
Bill not notched; hind nail elongate (Fig. 100) .... **ALAUDIDAE** (Larks).

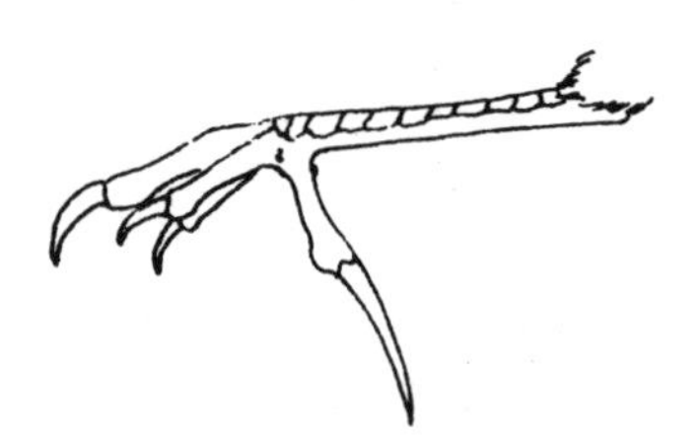

Figure 100

4. Tarsus booted (holorhinal) (Fig. 101) 5

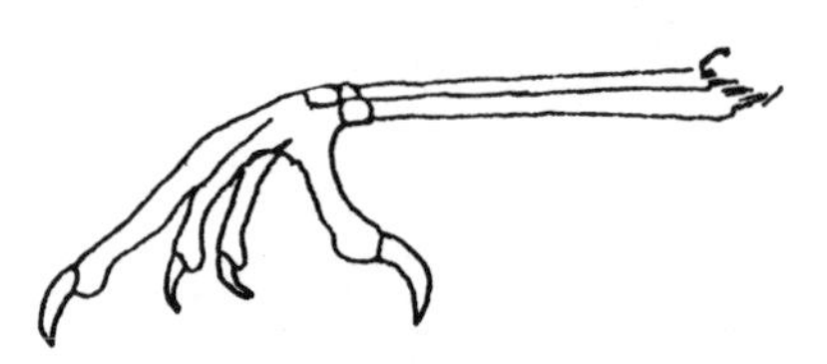

Figure 101

Tarsus not booted 9
5. Rictal bristles present 6
Rictal bristles absent .... **CINCLIDAE** (Dippers).
6. Bill short and flattened .... **PTILOGONATIDAE** (Silky Flycatchers).
Bill variable but not as above 7
7. Wings pointed; length of bird 6.5 to 12 inches .... **TURDIDAE** (Thrushes).
Wings rounded; length under 6 inches 8
8. Tail shorter than wings; plumage not lax .... **REGULIDAE** (Kinglets) (Usually considered part of SYLVIIDAE).
Tail longer than wings; plumage lax .... **CHAMAEIDAE** (Wren-tits).

9. Bill hooked at tip and notched near tip 10
   Bill may or may not be notched but never when hooked 11
10. Plumage greenish above, whitish below .... **VIREONIDAE** (Vireos).
   Plumage black, gray, and white .... **LANIIDAE** (Shrikes).

Figure 102

   Feet not scansorial (i.e. not adapted for climbing) 13
12. Bill slender, decurved; rectrices stiffened (Fig. 103a) .... **CERTHIIDAE** (Creepers).
   Bill with lower mandible upturned; rectrices not stiffened (Fig. 103b) .... **SITTIDAE** (Nuthatches).

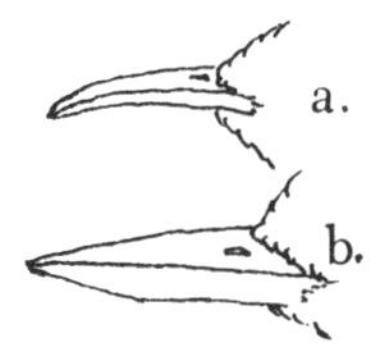

Figure 103

13. First primary rudimentary (less than half the second) 23
   First primary not rudimentary 14
14. First primaries more or less graduated; first conspicuously shorter but not rudimentary 15
   First primary little if any shorter than second 17
15. Nostrils exposed 16
   Nostrils largely concealed by rictal bristles .... **CORVIDAE** (Crows, Jays).

16. Small (4 to 6 inches) brown birds .... **TROGLODYTIDAE** (Wrens).
    Larger (7 to 12 inches); nostril bristles usually present. .... **MIMIDAE** (Catbird, Mockingbirds, Thrashers).
17. First primary longest; bill short, gape wide .... **HIRUNDINIDAE** (Swallows).
    First three primaries about equal 18
18. Upper mandible broadly toothed near base; males generally brilliantly colored (Fig. 104) .... **THRAUPIDAE** (Tanagers).

Figure 104

    Upper mandible not toothed 19
19. Bill extends back, parting feathers of forehead no rictal bristles; commisure rather abruptly bent downward along side of head (Fig. 105) .... **ICTERIDAE** (Blackbirds), etc.)

Figure 105

    Not as above 20
20. Bill stout at base, vaulted, conical or sometimes crossed, commisure less abruptly bent, gonydeal angle not pronounced; rictal bristles small but plainly visible (Fig. 106) .... **FRINGILLIDAE** (Finches, Sparrows, etc.)

Figure 106

Bill stout at base, vaulted, never conical nor crossed; gonydeal angle more pronounced; plumage sooty gray beneath; rictal bristles very small (Fig. 107) .... **PLOCEIDAE** (Weaver finches of the Genus **Passer**).

22. Bill notched at tip; brown crested birds .... **BOMBYCILLIDAE** (Waxwing).
Bill not notched, usually slender, more or less straight, somewhat flattened in some species; plumage usually rather brilliant (Fig. 108a and 108b) .... **PARULIDAE** (Warblers).

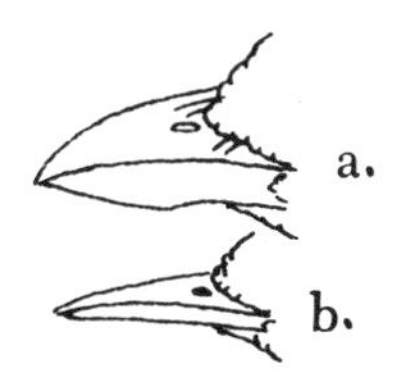

Figure 108

23. Second primary longest; wings pointed .... **STURNIDAE** (Starlings).
Second not longer than third 24
24. Second primary shorter; third to sixth longest 25
Second to fifth primaries equal; bill stout 26
25. Bill short and stout; plumage lax .... **PARIDAE** (Titmice)
Bill slender, moderately long; plumage somewhat lax .... **SYLVIIDAE** (Gnatcatchers).
26. First primary extremely rudimentary, sometimes lacking; bill as described in couplet 20; rictal bristles small (Fig. 107) .... **PLOCEIDAE** (Weaver-birds of Genus *Passer*).

First primary small but conspicuous, bill vaulted, rictal bristles rather conspicuous (Fig. 106) .... **FRINGILLIDAE** (Finches).

AN EXERCISE ON THE CHARACTERISTICS OF FAMILIES OF BIRDS AND THEIR DISTRIBUTION

The following pages are provided for the student to record diagnostic features of the families of birds and to record the world distribution of the families. A sample page is provided. It concerns the Order Struthioniformes, Family Struthionidae and is found on page 201.

The map should be completed by consulting the literature. Van Tyne and Berger, 1959, Fundamentals of Ornithology, John Wiley & Sons, New York, pages 376 to 552 is an excellent recent source. Use a bright colored ink on the maps for best results.

The characteristics of families should be recorded only as specimens of the various families are subjected to the use of the keys preceding this page. Properly done, this exercise will be of great assistance in helping you learn the orders and families of birds.

Order: (*STRUTHIONIFORMES* Family: STRUTHIONIDAE)

Synopsis of Family Characteristics:

Large: length to 72 in., to 300 lbs. Body plumage soft and lose (black in male, brownish in female), feathers sparse on head and most of neck. Thighs bare. Bill short and flat, eyes large, head small, neck long. Legs long and powerful; toes 2 (3rd and 4th).

Specimens identified (number and name): #2501 *Struthio camelus*, (Ostrich).

Distribution: Africa: open arid country (nonmigratory).

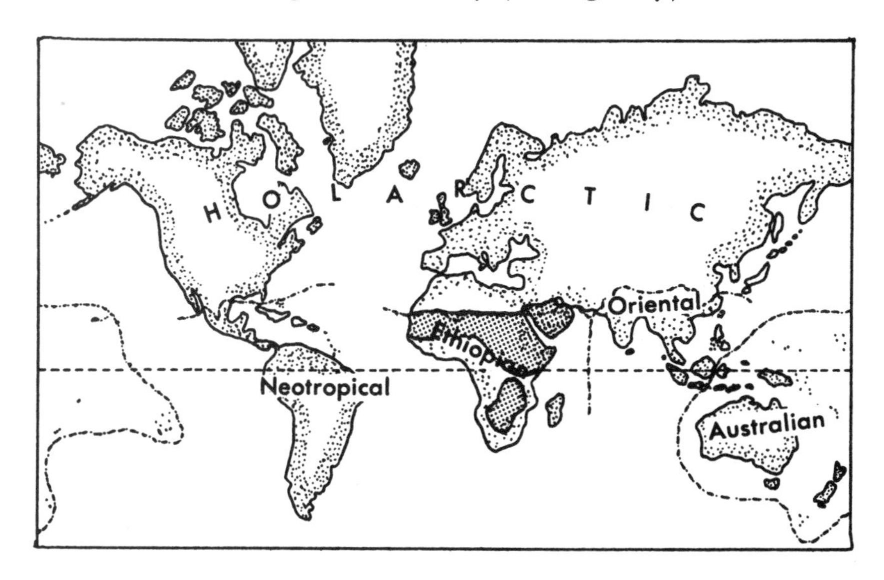

Order: *GAVIIFORMES* Family: GAVIIDAE

Synopsis of Family Characteristics:

Specimens identified (number and name): ____________________

____

Distribution:

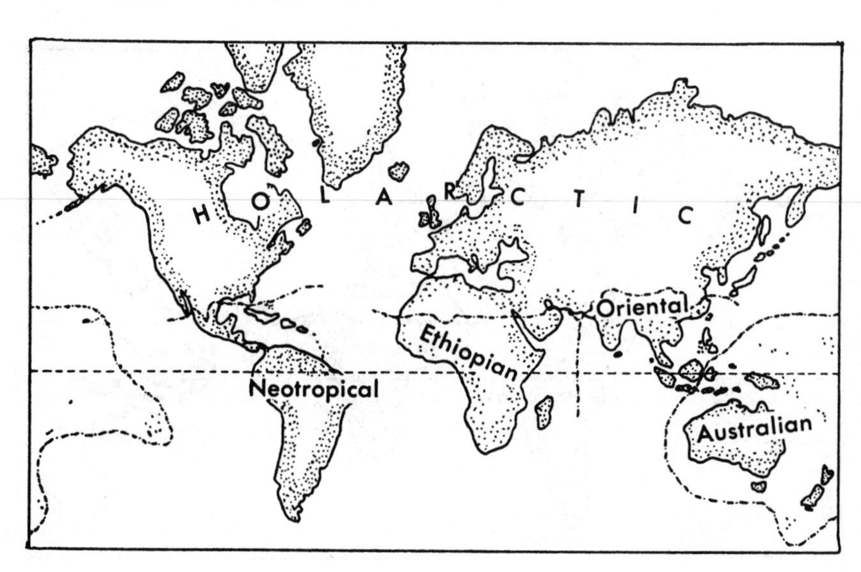

Order: *PODICIPEDIFORMES* Family: PODICIPEDIDAE

Synopsis of Family Characteristics:

Specimens identified (number and name): ______________________

____

Distribution:

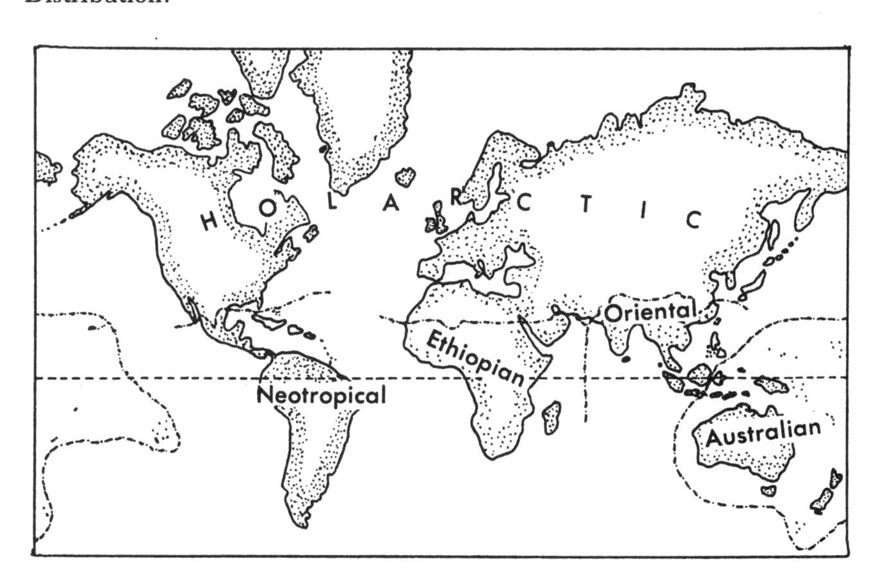

Order: *PROCELLARIIFORMES* Family: DIOMEDEIDAE

Synopsis of Family Characteristics:

Specimens identified (number and name): ______________________________

____

Distribution:

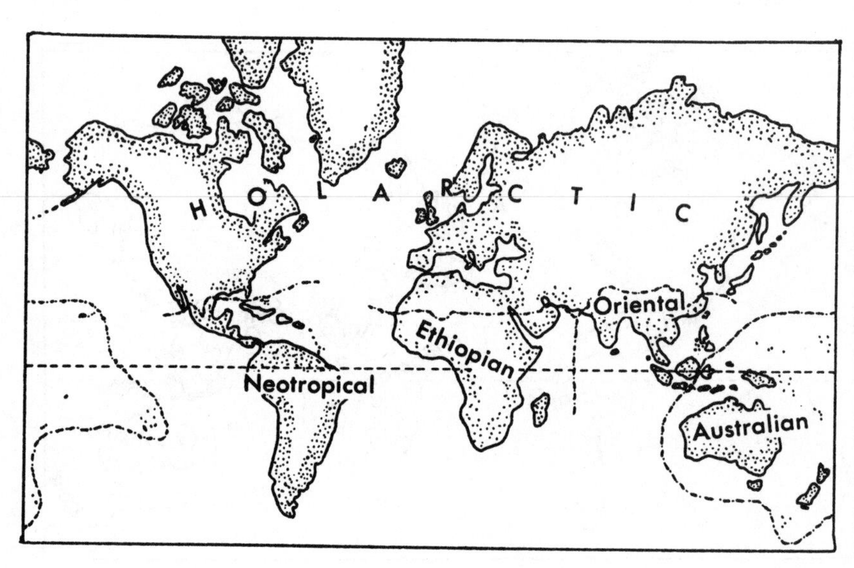

Order: *PROCELLARIIFORMES* Family: PROCELLARIIDAE

Synopsis of Family Characteristics:

Specimens identified (number and name): ______________________

____

Distribution:

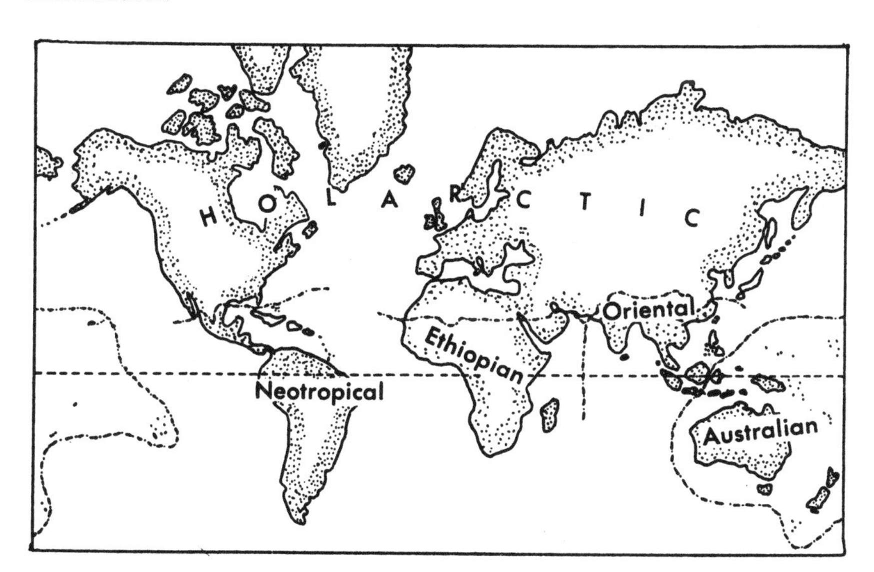

Order: *PROCELLARIIFORMES* Family: HYDROBATIDAE

Synopsis of Family Characteristics:

Specimens identified (number and name): ______________________

____

Distribution:

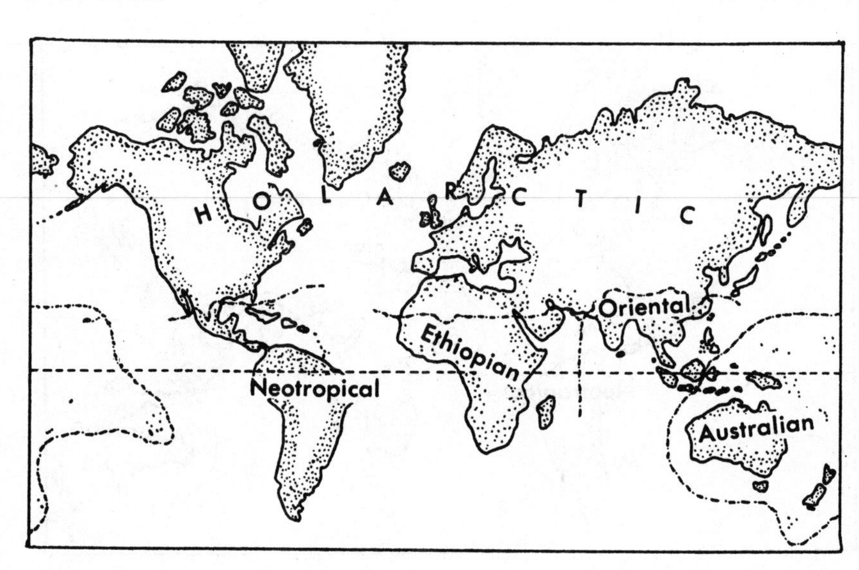

Order: *PELECANIFORMES* Family: PHAETHONTIDAE

Synopsis of Family Characteristics:

Specimens identified (number and name): ______________________

____

Distribution:

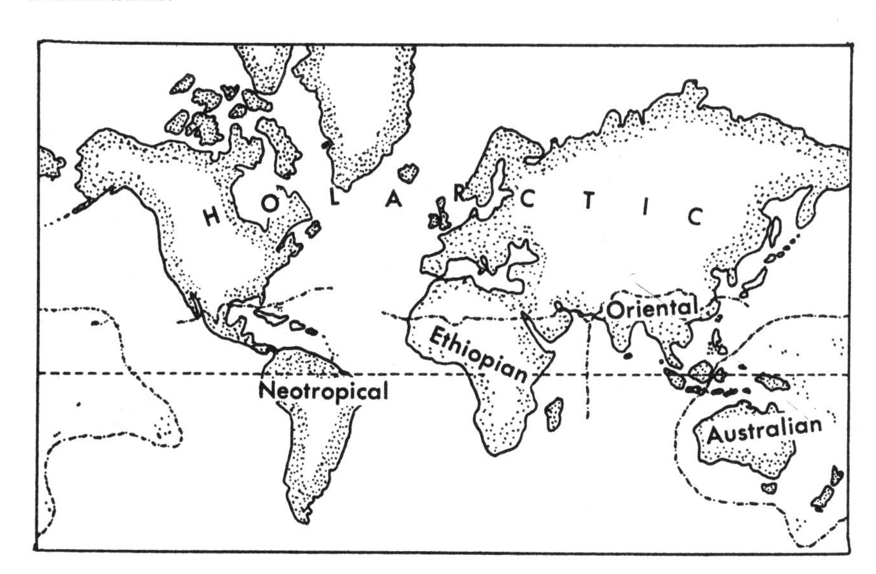

Order: *PELECANIFORMES* Family: PELECANIDAE

Synopsis of Family Characteristics:

Specimens identified (number and name): ______________________

____

Distribution:

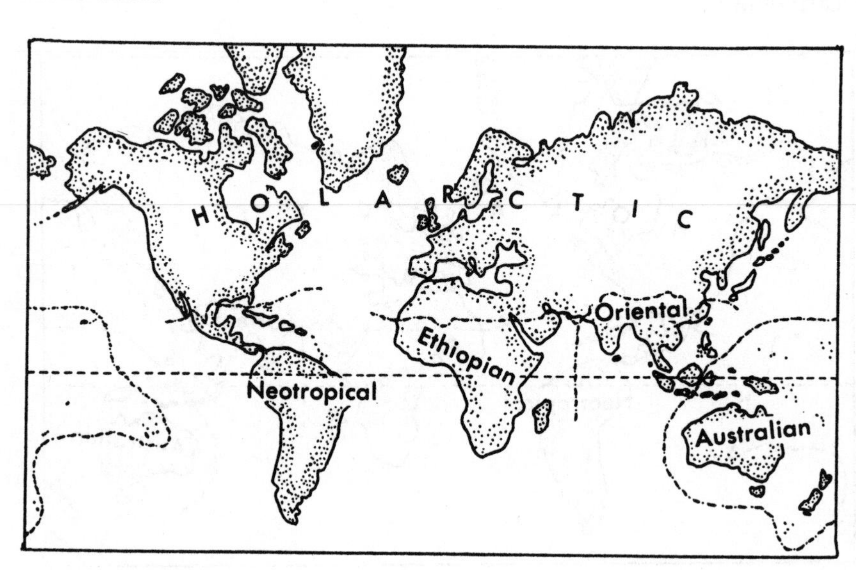

Order: *PELECANIFORMES* Family: SULIDAE

Synopsis of Family Characteristics:

Specimens identified (number and name): ______________________

____

Distribution:

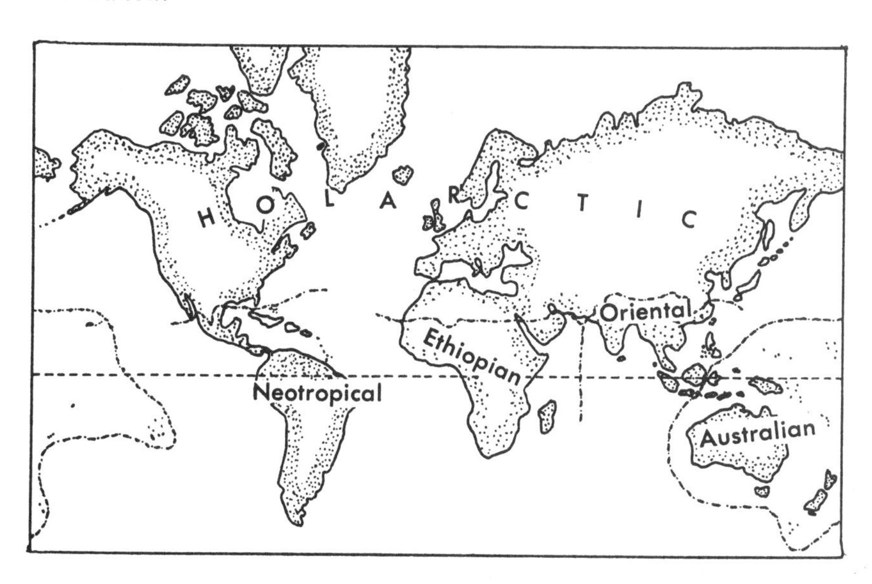

Order: *PELECANIFORMES* Family: PHALACROCORACIDAE

Synopsis of Family Characteristics:

Specimens identified (number and name): ____________________

____

Distribution:

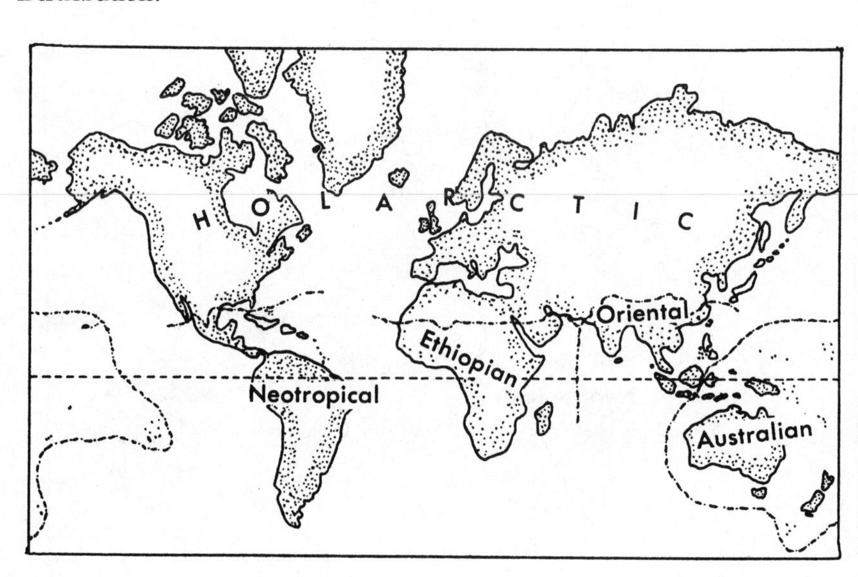

Order: *PELECANIFORMES* Family: ANHINGIDAE

Synopsis of Family Characteristics:

Specimens identified (number and name): ______________________

____

Distribution:

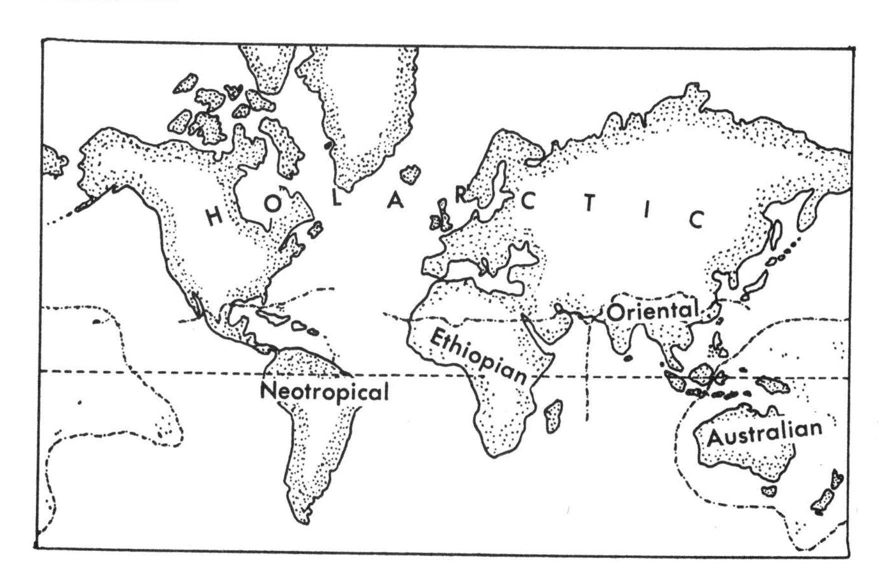

Order: *PELECANIFORMES* Family: FREGATIDAE

Synopsis of Family Characteristics:

Specimens identified (number and name): ______________________

____

Distribution:

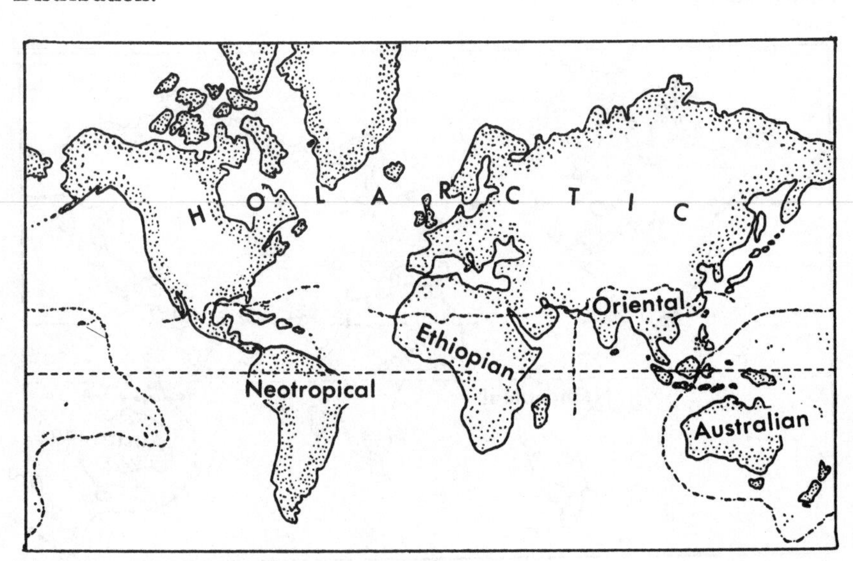

Order: *CICONIIFORMES* Family: ARDEIDAE

Synopsis of Family Characteristics:

Specimens identified (number and name): ______________________

____

Distribution:

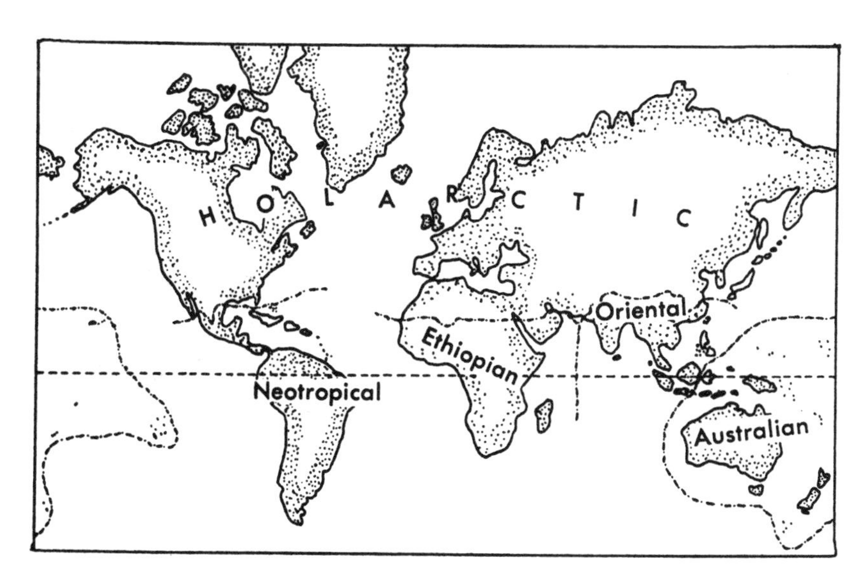

Order: *CICONIIFORMES* Family: CICONIIDAE

Synopsis of Family Characteristics:

Specimens identified (number and name): ____________________

____

Distribution:

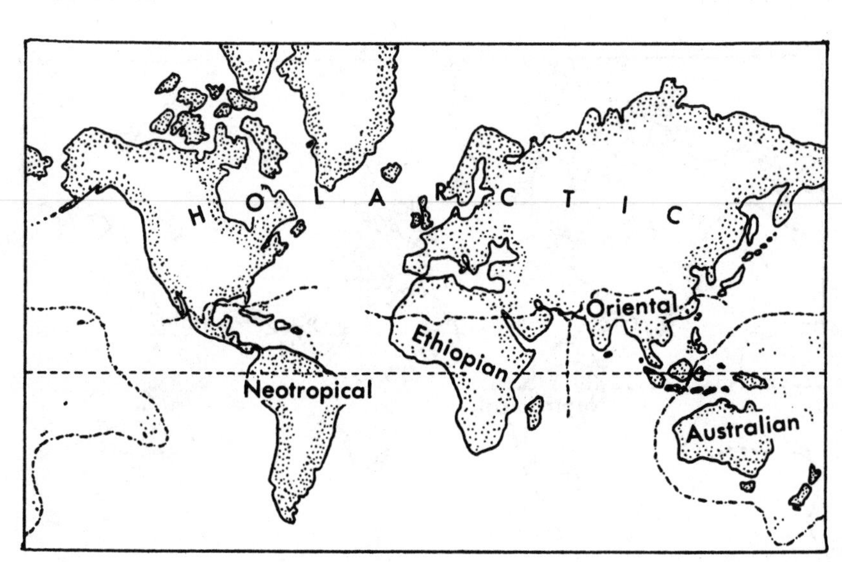

Order: *CICONIIFORMES* Family: THRESKIORNITHIDAE

Synopsis of Family Characteristics:

Specimens identified (number and name): ______________________

____

Distribution:

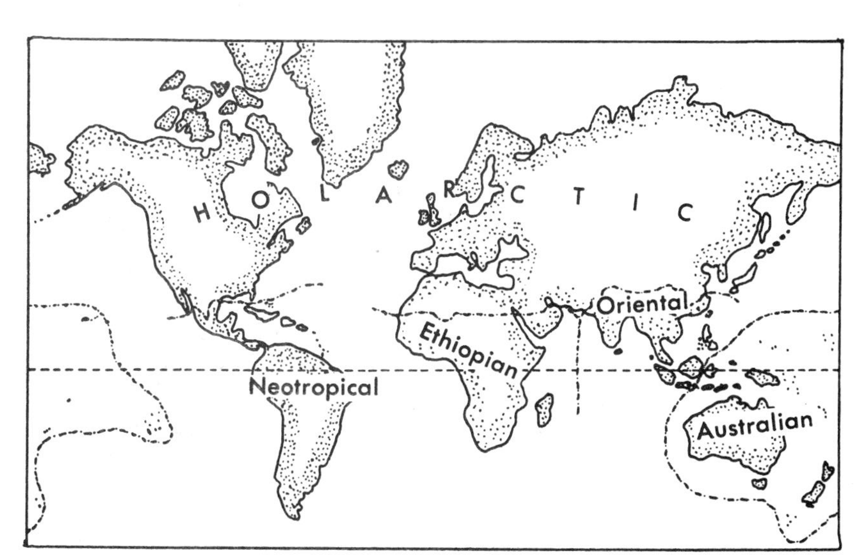

Order: *CICONIIFORMES* Family: PHOENICOPTERIDAE

Synopsis of Family Characteristics:

Specimens identified (number and name): ______________________

____

Distribution:

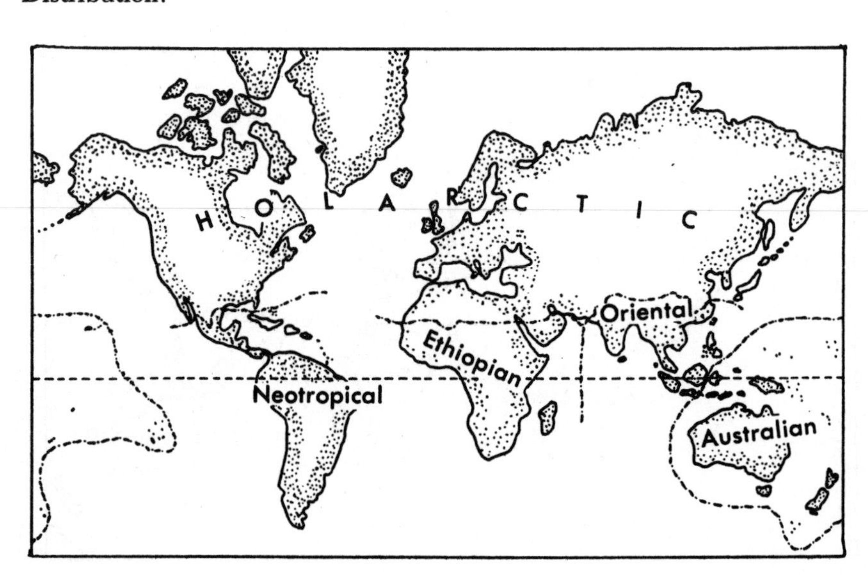

Order: *ANSERIFORMES* Family: ANATIDAE

Synopsis of Family Characteristics:

Specimens identified (number and name): ______________________

____

Distribution:

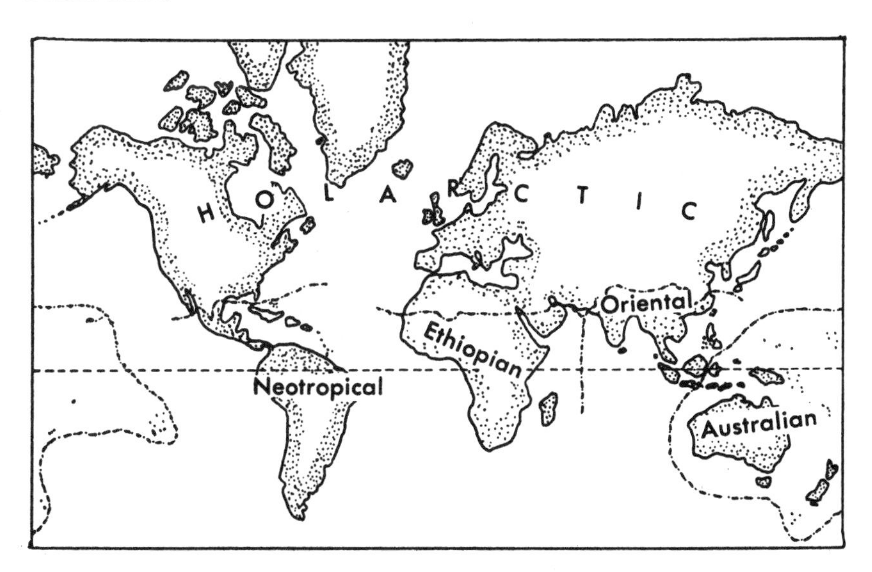

Order: *FALCONIFORMES* Family: CATHARTIDAE

Synopsis of Family Characteristics:

Specimens identified (number and name): ______________________

____

Distribution:

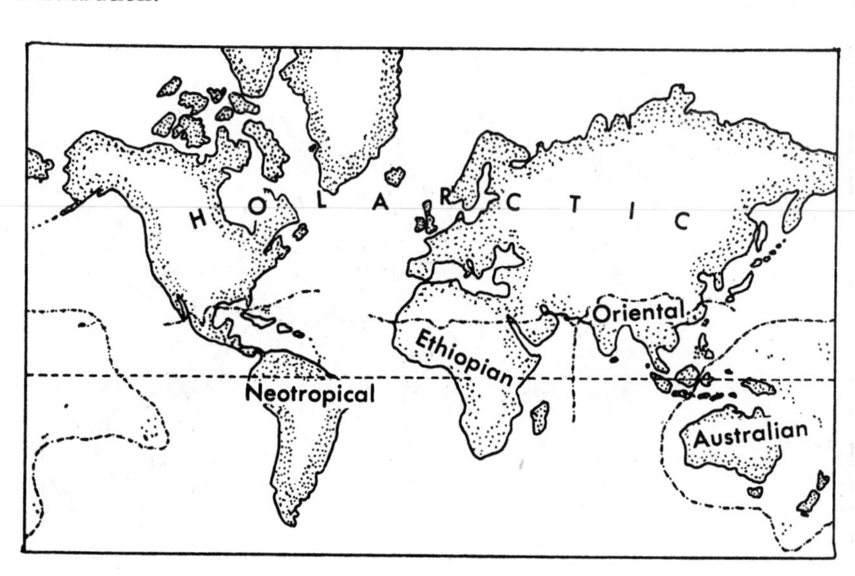

Order: *FALCONIFORMES* Family: ACCIPITRIDAE

Synopsis of Family Characteristics:

Specimens identified (number and name): ____________________

____

Distribution:

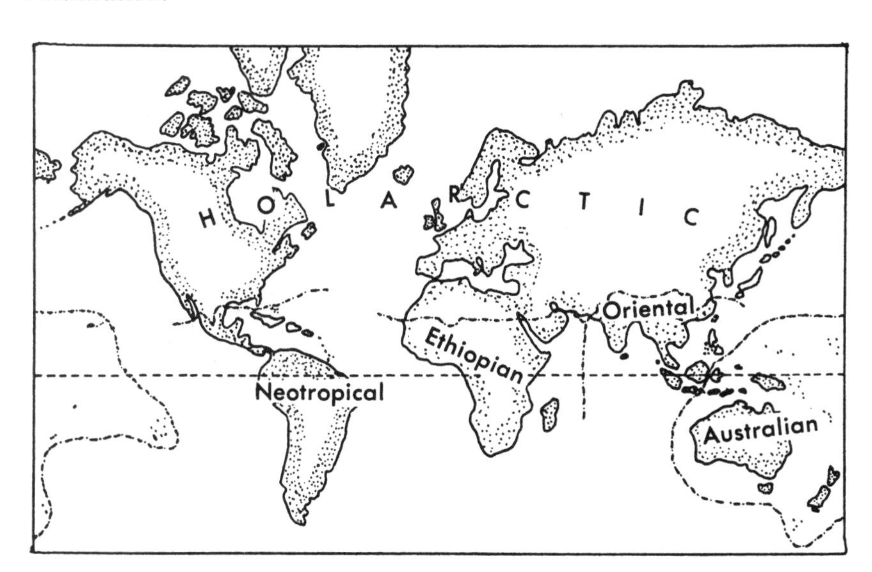

Order: *FALCONIFORMES* Family: PANDIONIDAE

Synopsis of Family Characteristics:

Specimens identified (number and name): ____________________

____

Distribution:

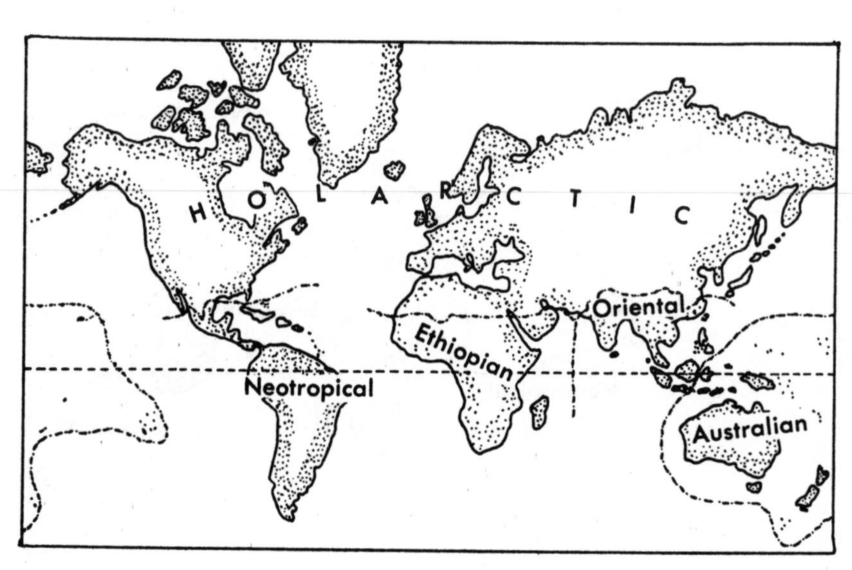

Order: *FALCONIFORMES* Family: FALCONIDAE

Synopsis of Family Characteristics:

Specimens identified (number and name): ______________________

____

Distribution:

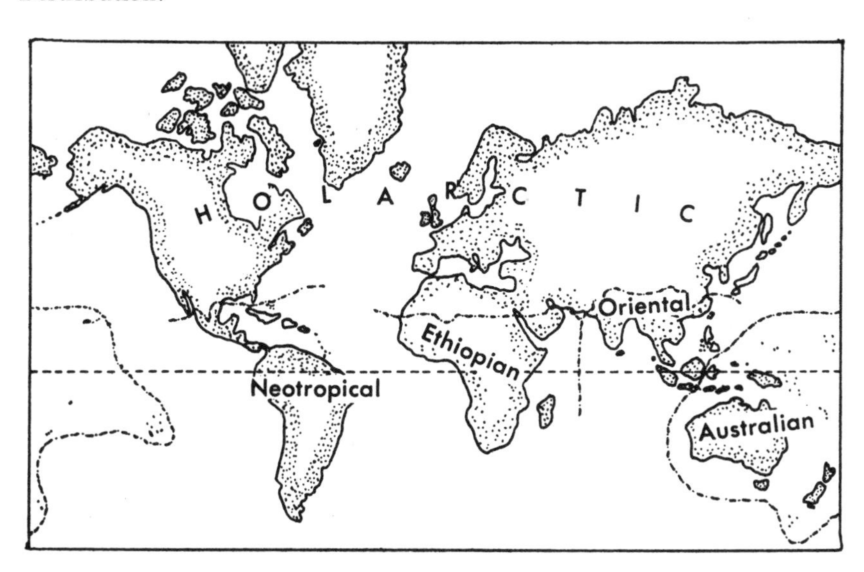

Order: *GALLIFORMES* Family: CRACIDAE

Synopsis of Family Characteristics:

Specimens identified (number and name): ______________________

____

Distribution:

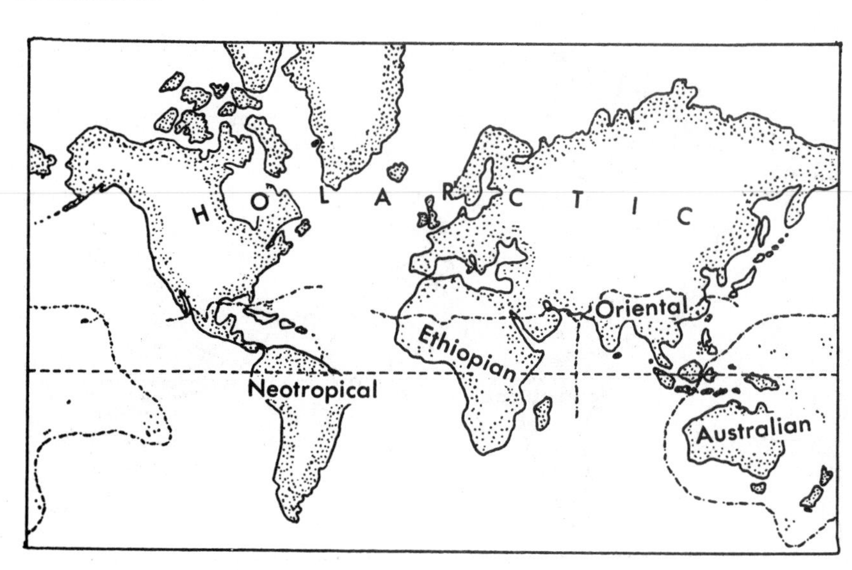

Order: *GALLIFORMES* Family: TETRAONIDAE

Synopsis of Family Characteristics:

Specimens identified (number and name): ______________________

____

Distribution:

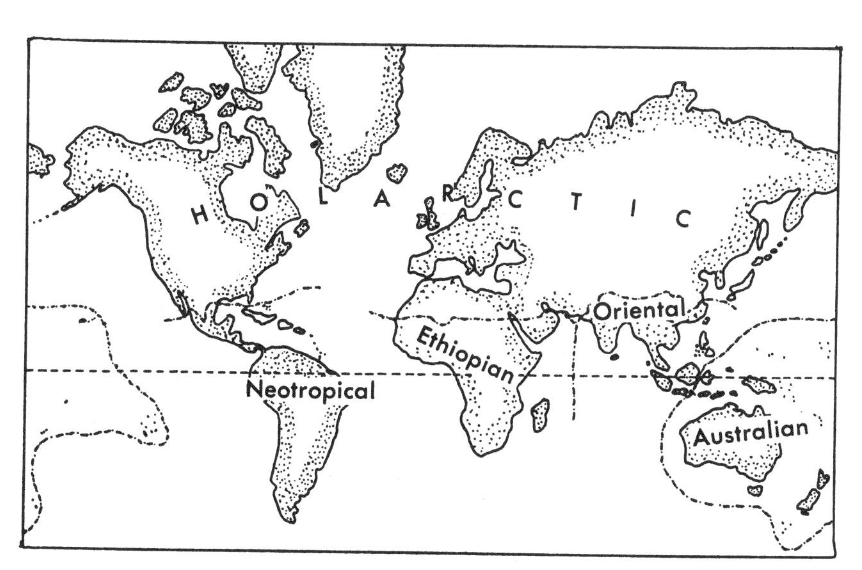

Order: *GALLIFORMES* Family: PHASIANIDAE

Synopsis of Family Characteristics:

Specimens identified (number and name): ____________________

____

Distribution:

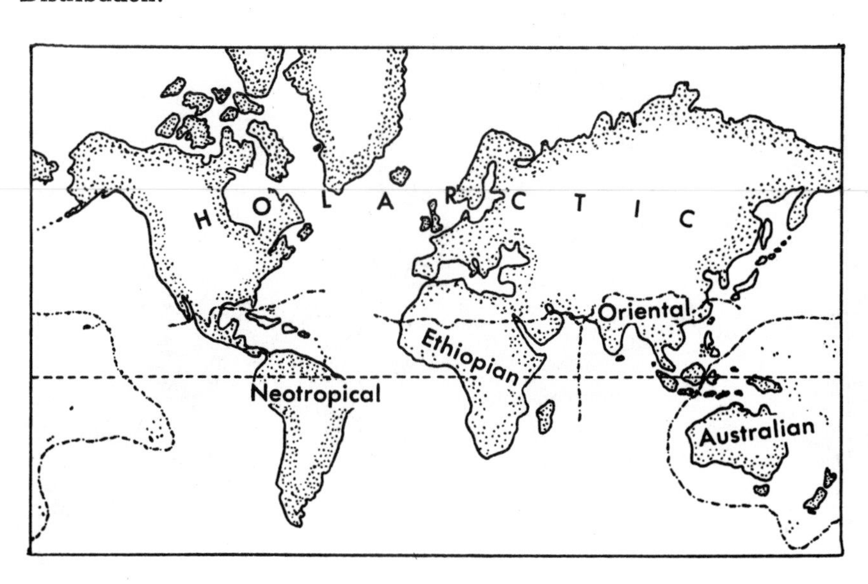

Order: *GALLIFORMES* Family: MELEAGRIDIDAE

Synopsis of Family Characteristics:

Specimens identified (number and name): ______________________

____

Distribution:

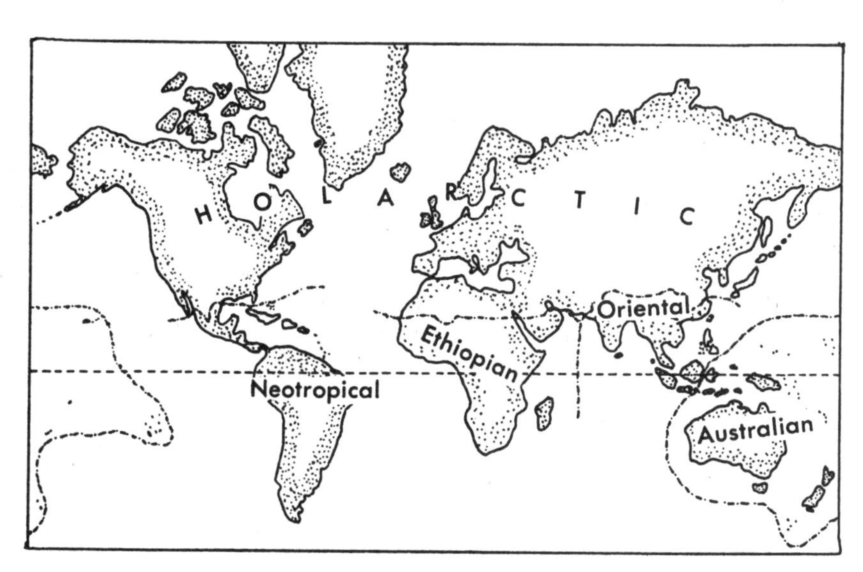

Order: *GRUIFORMES* Family: GRUIDAE

Synopsis of Family Characteristics:

Specimens identified (number and name): ____________________

____

Distribution:

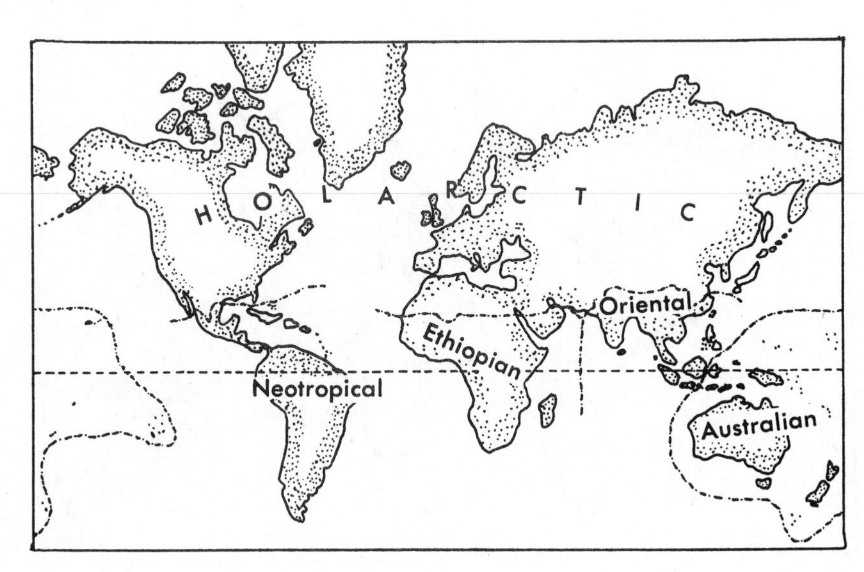

Order: *GRUIFORMES* Family: ARAMIDAE

Synopsis of Family Characteristics:

Specimens identified (number and name): ____________________

____

Distribution:

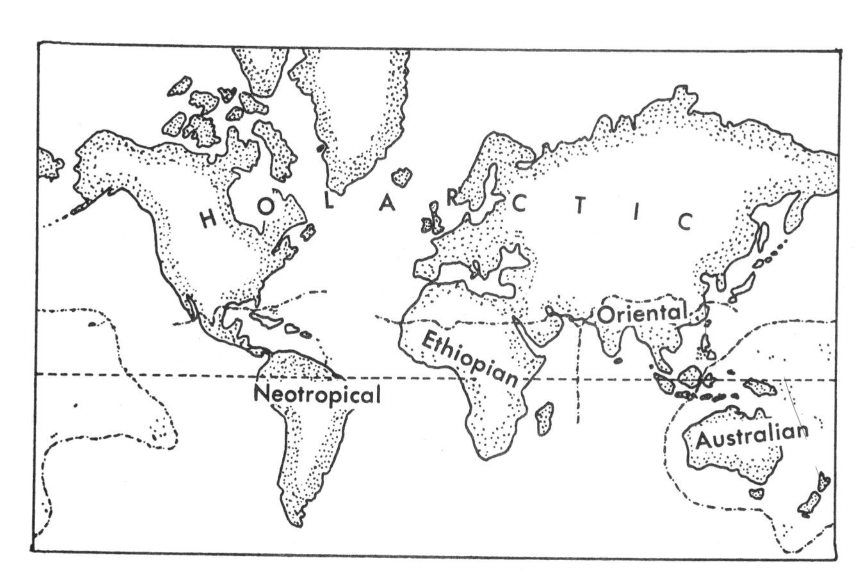

Order: *GRUIFORMES* Family: RALLIDAE

Synopsis of Family Characteristics:

Specimens identified (number and name): ______________________

____

Distribution:

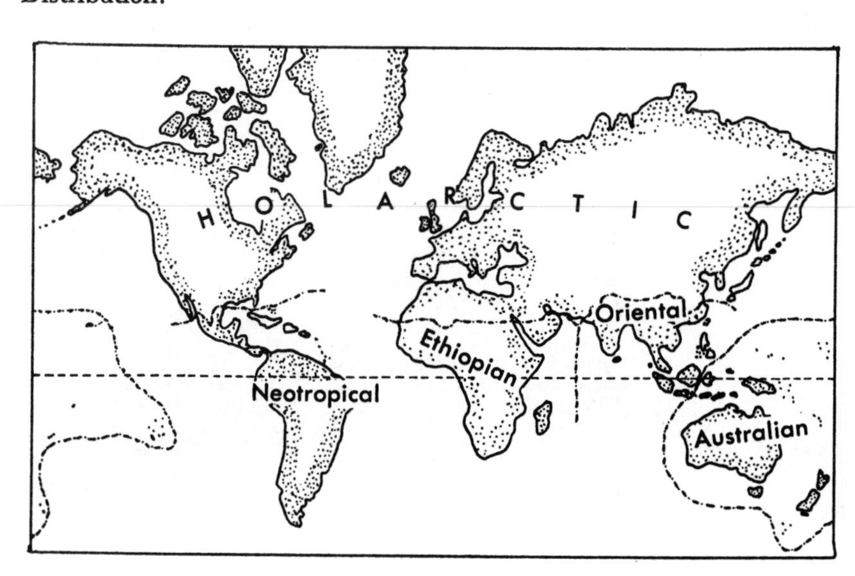

Order: *CHARADRIIFORMES* Family: JACANIDAE

Synopsis of Family Characteristics:

Specimens identified (number and name): ______________________

____

Distribution:

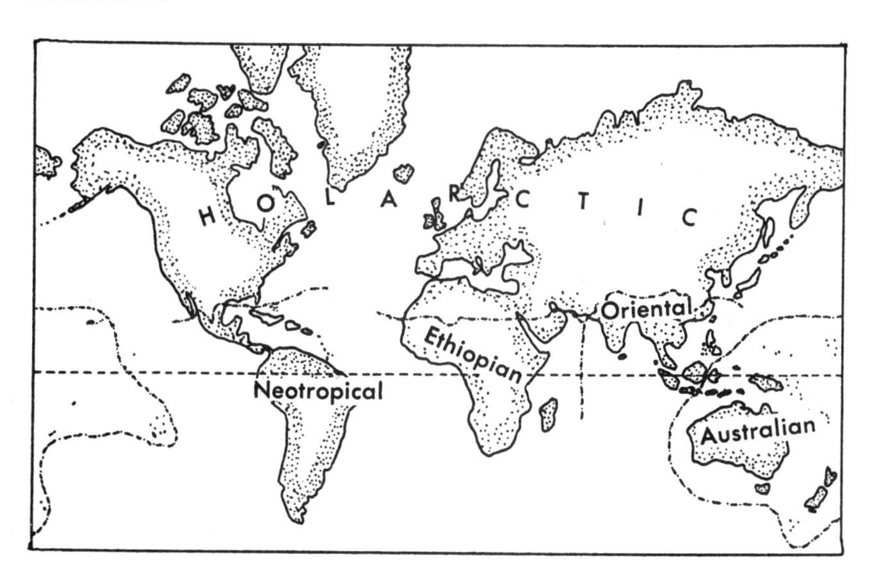

Order: *CHARADRIIFORMES* Family: HAEMATOPODIDAE

Synopsis of Family Characteristics:

Specimens identified (number and name): ______________________

____

Distribution:

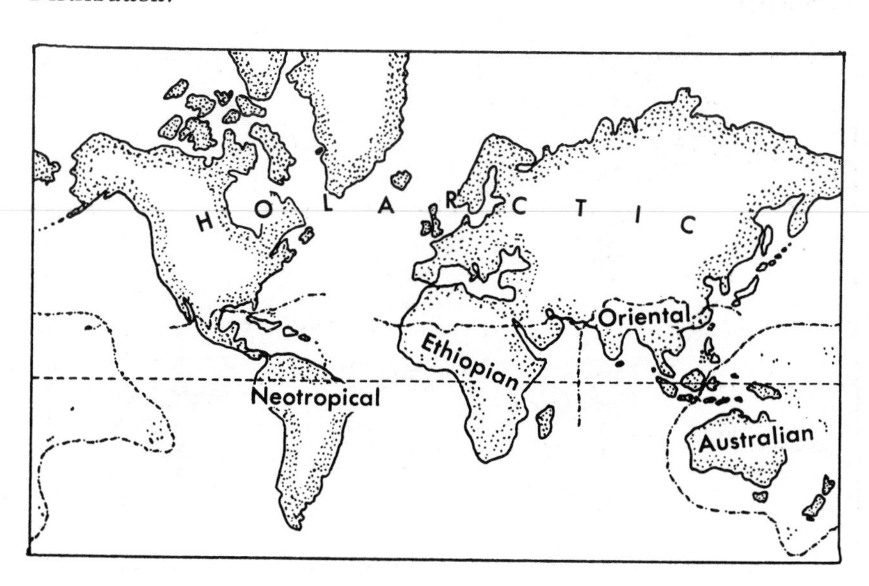

Order: *CHARADRIIFORMES* Family: CHARADRIIDAE

Synopsis of Family Characteristics:

Specimens identified (number and name): ______________________

____

Distribution:

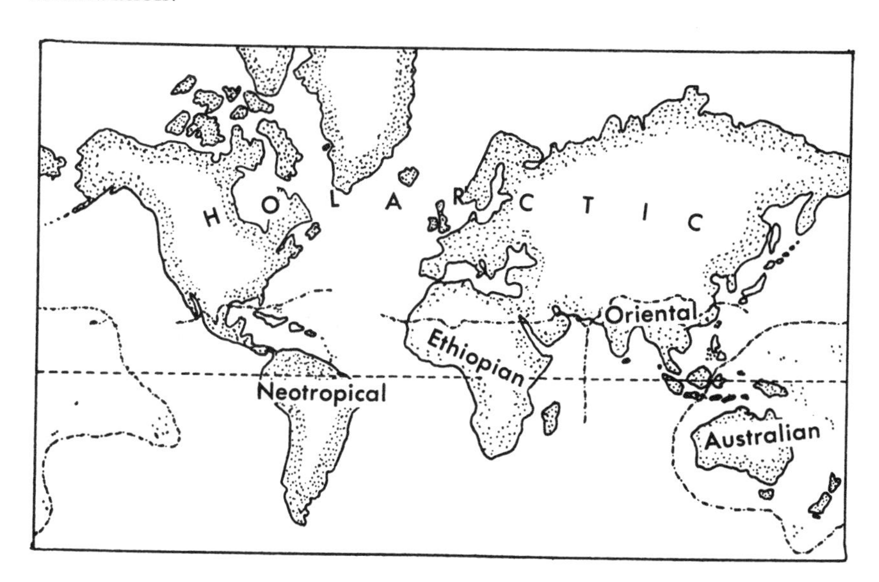

Order: *CHARADRIIFORMES* Family: SCOLOPACIDAE

Synopsis of Family Characteristics:

Specimens identified (number and name): ______________________

____

Distribution:

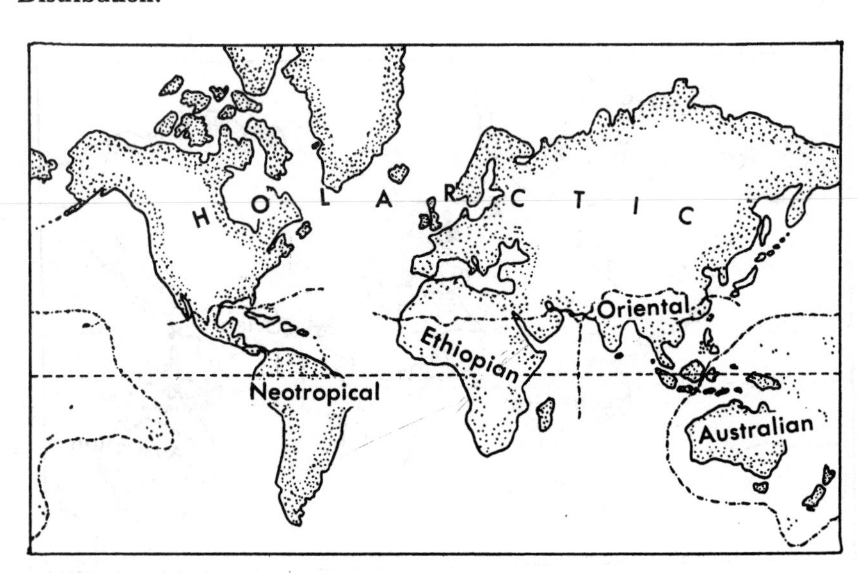

Order: *CHARADRIIFORMES* Family: RECURVIROSTRIDAE

Synopsis of Family Characteristics:

Specimens identified (number and name): ______________________

____

Distribution:

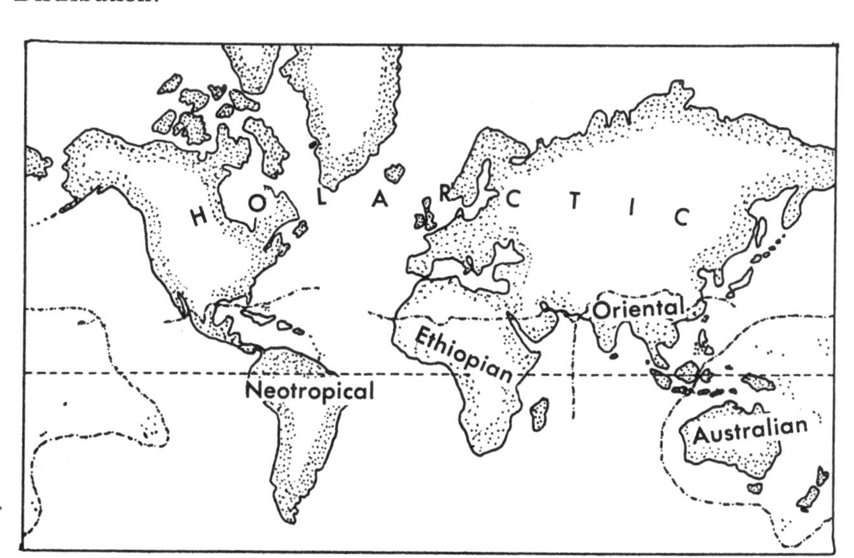

Order: *CHARADRIIFORMES* Family: PHALAROPODIDAE

Synopsis of Family Characteristics:

Specimens identified (number and name): ______________________

____

Distribution:

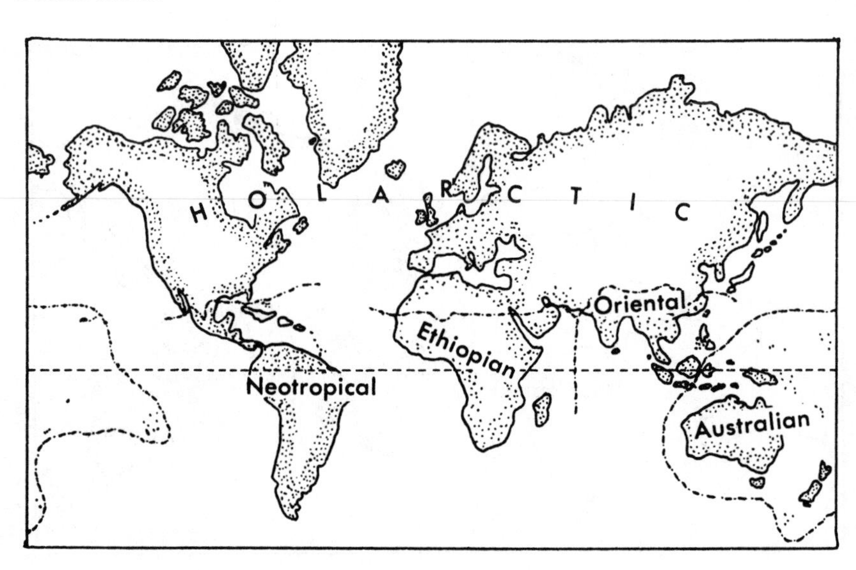

Order: *CHARADRIIFORMES* Family: STERCORARIIDAE

Synopsis of Family Characteristics:

Specimens identified (number and name): ______________________

____

Distribution:

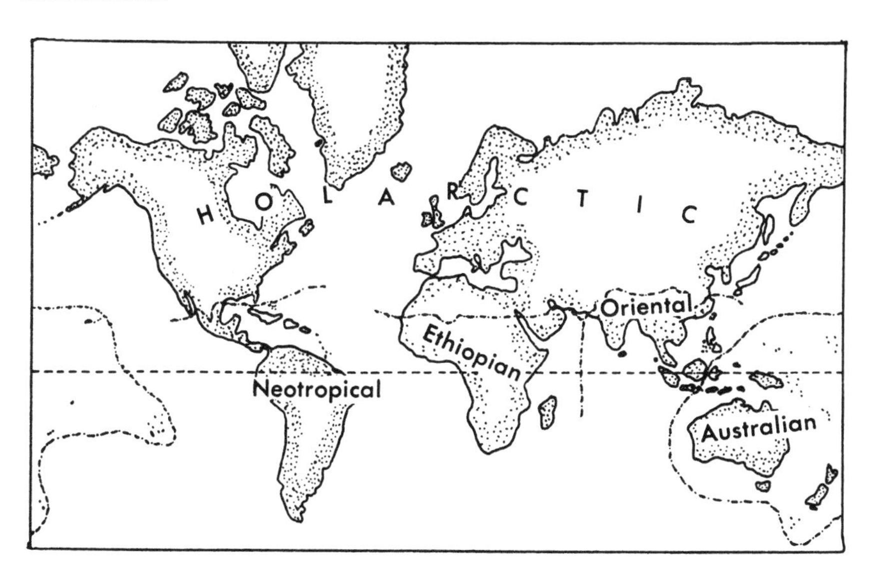

Order: *CHARADRIIFORMES* Family: LARIDAE

Synopsis of Family Characteristics:

Specimens identified (number and name): ______________________

____

Distribution:

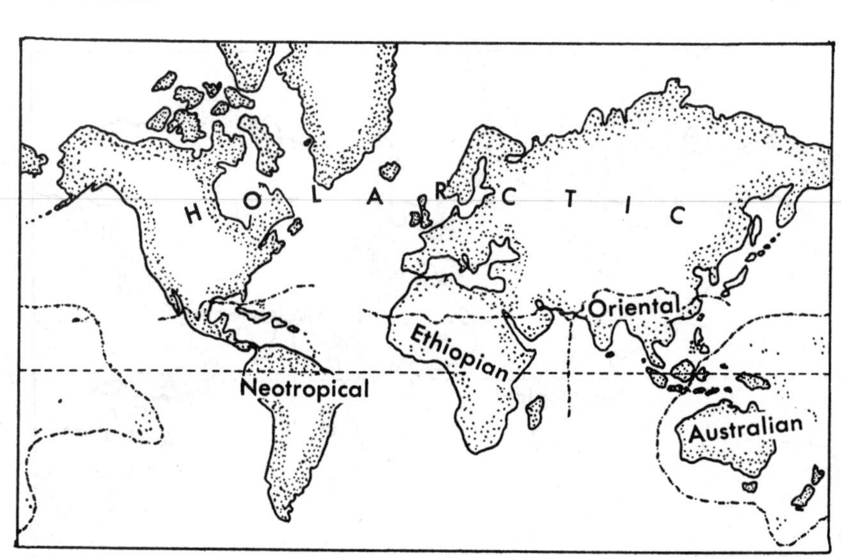

Order: *CHARADRIIFORMES* Family: RYNCHOPIDAE

Synopsis of Family Characteristics:

Specimens identified (number and name): ______________________

____

Distribution:

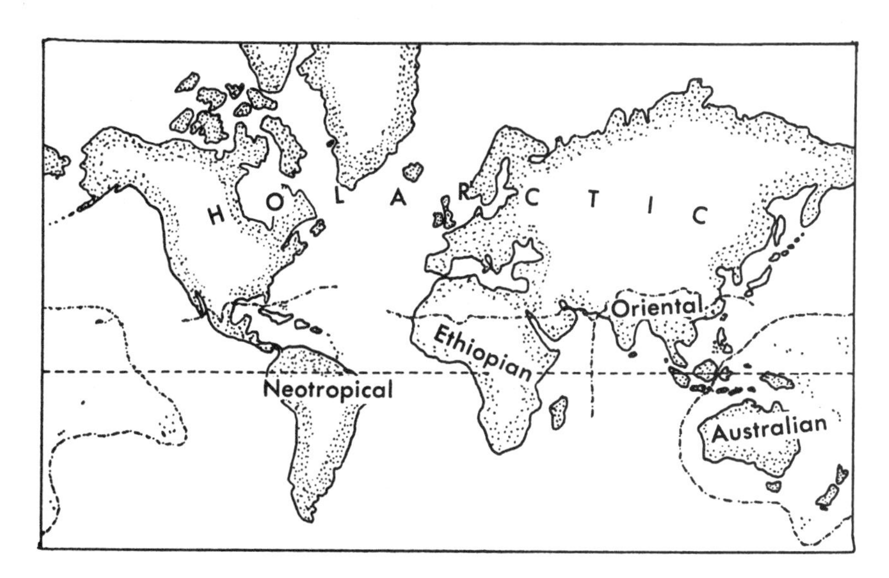

Order: *CHARADRIIFORMES* Family: ALCIDAE

Synopsis of Family Characteristics:

Specimens identified (number and name): ______________________

____

Distribution:

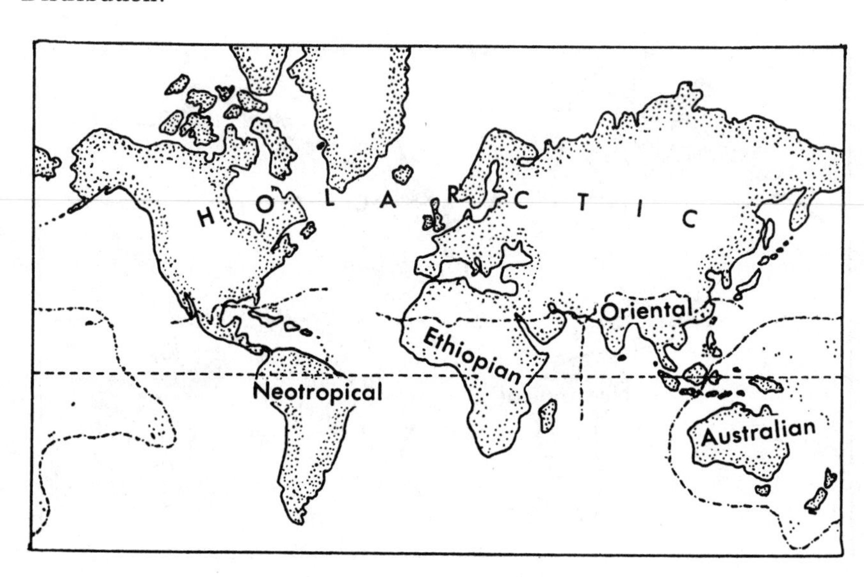

Order: *COLUMBIFORMES* Family: COLUMBIDAE

Synopsis of Family Characteristics:

Specimens identified (number and name): ______________________

____

Distribution:

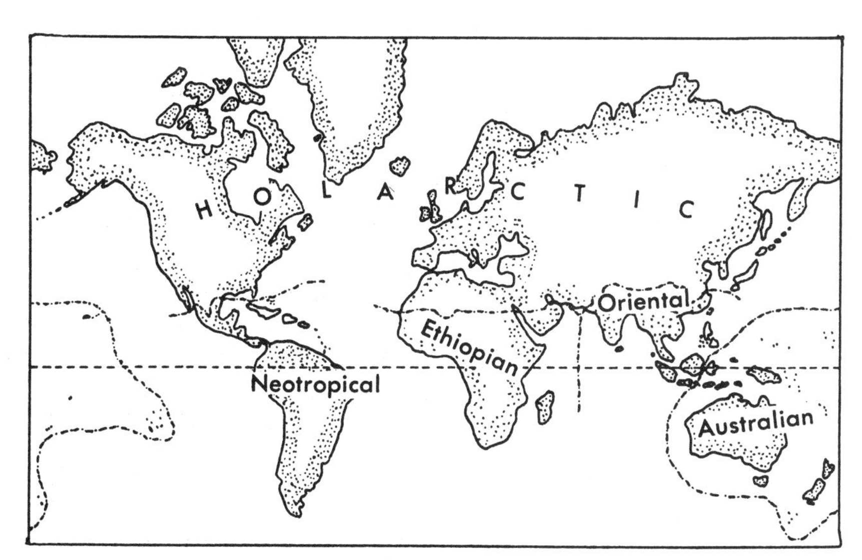

Order: *PSITTACIFORMES* Family: PSITTACIDAE

Synopsis of Family Characteristics:

Specimens identified (number and name): ____________________

____

Distribution:

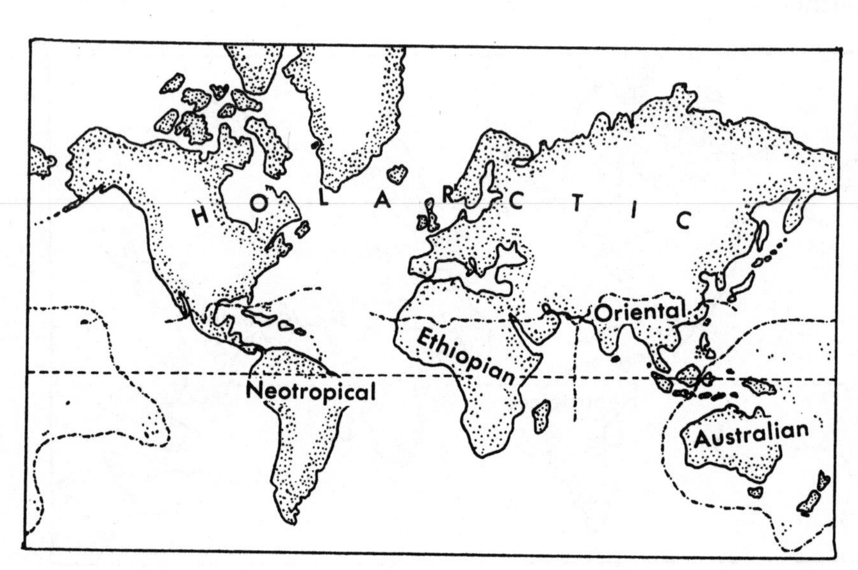

Order: *CUCULIFORMES* Family: CUCULIDAE

Synopsis of Family Characteristics:

Specimens identified (number and name): ______________________

____

Distribution:

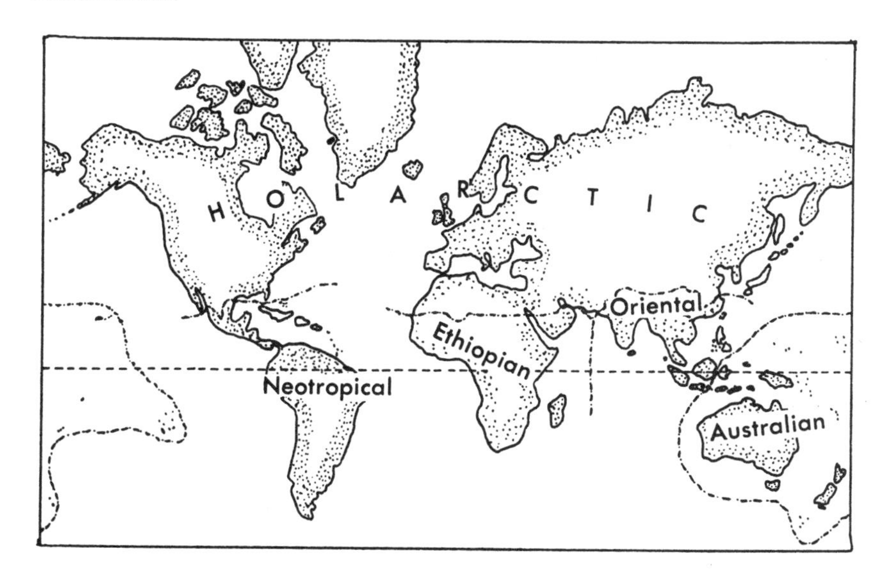

Order: *STRIGIFORMES* Family: TYTONIDAE

Synopsis of Family Characteristics:

Specimens identified (number and name): ____________________

____

Distribution:

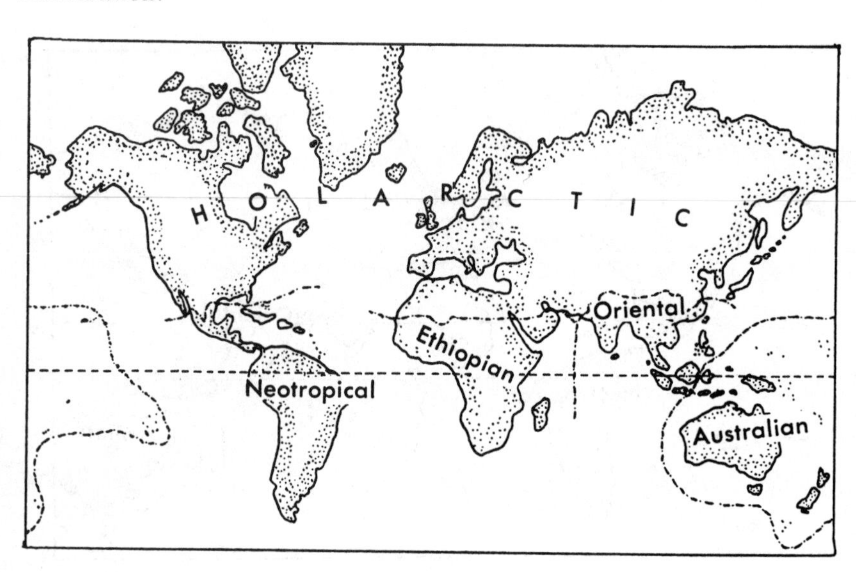

Order: *STRIGIFORMES* Family: STRIGIDAE

Synopsis of Family Characteristics:

Specimens identified (number and name): ______________________

____

Distribution:

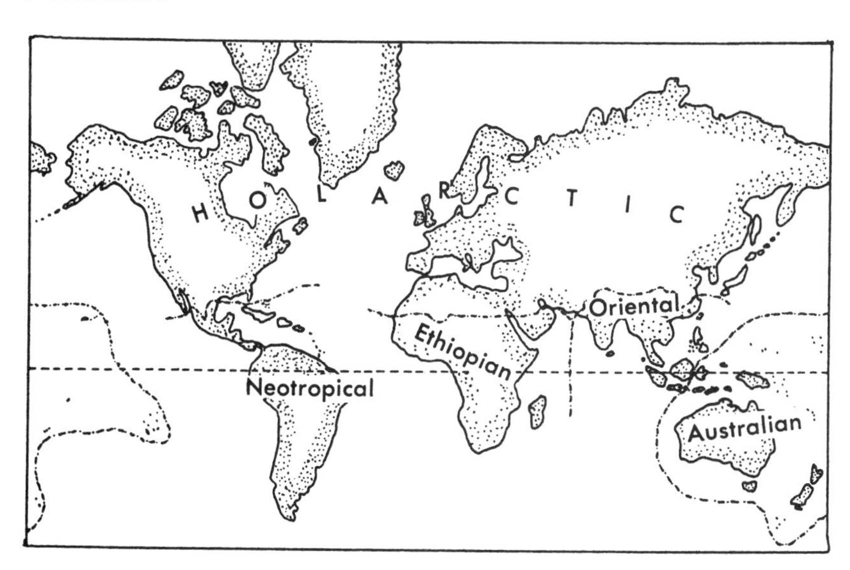

Order: *CAPRIMULGIFORMES* Family: CAPRIMULGIDAE

Synopsis of Family Characteristics:

Specimens identified (number and name): ______________________

____

Distribution:

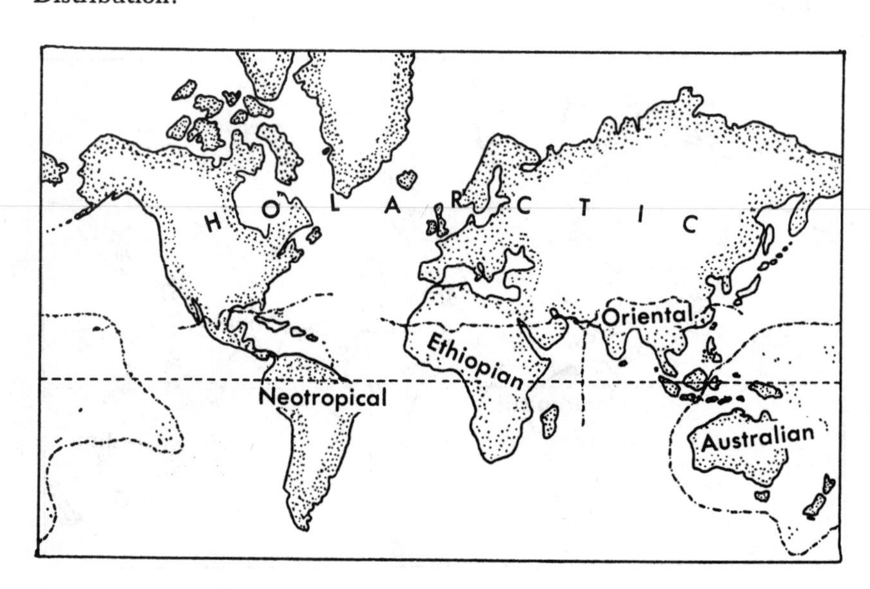

Order: *APODIFORMES* Family: APODIDAE

Synopsis of Family Characteristics:

Specimens identified (number and name): ______________________

____

Distribution:

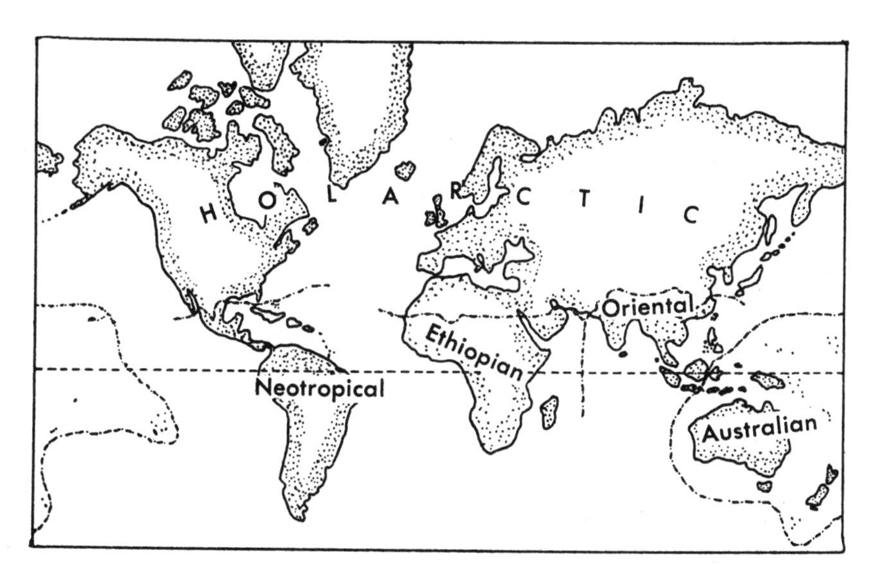

Order: *APODIFORMES* Family: TROCHILIDAE

Synopsis of Family Characteristics:

Specimens identified (number and name): ______________________

____

Distribution:

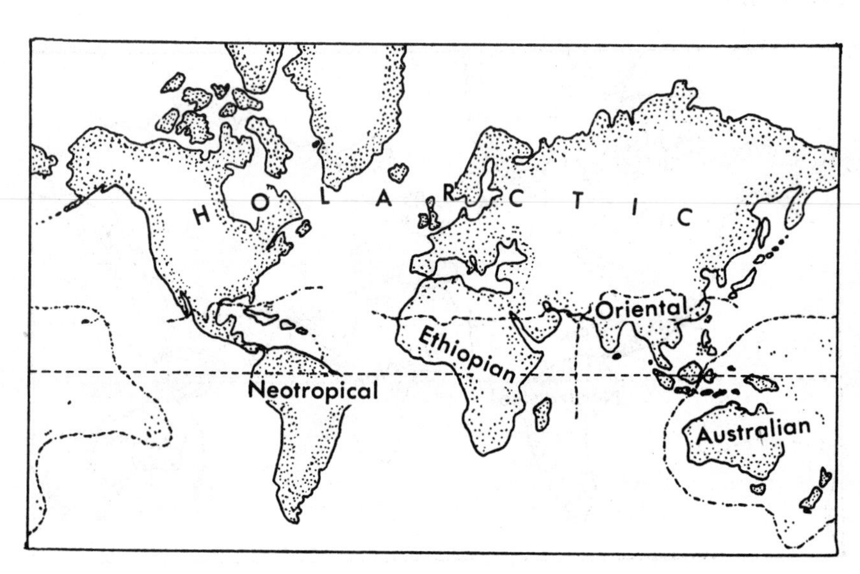

Order: *TROGONIFORMES* Family: TROGONIDAE

Synopsis of Family Characteristics:

Specimens identified (number and name): ____________________

____

Distribution:

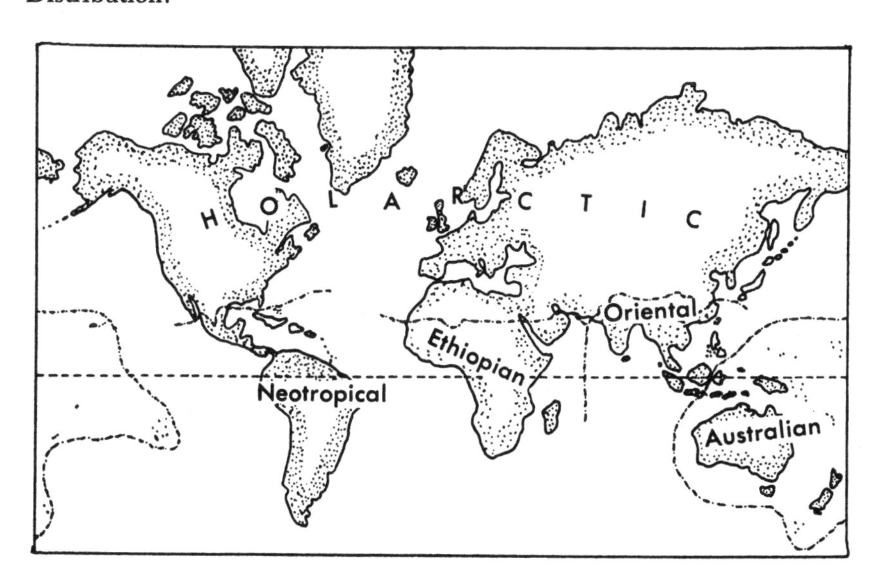

Order: *CORACIIFORMES* Family: ALCEDINIDAE

Synopsis of Family Characteristics:

Specimens identified (number and name): ______________________

____

Distribution:

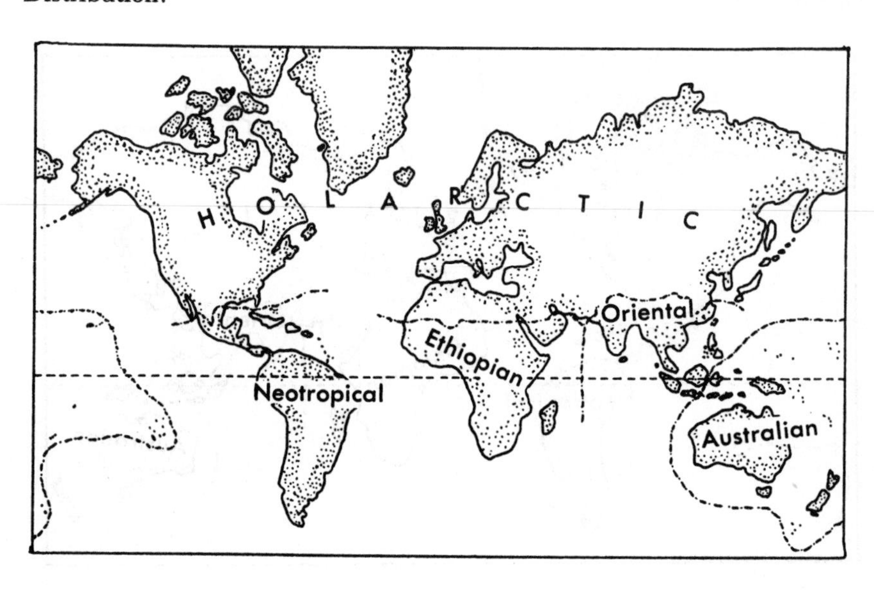

Order: *PICIFORMES* Family: PICIDAE

Synopsis of Family Characteristics:

Specimens identified (number and name): ______________________

____

Distribution:

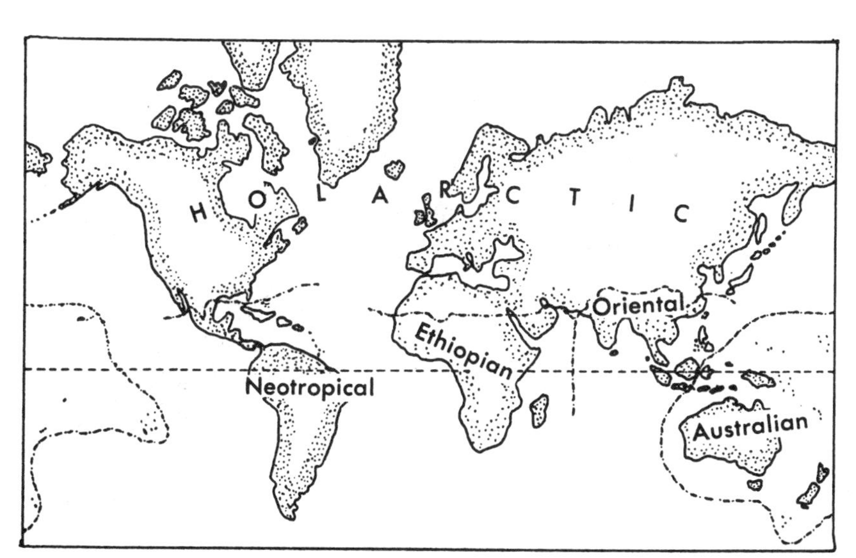

Order: *PASSERIFORMES* Family: COTINGIDAE

Synopsis of Family Characteristics:

Specimens identified (number and name): ____________________

____

Distribution:

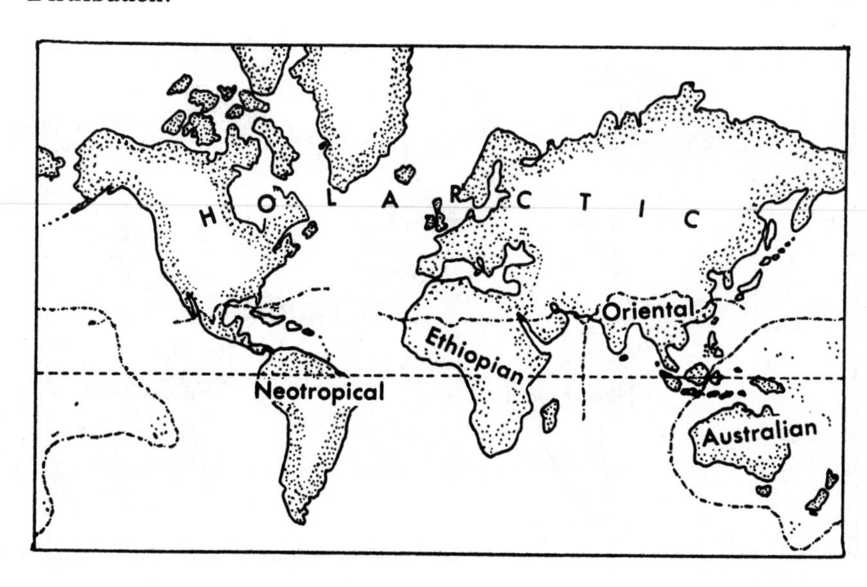

Order: *PASSERIFORMES* Family: TYRANNIDAE

Synopsis of Family Characteristics:

Specimens identified (number and name): ______________________

____

Distribution:

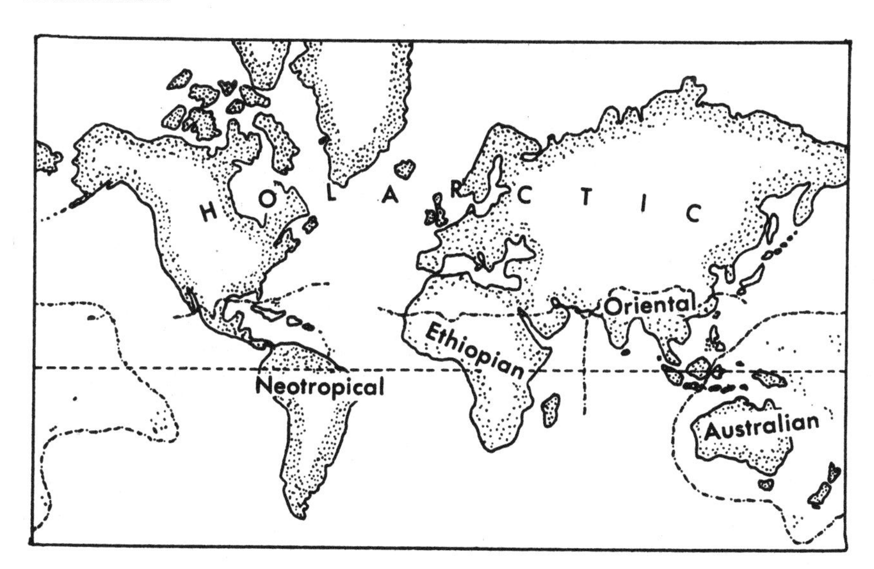

Order: *PASSERIFORMES* Family: ALAUDIDAE

Synopsis of Family Characteristics:

Specimens identified (number and name): ____________________

____

Distribution:

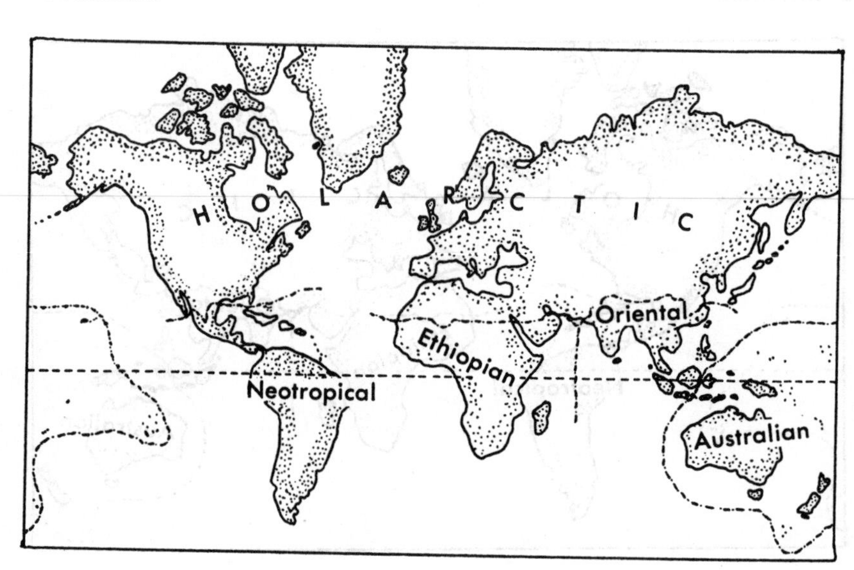

Order: *PASSERIFORMES* Family: HIRUNDINIDAE

Synopsis of Family Characteristics:

Specimens identified (number and name): ____________________

____

Distribution:

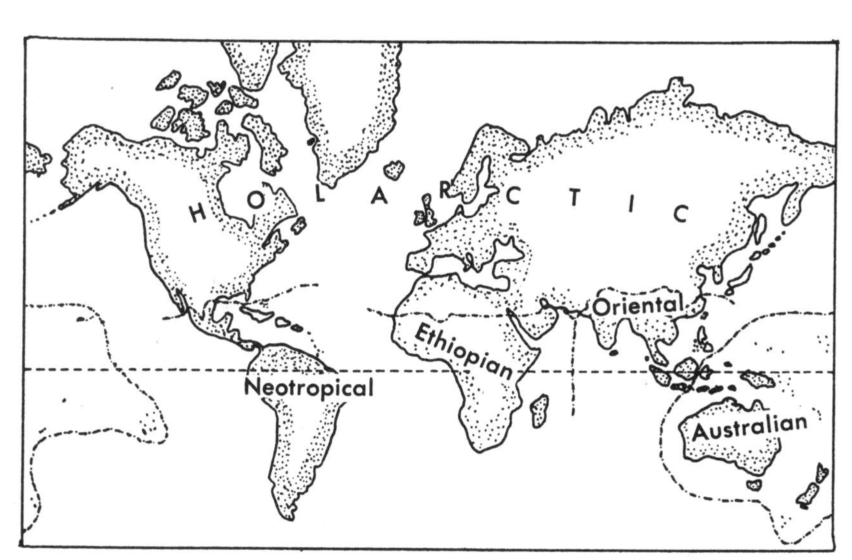

Order: *PASSERIFORMES* Family: CORVIDAE

Synopsis of Family Characteristics:

Specimens identified (number and name): ____________________

____

Distribution:

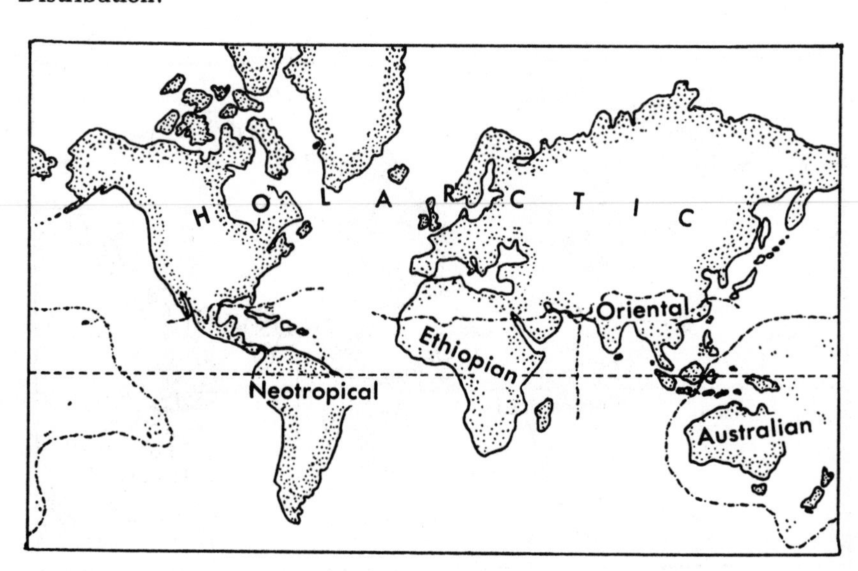

Order: *PASSERIFORMES* Family: PARIDAE

Synopsis of Family Characteristics:

Specimens identified (number and name): ______________________

____

Distribution:

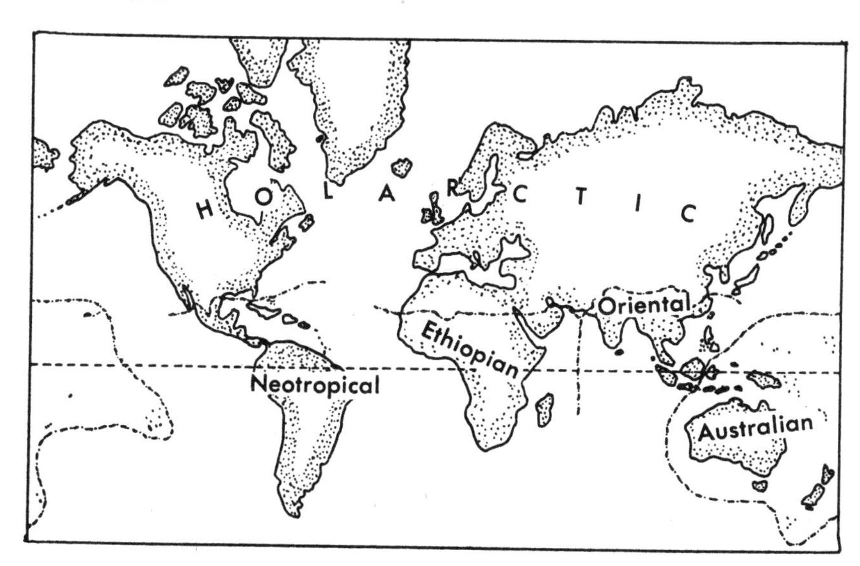

Order: *PASSERIFORMES* Family: SITTIDAE

Synopsis of Family Characteristics:

Specimens identified (number and name): ______________________

____

Distribution:

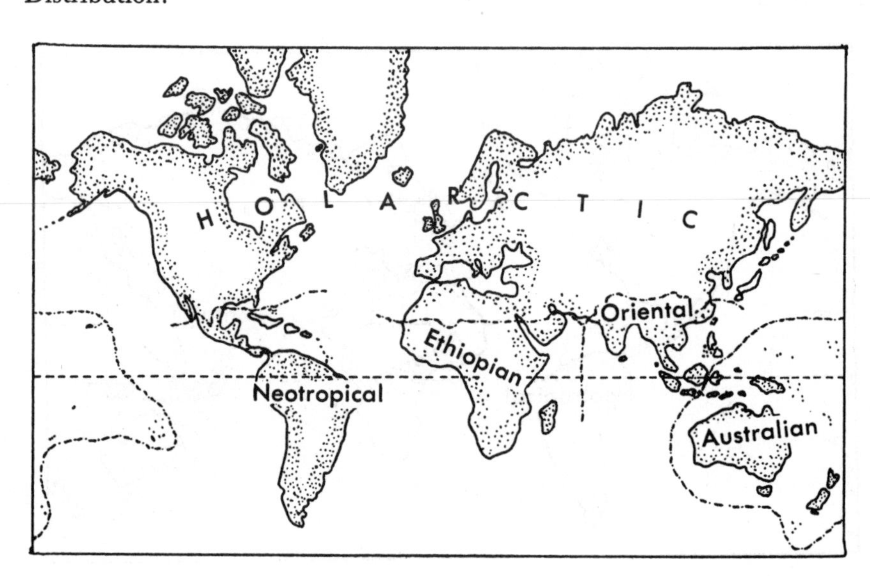

Order: *PASSERIFORMES* Family: CERTHIIDAE

Synopsis of Family Characteristics:

Specimens identified (number and name): ______________________

____

Distribution:

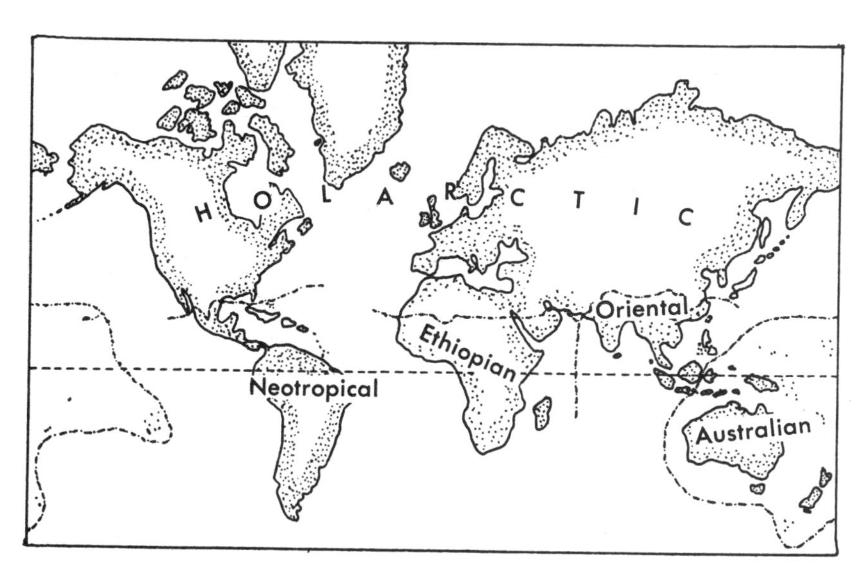

Order: *PASSERIFORMES* Family: CHAMAEIDAE

Synopsis of Family Characteristics:

Specimens identified (number and name): ______________________

____

Distribution:

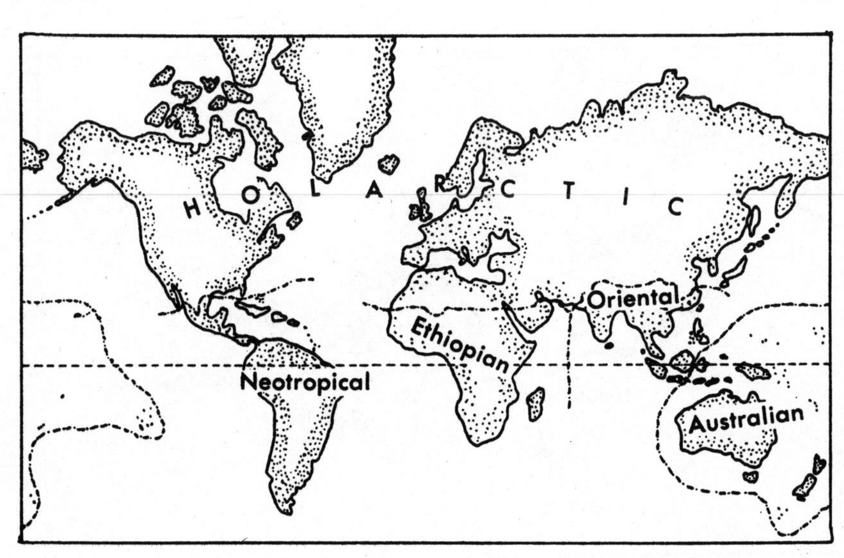

Order: *PASSERIFORMES* Family: CINCLIDAE

Synopsis of Family Characteristics:

Specimens identified (number and name): ______________________

____

Distribution:

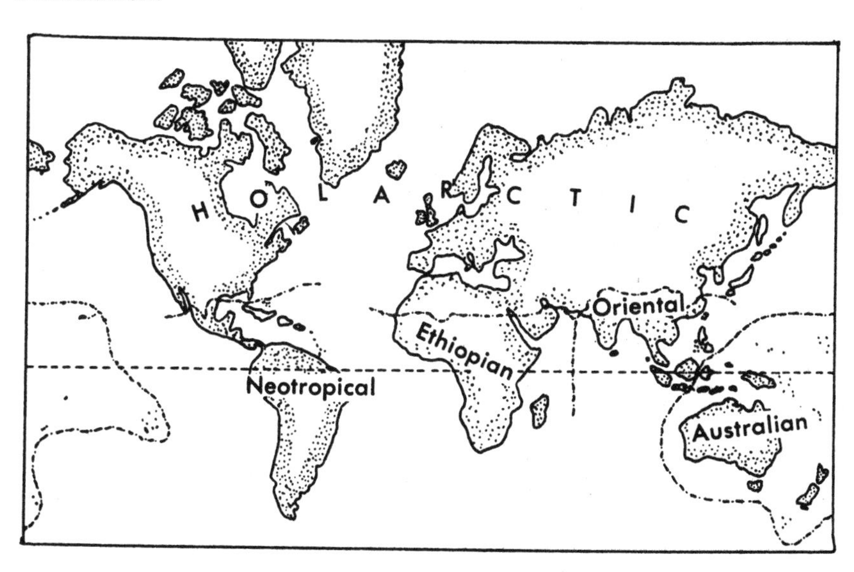

Order: *PASSERIFORMES* Family: TROGLODYTIDAE

Synopsis of Family Characteristics:

Specimens identified (number and name): ______________________

____

Distribution:

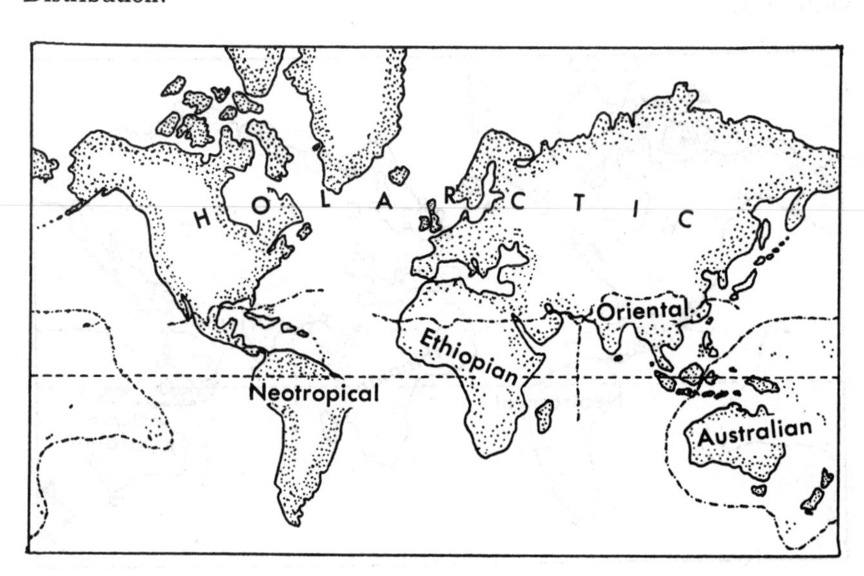

Order: *PASSERIFORMES* Family: MIMIDAE

Synopsis of Family Characteristics:

Specimens identified (number and name): ______________________

____

Distribution:

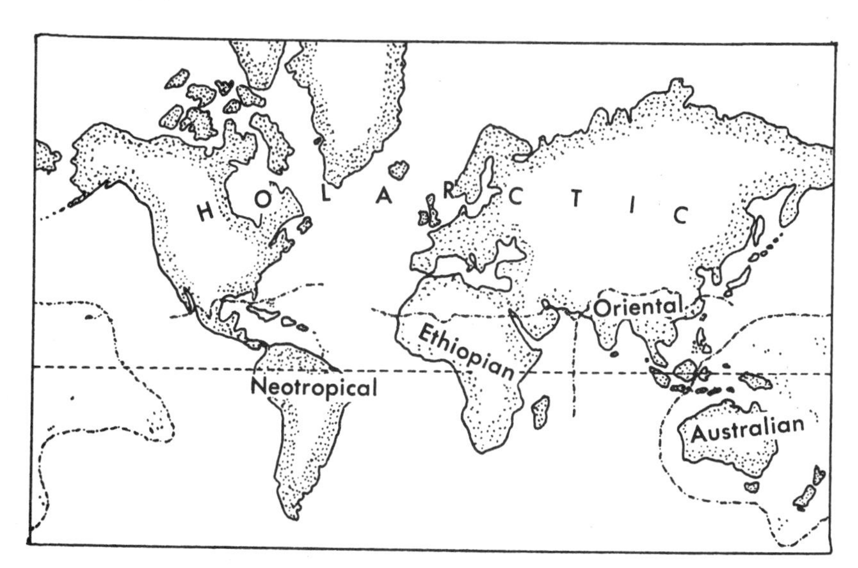

Order: *PASSERIFORMES* Family: TURDIDAE

Synopsis of Family Characteristics:

Specimens identified (number and name): ______________________

____

Distribution:

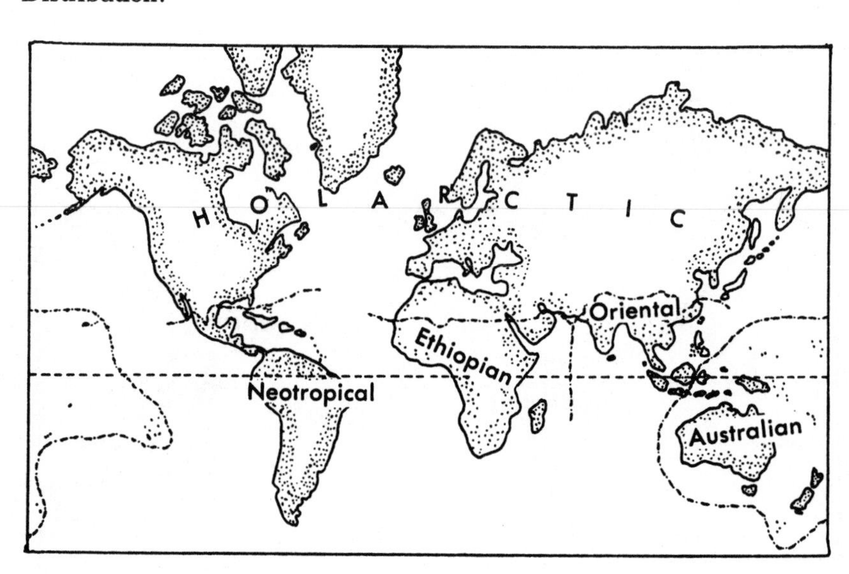

Order: *PASSERIFORMES* Family: SYLVIIDAE

Synopsis of Family Characteristics:

Specimens identified (number and name): ______________________

____

Distribution:

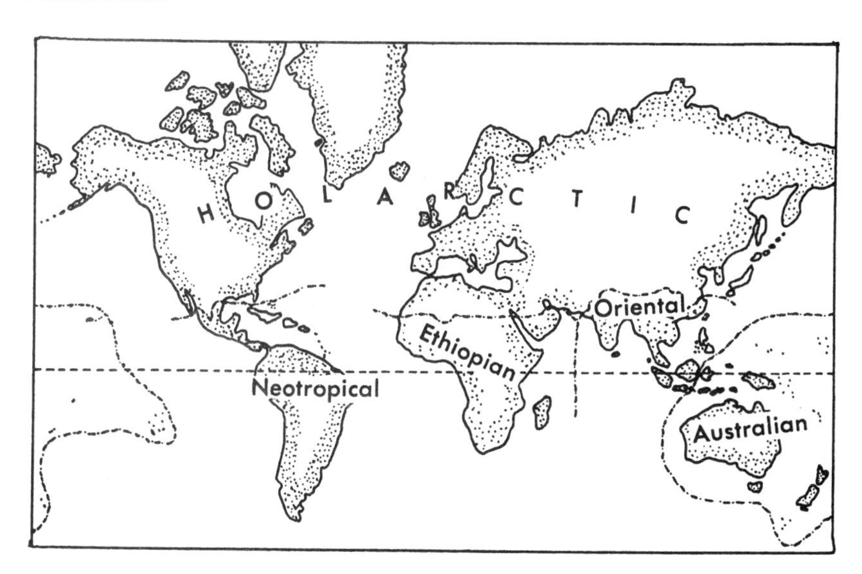

Order: *PASSERIFORMES* Family: PRUNELLIDAE

Synopsis of Family Characteristics:

Specimens identified (number and name): ______________________

____

Distribution:

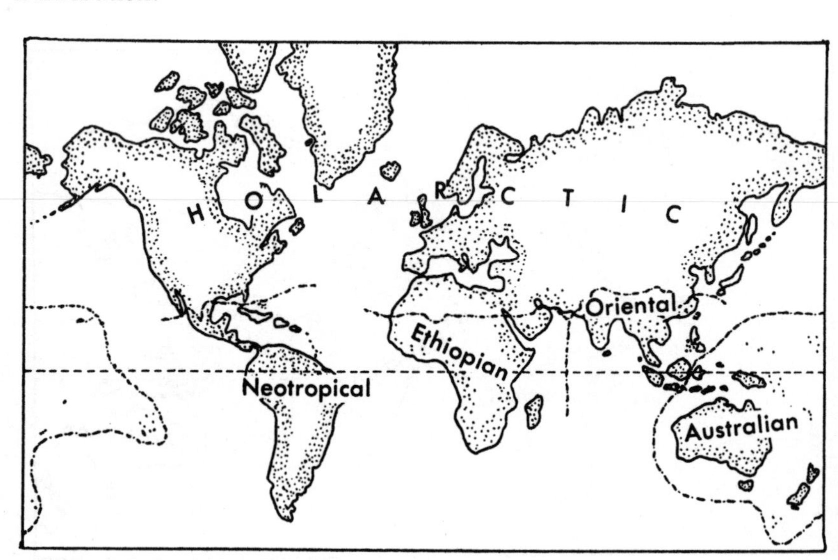

Order: *PASSERIFORMES* Family: MOTACILLIDAE

Synopsis of Family Characteristics:

Specimens identified (number and name): ____________________

____

Distribution:

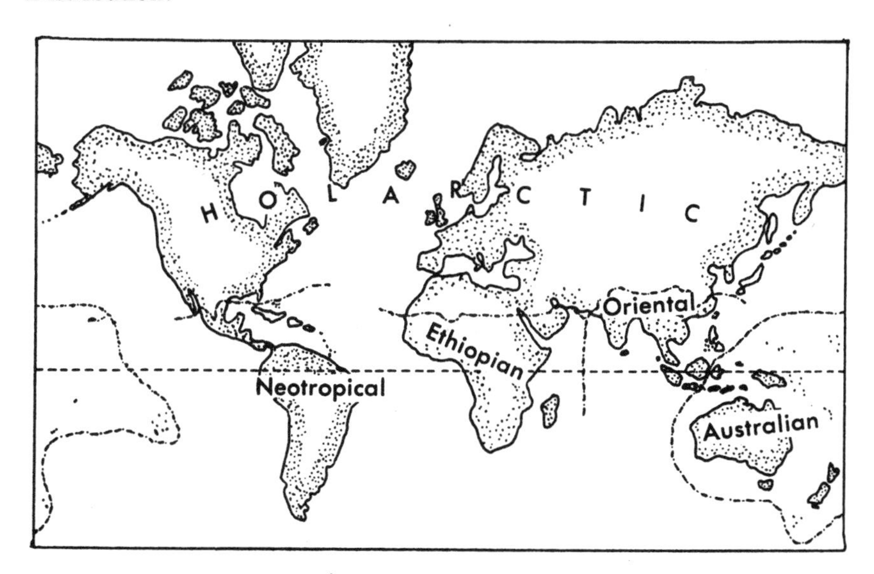

Order: *PASSERIFORMES* Family: BOMBYCILLIDAE

Synopsis of Family Characteristics:

Specimens identified (number and name): ______________________

____

Distribution:

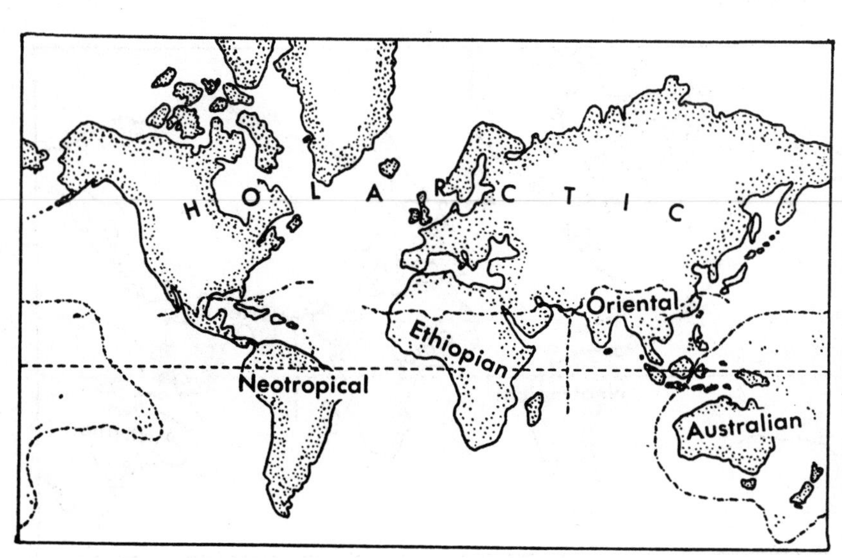

Order: *PASSERIFORMES* Family: Ptilogonatidae

Synopsis of Family Characteristics:

Specimens identified (number and name): ____________

____

Distribution:

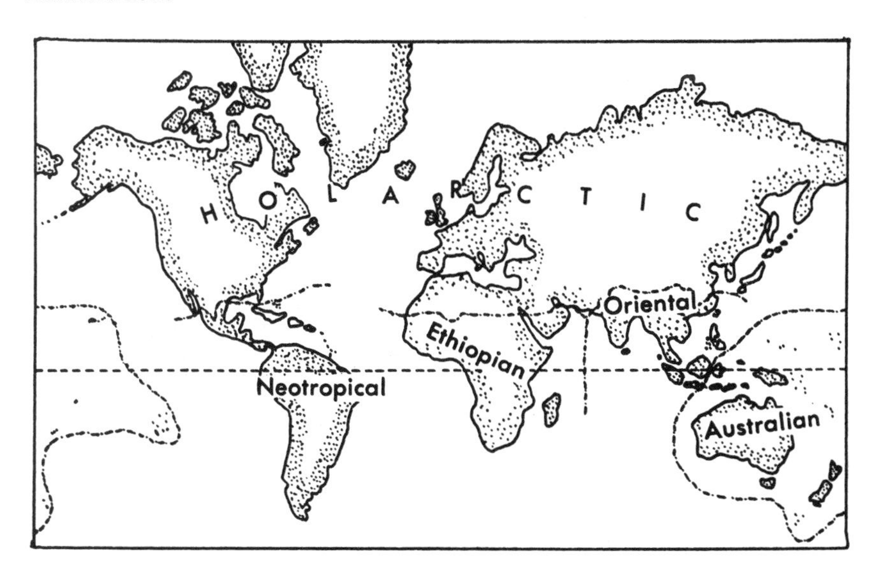

Order: *PASSERIFORMES* Family: LANIIDAE

Synopsis of Family Characteristics:

Specimens identified (number and name): ____________________

____

Distribution:

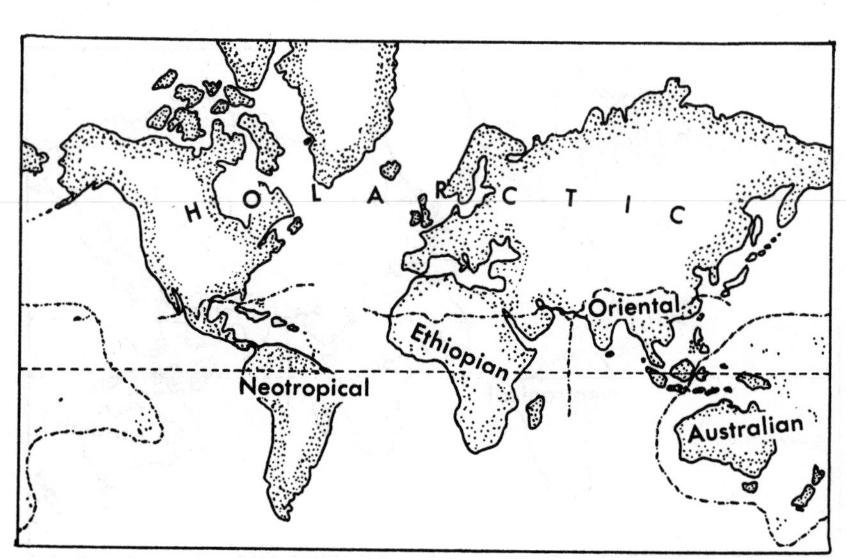

Order: *PASSERIFORMES* Family: STURNIDAE

Synopsis of Family Characteristics:

Specimens identified (number and name): ______________________

____

Distribution:

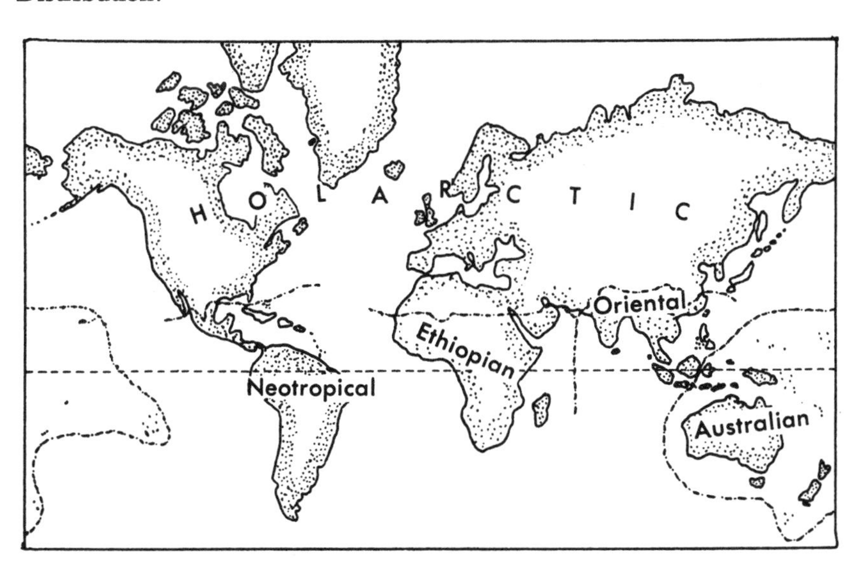

Order: *PASSERIFORMES* Family: VIREONIDAE

Synopsis of Family Characteristics:

Specimens identified (number and name): ______________________________

____

Distribution:

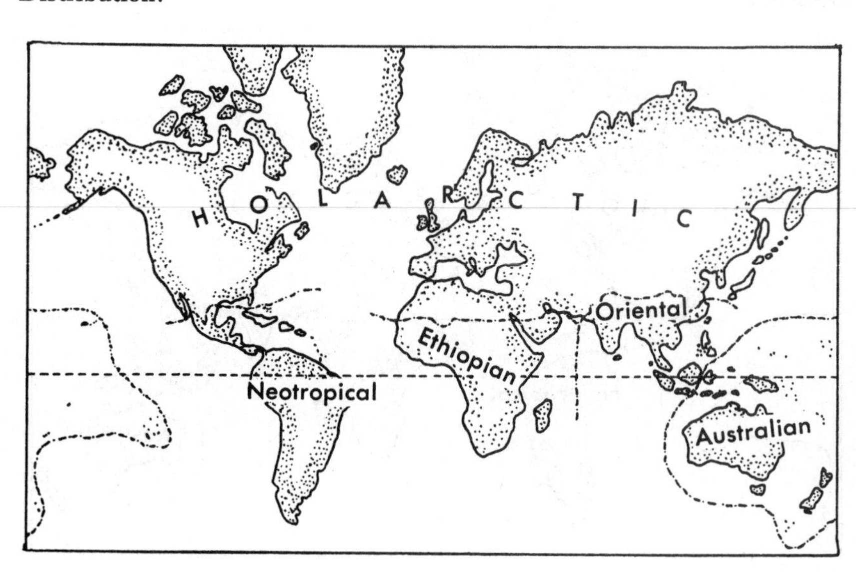

Order: *PASSERIFORMES* Family: PARULIDAE

Synopsis of Family Characteristics:

Specimens identified (number and name): ______________________

____

Distribution:

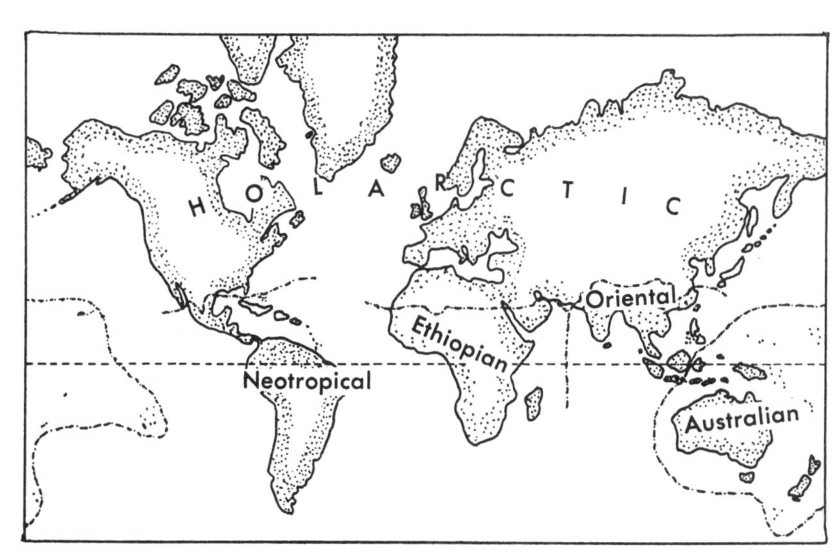

Order: *PASSERIFORMES* Family: PLOCEIDAE

Synopsis of Family Characteristics:

Specimens identified (number and name): ______________________

____

Distribution:

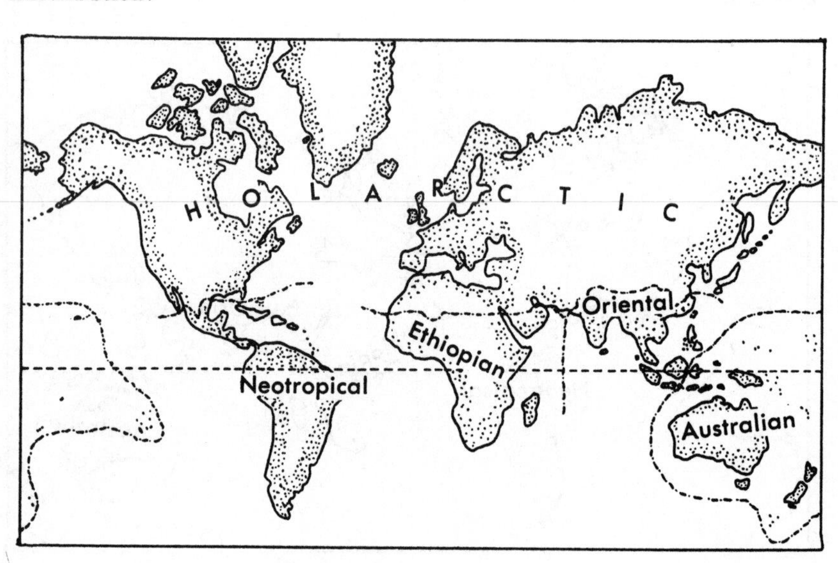

Order: *PASSERIFORMES* Family: ICTERIDAE

Synopsis of Family Characteristics:

Specimens identified (number and name): ______________________

____

Distribution:

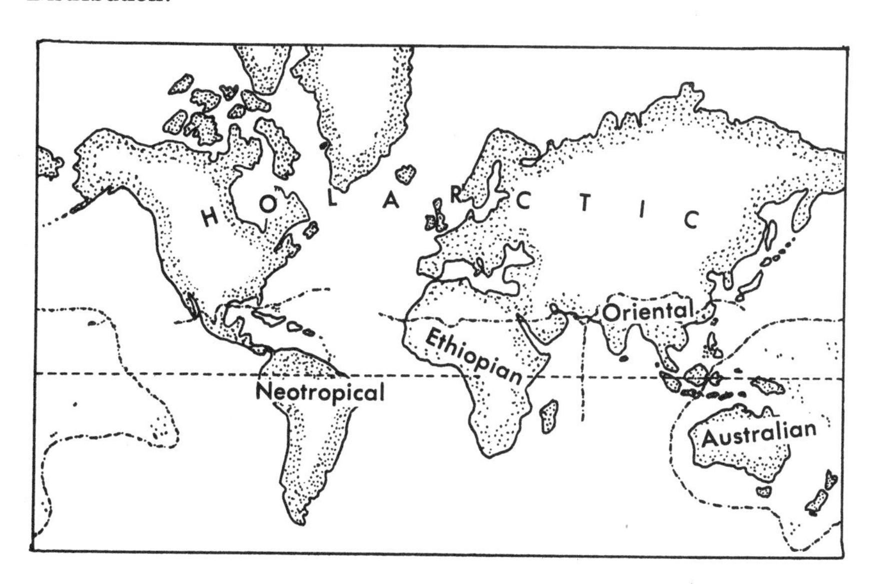

Order: *PASSERIFORMES* Family: THRAUPIDAE

Synopsis of Family Characteristics:

Specimens identified (number and name): ______________________________

____

Distribution:

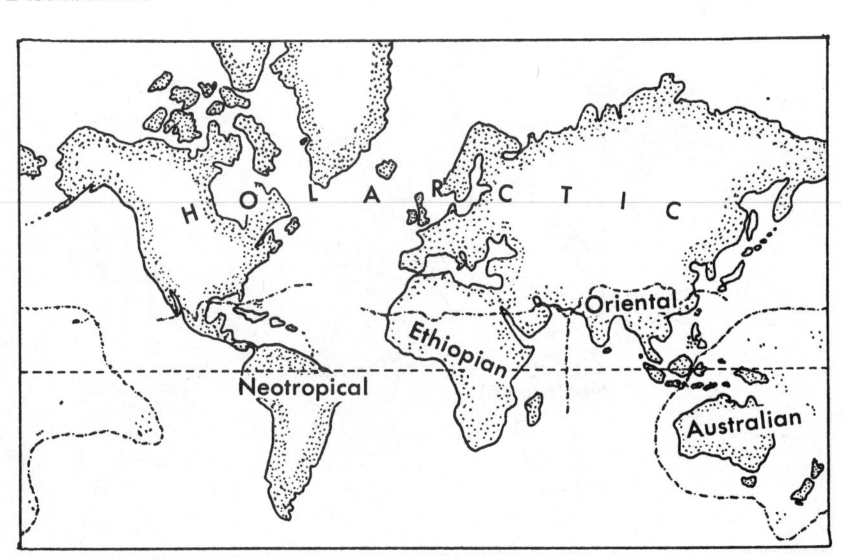

Order: *PASSERIFORMES* Family: FRINGILLIDAE

Synopsis of Family Characteristics:

Specimens identified (number and name): ______________________

____

Distribution:

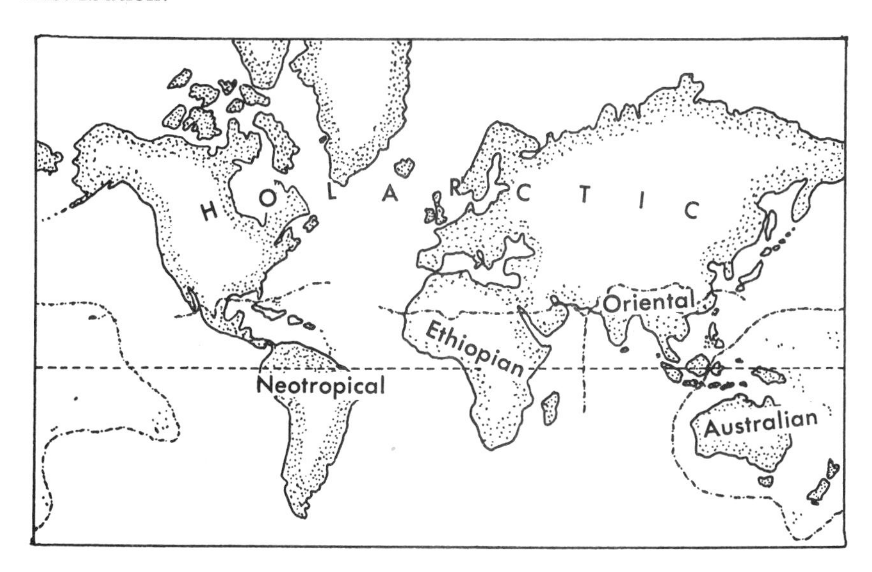

APPENDIX B

Some Suggested Problems in Ornithology

The following list of suggested problems is but a brief one selected from among the multitude of possibilities. An experience with research on the undergraduate level is becoming more and more desirable in the eyes of college teachers.

The student will learn that research is not always the smooth execution of a plan. Whether the plan is simple or complex, there are pitfalls to be encountered. The measure of research quality lies more in thoughtful planning and execution of the project than in the result obtained. This is not to imply that results are unimportant, but rather that the validity of results is dependent upon the care of execution. A carefully thought out plan will help eliminate pitfalls. Frequent consultation with the instructor is essential.

Do not attempt a problem for which the equipment or facilities needed are not available. Carefully study the literature (sources appear at the end of this section) before attempting to undertake any actual work. If available, reports on the same or similar research efforts should prove helpful. In reading these papers, notice the organization of the paper, method of citing references, how summaries relate to the main body of the work, the bibliography, etc. Keep in mind that an orderly, intelligible report of the project is the logical conclusion of the work.

In the following annotated list of suggested projects occasional special references are cited. This is by no means to be construed as the only source, but is cited merely to help the student get a start. One reference generally leads to others and these to still more, etc.

LIFE HISTORY PROBLEMS

Life histories of birds generally require a great deal of direct observation over relatively long periods of time. Such time periods may not

3. Incubation studies. Determination of the incubation period for the eggs of any species. It should be noted that a single observation is less valid than a number of observations. See Davis, David E. 1955. *Breeding Biology of Birds* in *Recent Studies in Avian Biology* (Edited by Albert Wolfson). Univ. Illinois Press, Urbana. pp. 264-308.
4. Incubation studies. Description of the incubation behavior of any species. See Davis (1955) as cited.
5. Measurement of growth of nestlings of any species. (See Stoner, Dayton, 1939. Temperature, Growth and Other Studies of the Eastern Phoebe. *N.Y. State Museum Circ.* 22, Albany, and Davis (1955) cited, especially p. 90.)
6. Composition of Phoebe Nests. Preliminary studies have shown us that there appears to be a relationship between the organic content – inorganic content ratio and the degree of bottom support of Eastern Phoebe (*Sayornis phoebe*) nests. Nests from the previous season were collected during the winter. Careful measurements of the support surfaces, side and bottom, were made. They were dried at low heat, pulverized in a Waring blender, and a sample of 200 to 300 gms. was taken from each nest. This sample, in an aluminum alloy pan, was then fired in a kiln, thus the combustible organic material was oxidized and remained only as ash. The fired sample was then promptly weighed and the difference determined. Weighing must be done on an analytic balance.
   Several species of swallows, robins, and a few other bird species might be similarly investigated.
7. A study of woodpecker cavities. Most woodpeckers drill two kinds of cavities in trees and the like. Any one or more species can be analyzed with respect to preferred tree species, height of cavity

above ground, orientation (north, east, south, west) of opening, etc. with comparisons between the two cavity types.

TERRITORY STUDIES

1. The Belted Kingfisher is known to have generally well defined territories for feeding. These are linear and comprise a certain length of stream. By walking along a stream the birds can be driven ahead until the territory extremity is reached at which point the kingfisher generally soars overhead to retain a position on his territory. Comparison of different ecological situations might be made to determine relative size of territories.
2. A grid of appropriate size is easily adapted for territory studies as well as population studies for a species. Lay out grid (e.g. 100 meters x 100 meters in 10 meter squares) and make a number of copies of a map of the grid. Place yourself at an advantageous observation point where you are relatively unnoticed. Record position of singing males through the several days of territory establishment. This is easily adaptable to marsh and open field nesting species.

FOOD AND FEEDING

1. Analysis of contents of owl pellets. Owls regurgitate many of the undigestible parts of their prey. Consisting of mixtures of hair, bones, scales, sclerites of insects, and the like, these materials take the form of an ovoid pellet. They can often be found in large numbers under a roost tree or other roosting place. The bones can generally be specifically identified by using comparative materials or by recourse to keys in the literature. See Glass, B.P. 1951, *A Key to the Skulls of North American Mammals*. Burgess Publ. Co., Minneapolis, Minnesota.
2. Color preference by seed-eating species. Establish a platform feeding station to attract a group of seed-eating birds. Once established, a compartmented tray bearing counted coarse-cracked corn, dyed with food coloring can be placed on the platform. Regular attention is needed. Never let any compartment be completely emptied. Rotate the colors in the compartments. Treat results statistically.
3. Grit, small pebbles found in the gizzards of game birds, can be collected by seeking the collaboration of hunters. This grit can be analyzed for type of rock, size, relation of size, total grit content to total weight of the bird, etc.

MIGRATION AND ORIENTATION

1. Make a daily or bidaily census of one or more migratory species during the migration season. Keep careful records of weather condi-

tions (temperature, precipitation, cloud cover, barometric pressure, relative humidity) to determine if any relation between certain individual or combinations of weather conditions influences migration of the species concerned.

2. Using any available species which can be live trapped (a permit is required from both federal and state governments to trap migratory species) repeat one or more of the celestial orientation experi-

Starling (*Sturnus vulgaris*). (Herman, Carlton M. 1955. *Diseases of Birds*. In: Wolfson, Albert, *Recent Studies in Avian Biology*. Univ. Illinois Press, Urbana. pp. 450-467.)

2. Ectoparasites of House Sparrow or other species. (See Herman, 1955, cited above.)
3. A study of inhabitants of bird nests. Any one of many aspects of this problem may comprise a problem for investigation. Birds' nests often bear uninvited inhabitants including insects, mites, mice and squirrels. (Hicks, Ellis A. 1959, *A Check List and Bibliography on the Occurrence of Insects in Birds' Nests*. Iowa State University Press, Ames, Iowa. A supplement to the foregoing was published in 1962.)

POPULATIONS

Population studies may take many directions and attempt to show diverse objectives.

1. A breeding bird plot census in an abandoned orchard (covering an area calculated to show a fair sample) can be compared to a sprayed commercial orchard, (plot of the same size). (See chapter 11.) and Gibb, John A., 1961, *Bird Populations* in A. J. Marshall, *Biology and Physiology of Birds*. Academic Press, New York. pp. 413-446.
2. A lineal census of singing males taken during the breeding season for a particular species and in a likely ecological situation might be compared with a similar census taken in a less likely area. For example, a two mile census along a creek or river with wooded borders could be compared to a two mile sample taken along a stream in relatively open pastures.

3. A roadside census through town and country (taken in winter) of previous years nests of the Baltimore Oriole (or any other species of oriole). Continued over a period of many years this investigation could yield significant data relating to variation in abundance of the species.

BEHAVIOR

1. Observe flocks of any gregarious species (e.g. Starlings, *Sturnus vulgaris,* in winter) while perched in a tree, on utility lines, on a fence, or the like. Record how the birds react to each other. Often a hierarchy of social order can be determined. Carefully record the intricacies of movement in hierarchy establishment, if such exists, in the species. Compare perching dominance with flight leadership of the flock. Compare dominance establishment in flocks of the same species as the season progresses. (See Nichols, J. T. 1931 Notes on the Flocking of Shore Birds. *Auk* 48:181-185. Also Hinde, R. A. 1961 *Behavior,* in Marshall, A. J. *Biology and Comparative Physiology of Birds,* Vol. II. Academic Press, New York. pp. 393-395, 407-411.)
2. Many behavioral aspects of the life cycle of birds are worthy investigations. Some of these are: behavior involved in intimidation and display in territory establishment; approach patterns and other behavioral aspects of parents in caring for their young; patterns used by adults to entice grown nestlings from the nest; behavior elicited by various call notes by a species. (See Hinde, 1961, cited, and Armstrong, E. A. 1947 *Bird Display and Behavior,* Oxford University Press, New York.)

SOURCES

Following is a list of major sources in ornithology. Any investigation should involve the literature (1) as a background on which to build, (2) as a source of ideas for further investigation, (3) as a means of testing, by comparison, the results of your investigation, (4) as a source of facts to be used by investigators who hope to integrate results of many individual researches and synthesize them into major biotic principles.

The sources listed here may be considered as but a brief introduction to the literature in ornithology.

A. PERIODICAL LITERATURE.

Audubon Field Notes. A bimonthly journal published by the National Audubon Society in collaboration with the U. S. Fish and Wildlife Service.

The Auk. A quarterly journal published by the American Ornithologists' Union.

Biological Abstracts. Semimonthly; contains abstracts of papers from many of the world's major ornithological journals, books, etc.

Bird-Banding. A quarterly journal published for the Northeastern Bird-Banding Association, the Eastern Bird-Banding Association, and the Inland Bird-Banding Association.

The Condor. A bimonthly journal published by the Cooper Ornithological Society.

be obtained separately.

B. ENCYCLOPEDIC LITERATURE.

AMERICAN ORNITHOLOGISTS' UNION, *Check-list of North American Birds,* American Ornithologists' Union, 1957.

BENT, ARTHUR CLEVELAND, *Life Histories of North American Birds.* See complete list at end of Chapter 10, 1919 to 1958.

CHAPMAN, FRANK M., *Handbook of Birds of Eastern North America,* 2nd Edition. New York: D. Appleton-Century Co., 1940.

KNOWLTON, F. H., *Birds of the World.* New York: Henry Holt and Co., 1909.

MARSHALL, A. J., Editor, *Biology and Comparative Physiology of Birds,* Volume 1. New York: Academic Press, 1960.

————, *Biology and Comparative Physiology of Birds,* Volume II. New York: Academic Press, 1961.

NEWTON, ALFRED, *A Dictionary of Birds.* London: Adam and Charles Black, 1896.

PALMER, RALPH S., *Handbook of North American Birds,* Volume I, *Loons through Flamingos.* New Haven, Conn.: Yale University Press. (The first of a multivolume undertaking), 1962.

Index

T

Z